★
**THE MOST
IDIOSYNCRATIC
HOTEL GUIDE
IN
THE
WORLD**

★ Cover by Neil Davenport
(Portal Gallery, London, England)

★ Illustrations by Natacha Ledwidge

THE
300 BEST HOTELS
IN THE WORLD

CHOSEN BY RENE LECLER

Ticknor & Fields
New Haven and New York
1983

Library of Congress Cataloging in Publication Data

Lecler, René.
    The 300 best hotels in the world.
    1. Hotels, taverns, etc. – Directories.   I. Title.
II. Title: Three hundred best hotels in the world.
TX907.L53   1983   647'.94   82-10778
ISBN 0-89919-160-6

Printed in Hong Kong

00 10 9 8 7 6 5 4 3 2 1

CONTENTS

FOREWORD

Welcome to the fourth edition of THE 300 BEST HOTELS IN THE WORLD. If you are a new reader, you are in good company. By now, this little book has become rather famous (some would say notorious . . .) even in the remotest parts of the world. I have found eager readers on a coastal steamer in Indonesia, a dude ranch in Arizona, in the Paris 'Metro', on Wilshire Boulevard and on beaches from Jamaica to Malaysia and, almost every time, such encounters have given rise to quite fascinating conversations with people who, in a world suffering so badly from creeping mediocrity, still care for quality.

Not long ago, as I waited for an appointment in a lobby of a Cairo hotel with a gift copy of the book under my arm, a lady doctor from Denver, Colorado, saw it, talked to me about it and said: 'My friends and I never go anywhere without it . . .' When it emerged that I had written it she sat down with sheer surprise and we began a conversation which eventually made me late for my appointment. I did not care. She had some marvellous ideas. Her last words to me were: 'Please, whatever you do, don't go "commercial". . . .' There is absolutely no chance of that and for the record here and now, let us say this: what makes THE 300 BEST HOTELS IN THE WORLD different from other guidebooks is that *we do not accept advertising* of any kind, either officially or unofficially. There is no commercial connection. Entry in the book is totally free of charge and if I visit a hotel for the first time, the chances are very high that I will do so incognito. Hotel people whose establishments are listed never really know whether they are in or out until a new edition is published. By now of course, having visited approximately 3,000 hotels in 102 countries, it is inevitable that people should know me – there is nothing I can do about that – and the friendship and approval of real hotel experts is very precious to me.

Apart from the sheer fun of it, and the agony of making the final choice, the most moving thing about writing this book is the vast number of people in widely different circumstances and far-away places who have taken the trouble of putting pen to paper to tell me what they thought of it. The last edition gave rise to some 1,500 letters – enough to start a stamp collection – and most of them have been tremendously helpful. People *do* care about the hotels they stay in and they are far more aware of the intricacies of hotelkeeping than one would imagine. One Toronto businessman who travels constantly wrote to me to say that as a rule he just has to walk into a hotel and within ten minutes he knows whether he is going to like it or not. It's the same for me – a kind of sixth sense. In the Caribbean recently, I was the despair of close friends because I walked into six different hotels and walked out again. They would not have been right in this book and I am still pretty sure my instinct was right.

Inevitably, more than a few people have accused me of being a snob. If being a snob means caring for quality, I plead guilty and I would endorse Oscar Wilde's words: 'My tastes are very simple – I only like the best'. That goes for hotel architecture and decor, management expertise, the quality of service and, especially in far distant places, the recognition of a job well done in difficult circumstances. If a man manages to run a good hotel in the middle of the Sahara Desert, I take my hat off to him. I do not care two figs if a hotel belongs to this or that company, this or that chain. If it gives me what I want, with genuine friendliness and a touch of panache, that hotel will make it.

In this edition, I have sent some forty hotels to the guillotine, including three world-famous ones (in New York, Athens and Madrid) – a fact which will certainly make eyebrows go up. In these instances, the hotels were so well known and so historically important that their management traded on past glories but failed to relieve the plumbing of its gurgles or the façade of its peeling paint. I am all for tradition, indeed I bend over backwards to pay it tribute, but in the long run one cannot forgive neglect.

Over the years I have gradually veered

away from listing too many hotels in the world's big cities where there are many more than are listed here. The reason for this is simple: I believe that most habitual travellers know where they are going to stay in New York, Paris or London and there is no merit in my telling them about another place when they are always likely to return to their first love. Listing a hotel in some difficult, remote place is much more worthwhile.

Since there are so many great modern hotels everywhere, I have also tended to settle on hotels which are different, amusing, odd or have a unique aura. One Californian advertising agent read the last edition and promptly went off to Peponi's in Lamu, Northern Kenya and then wrote to me: 'This was for me the place of a lifetime – not the kind of hotel I am used to but one which I will never forget'. I am glad he liked it and he and others will find quite a number of 'odd' hotels in this edition. One of the great joys of doing this work is to travel to some distant and exotic place like, for instance, Papua New Guinea or, not so exotic, the Adirondacks, and find a hostelry which has real authenticity.

It will become evident when you read this book that I do 'love' hotels – their history, their character, the people who work in them. However, this affection is merely the by-product of my own unchanging obsession with travel – an occupation which over more than two decades I have been able to enjoy through my work as Travel Editor of HARPERS & QUEEN, England's and Europe's most prestigious magazine. To HARPERS & QUEEN, its editor and management, go my thanks for a lifetime of personal discovery.

Now, for those who are joining us for the first time, let us make a few things clear.

★ I do not award stars or grade hotels in any way. Long ago I decided that to give three stars to this one and two stars to that one was merely an expression of the selector's own judgment. As the cover states, this is 'the most idiosyncratic hotel guide in the world' and we stick to it. The hotels listed are those I like and it is up to you, the reader, to say whether you

agree or not. This is an intensely *personal* guide.

★ If a hotel is not in the book, it does not necessarily mean that it is no good – simply that I do not know it. I try to give as wide a geographical spread as possible, given the limitations of one man and a small team of consistent and trustworthy advisers.

★ I do not compare one hotel with another. How can one compare a hotel in Florida with one in Vienna? Nor can one compare a resort hotel with a big-city hotel. What I am saying is simply this: if I were in this or that place, this is the hotel I would choose.

★ I make no allowances for second best nor do I, on the whole, list hotels which I *think* are going to be great. Take Hong Kong for example, a city where there is an abundance of excellent hotels. For years I have only listed two because these two are so far above the others that comparisons are odious. Yet people will inevitably say to me: 'What about the Hong Kong Regent?' Quite – a superb hotel in anyone's estimation. But it has only been open a short while and in a place like Hong Kong where the competition is fierce and based on the finer points of hotelmanship, the Regent needs time. I am sure it will make it.

★ I do not only choose large hotels. One in this book has a total of nine rooms and another nearly two thousand. I have nothing against hotel chains – some of them are quite well represented. But in a world where the similarities proliferate, I tend to choose the one-off.

★ Some people have also accused me of choosing only expensive hotels. This is absolutely untrue. Some hotels in this book are perfectly reasonable in price. It is simply that in these inflationary days, the best can never be cheap.

★ The factual half of each entry can give trouble since it is supplied by the hotel people themselves and while one can tone down their enthusiasm, one is not always able to measure, for example, a bathroom in the South Pacific. Room standards also vary – due to situation, improvements being made in some other part of the hotel or a hundred other reasons. The best way to insure yourself against disappointments is to ask to see your room *before* your luggage is taken up. If the hotel man is a real professional, he won't mind in the least.

★ A final caveat. This hotel guide is written by a European so the book tends to be overweighted by European considerations arising out of background, history and living habits. Most American readers have happily understood this and accepted the different point of view.

In the last edition I went to some lengths to describe how I actually selected a particular hotel. Another question people very often ask me is about the general hotel picture. Where do I think hotels are going? Up or down? Obviously, this is an extremely difficult question to answer and one can only do it in vague generalisations. In the United States for instance, I believe that the *good* hotels are getting better all the time and their standards of service and convenience are very high indeed. Also keeping their end up are Europe's older grand hotels – somehow they seem to have adapted to the changes in society and provide a type of accommodation which is still very much in demand. One wishes the same could be said for the thousands of newer hotels springing up in and around the big cities – unspeakable monstrosities of concrete and plastic which one should avoid at all costs. In Europe, the real winners in the quality stakes are, in my opinion, the country hotels – especially in Britain, France and Italy. In their case, small is beautiful and they seem to have gained a new lease of life.

There is little doubt in my mind that when every aspect is taken into consideration – architecture and decor, service and management skills – hotels in Southern Asia and the Far East are scoring points at every turn and their excellence is now a legend. Hotels in Hong Kong, Singapore and Japan for instance compare extremely favourably with the best in the world and service is their greatest asset. As for South America and the greater part of Africa, these are, alas, hotel deserts. Two final points for those who read this book. Do write in, give your opinions, air your views, tell us where you think we are right or wrong and in fact help us by making the next edition even better. THE 300 BEST HOTELS IN THE WORLD relies on your experiences.

As we have stated, the book is totally non-commercial and it thrives on its sales alone. If you like the book, tell your friends, talk about it, spread the word and help us insure that THE 300 BEST HOTELS IN THE WORLD becomes for the many what it is for the few – the standard travel companion for all those who value quality in their travels.

Bon voyage.

HOTEL REPRESENTATION AND RESERVATION COMPANIES

ADDRESSES AND TELEPHONE NUMBERS CHANGE FREQUENTLY.
IN CASE OF DOUBT, READERS SHOULD CONSULT THEIR LOCAL DIRECTORY
AND/OR ACCREDITED TRAVEL AGENT.

AER LINGUS
LONDON: Aer Lingus House, 51 Poland Street, London, W1V 4AA. 01-734-1212
NEW YORK: 122 East 42nd Street, New York, N.Y. 10017. (212) 557-1090 (Executive offices); (212) 557-1110 (Reservations)
and worldwide

AIR FRANCE
LONDON: 158 New Bond Street, London, W1Y 0AY. 01-499-9511
NEW YORK: 666 Fifth Avenue, New York, N.Y. 10019. (212) 247-0100
and worldwide

AIRTOURS INTERNATIONAL
FRANKFURT: Gartnerweg 4–8, D-6 Frankfurt/m. 79-281

MARK ALLAN TRAVEL LTD
LONDON: 130 Mount Street, Berkeley Square, London, W1Y 5HH. 01-491-3200

AMERICAN WOLFE INTERNATIONAL
NEW YORK: 500 Fifth Avenue, New York, N.Y. 10036. (212) 730-8100

ASTIR HOTEL CO INC
LONDON: 204–208 Tottenham Court Road, London, W1P 9LA. 01-636-0818
BRUSSELS: 75 Defacqz Street, 1050 Brussels, Belgium. (02) 538-8112

ATESA
PARIS: 28 Rue Saint Marc, 75002 Paris, France. 073-3440

AUSTRIAN AIRLINES
LONDON: 50/51 Conduit Street, London, W1R 0NP. 01-439-0741

BAHAMAS RESERVATION SERVICE
LONDON: 23 Old Bond Street, London, W1X 4PQ. 01-491-4800
U.S.A.: 255 Alhambra Circle, Coral Gables, Fl. 33143. (305) 442-4860
FRANKFURT: Poststrasse 2–4, 6000 Frankfurt/m. (0611) 25 20 27

BEST WESTERN HOTELS
U.S.A.: P.O. Box 10203, Phoenix, Arizona, Az. 85064 (2602) 957-4200 tollfree except Arizona (1-800) 528-1234

BRENDAN TOURS
U.S.A.: 510 West Sixth Street, Los Angeles, Ca. 90014. (213) 488-9191

BRITISH AIRWAYS
LONDON: West London Terminal, Cromwell Road, London, SW7 4ED. 01-370-5411

BRITISH TRANSPORT HOTELS LTD
LONDON: St. Pancras Chambers, Euston Road, London, NW1 2TU. 01-387-2878
NEW YORK: 185 Madison Avenue, New York, N.Y. 10006. (212) 684-1820

R. M. BROOKER LTD
U.K.: P.O. Box 90, 1 Old Hall Street, Liverpool, L69 3EP. (051) 236-9306/7

CANADIAN NATIONAL RAILWAYS
LONDON: 17 Cockspur Street, London, SW1Y 5BS. 01-930-2156
CANADA: CN Hotels, 4th Floor, 700 Dorchester Boulevard West, Montreal, Quebec, Canada. (514) 877-3643

CIGA—ITALIAN GRAND HOTELS LTD
LONDON: 67 Jermyn Street, London, SW1. 01-930-4147
NEW YORK: 745 Fifth Avenue, New York, N.Y. 10022. (212) 935-9540
FRANKFURT: Barckhausstrasse 4, D-6000 Frankfurt/m. (0611) 72 97 44
ROME: Via Piemonte 32, 00187 Rome. 475-7198
PARIS: 22 rue de L'Arcade, Paris 75008. 265-8434

JOYCE B. CLARKE ASSOC
MONTREAL: Suite 402, 1117 St. Catherine West, Montreal, 43B 149. (514) 844-4421

COMFORT HOTELS INTERNATIONAL
WASHINGTON: 1735 Eye Street, N.W. Washington D.C., DC 20006. (202) 872-0770

CUNARD
LONDON: see Windotel Ltd
NEW YORK: Cunard, 555 Fifth Avenue, New York, N.Y. 10017. (212) 880-7390

DAN HOTELS CORPORATION
LONDON: Roxburghe House, 273/287 Regent Street, London, W1R 7PB. 01-499-4597
NEW YORK: 120 East 56th Street, New York, N.Y. 10022. (212) 752-6120
TEL AVIV: 99 Hayarkon Street, Tel Aviv, Israel. 03-241141
ZURICH: Talstrasse 82, 8001 Zurich, Switzerland. 01-211-7302

CLAUDE L.C. DUTEIL
PARIS: 11 rue de Rome, Paris 75008. 522-1034

MURIEL FLEGER INTERNATIONAL
ONTARIO: 500 University Avenue, Toronto, Ontario, Canada, M5G 1V7

FOUR SEASONS HOTELS LTD
LONDON: Inn on the Park, Hamilton Place, London, W1A 1AZ. 01-499-0888
CANADA: 1100 Eglinton East Avenue, Toronto, Ontario M3C 1H8. (416) 449 1750
NEW YORK: 32 East 70th Street, New York, N.Y. 10021. (212) 570 9280

GERMAN NATIONAL TOURIST OFFICE
NEW YORK: 747 Third Avenue, New York, N.Y. 10017. (212) 308-3300
LONDON: 61 Conduit Street, London, W1R 0EN. 01-734-2600

GOLDEN TULIP HOTELS RESERVATION SERVICE
See K.L.M. Royal Dutch Airlines

HILTON RESERVATION SERVICE
LONDON: 6 Bedford Avenue, London, WC1. 01-631-1767
NEW YORK: 401 Seventh Avenue, New York, N.Y. 10001. (212) 594-4500 and worldwide/any Hilton Hotel

HOTEL REPRESENTATIVES INC—(HRI—The Leading Hotels of the World)
LONDON: 15 New Bridge Street, London, EC4. 01-583-3050
NEW YORK: 770 Lexington Avenue, New York, N.Y. 10021. (212) 838-7874
and worldwide

IBERIAN SERVICE LTD
LONDON: 116 Judd Street, London, WC1H 9NS. 01-278-1425

INTER-CONTINENTAL HOTELS CORP
LONDON: 13/14 Hanover Street, London, W1R 0LU. 01-493-7578
NEW YORK: 200 Park Avenue, New York, N.Y. 10166. (212) 973-3800
and worldwide/any Inter-Continental Hotel

IRISH TOURIST BOARD
LONDON: Ireland House, 150 New Bond Street, London, W1Y 0AQ. 01-493-3201
NEW YORK: 590 Fifth Avenue, New York. N.Y. 10036. (212) 246-7400

ISRAEL HOTEL REPRESENTATIVE
NEW YORK: 120 East 56th Street, New York, N.Y. 10022. (212) 752-6120

JAPAN TRAVEL BUREAU INTERNATIONAL INC
NEW YORK: 45 Rockefeller Plaza, New York, N.Y. 10020. (212) 246-8030

HARRY JARVINEN & ASSOCIATES
NEW YORK: 25 West 43rd Street, New York, N.Y. 10036. (212) 354-2077
LOS ANGELES: 1717 North Highland Avenue, Los Angeles, Ca. 90028. (213) 462-6391 tollfree except Ca. (1-800) 421-0767

K.L.M. ROYAL DUTCH AIRLINES (Golden Tulip Hotels Reservation Service)
LONDON: Time and Life Building, 153 New Bond Street, London, W1Y 0AD. 01-568-9144
NEW YORK: 437 Madison Avenue, New York, N.Y. 10022. (212) 247-7950

KNIGHTSBRIDGE MARKETING SERVICE INC
FRAMINGHAM: 1661 Worcester Road, Mass 01701, U.S.A. (800) 982-4770 (Mass); (800) 255-2230 tollfree elsewhere

LANDMARK INTERNATIONAL HOTELS LTD
LONDON: Landmark House, 1 Great Scotland Yard, London, SW1A 2HJ. 01-930-1735

NICHOLAS LAWSON LTD
LONDON: 30 Old Bond Street, London, W1Y 3AD. 01-491-7431

RALPH LOCKE
NEW YORK: 315 East 72nd Street, New York, N.Y. 10021. (212) 628-8149. Outside New York (800) 223-1108

LOEWS REPRESENTATION INTERNATIONAL
LONDON: The Churchill Hotel, 30 Portman Square, London, W1H 0AJ. 01-486-3213
NEW YORK: 666 Fifth Avenue, New York, N.Y. 10019. (212) 841-1111
and worldwide

MARRIOTT HOTELS INC
LONDON: 25 Southampton Street, London, WC2E 7JH. 01-836-8521
U.S.A.: Marriott Drive, Washington, D.C. 20058. (800) 228-9290 tollfree

McDONOUGH HOTELS
U.S.A.: P.O. Box 1825, Parkesburg, W.V. 26101. (800) 624-1921

MERIDIEN RESERVATION INTERNATIONAL
LONDON: Air France House, 158 New Bond Street, London, W1Y 0AY. 01-493-0609
NEW YORK: 1350 Avenue of the Americas, New York, N.Y. 10019. (212) 841-7499
and any Air France office worldwide

JOHN MILLER
SYDNEY: Scottish House, 17/19 Bridge Street, Sydney, N.S.W. 2000. 241-2727

DAVID B. MITCHELL & CO INC
NEW YORK: 200 Madison Avenue, New York, N.Y. 10016. (212) 371-1323

MORRIS ASSOCIATES LTD
LONDON: Premier House, 150 Southampton Row, London, WC1B 5AL. 01-278-8091

RAY MORROW ASSOCIATES
U.S.A.: 360 Main Street, Ridgefield, Connecticut, Ct 06877. (203) 438-3793 tollfree
except Ct (800) 243-9420

ERNEST J. NEWMAN INC
NEW YORK: 770 Broadway, New York, N.Y. 10003. (212) 420-0360

OBEROI HOTELS
LONDON: Loews Representation International, The Churchill Hotel, 30 Portman
Square, London, W1H 0AJ. 01-486-3213
DELHI: 7 Sham Nath Marg, Delhi 110054. 221-411
and worldwide

PREFERRED HOTELS ASSOCIATION
TORONTO: Prince Hotel, 900 York Mills Road, Toronto, Canada M3B 3H2. (800)
323-7500 (U.S.A. except Illinois), (800) 942-7400 (Illinois)

PRESTIGE HOTELS
LONDON: 13–14 Golden Square, London, W1R 3AG. 01-734-6446

PRINCESS RESERVATION SERVICE
FRANKFURT: 6000 Frankfurt/m, Rossmarkt 10. (0611) 29 53 53

QANTAS AIRWAYS
LONDON: 500 Chiswick High Road, London, W4 5RW. 01-995-1344
NEW YORK: 542 Fifth Avenue, New York, N.Y. 10022. (800) 227-4500

REGENT INTERNATIONAL HOTELS
LONDON: 149 Sloane Street, London, SW1X 9BZ. 01-730-8687
NEW YORK: 122 East 55th Street, New York, N.Y. 10022. (212) 935-4950

ROBERT REID ASSOCIATES
LONDON: Walmar House, 288 Regent Street, London, W1R 5HE. 01-580-8313/4
NEW YORK: 1270 Avenue of the Americas, New York, N.Y. 10020. (212) 757-2444

RELAIS ET CHATEAUX
PARIS: Hotel de Crillon, 10 Place de la Concorde, 75008 Paris. 742-0020

ROCKRESORTS RESERVATIONS INC
NEW YORK: 30 Rockefeller Plaza, New York, N.Y. 10019. (212) 765-5950

SCOTT CALDER INTERNATIONAL
NEW YORK: 295 Madison Avenue, New York, N.Y. 10017. (212) 535 9530

SERGAT
PARIS: 9 rue Guenegaud, 75006 Paris. 325-3429

SHERATON RESERVATIONS
LONDON: Roxburghe House, 273 Regent Street, London, W1R 8BJ. 01-636-6411
BOSTON: Sixty State Street, Mass. 02109, U.S.A. (617) 367-3600, tollfree (800) 325-3535
and Sheraton Hotels/Sheraton Reservation offices worldwide

SOFITEL—First French Hotels
LONDON: 8th Floor, 16 Berkeley Street, London, W1X 5AE. 01-499-0734
PARIS: 8 rue Louis Armand, 75738 Paris 15. 554-9500

STEIGENBERGER RESERVATION SERVICE
LONDON: 12A Maddox Street, London, W1R 9PL. 01-629-9792
NEW YORK: 40 East 49th Street, New York, N.Y. 10017. (212) 593-2988
and worldwide

SUPEREPS INTERNATIONAL
LONDON: Suite 433, High Holborn House, 52 High Holborn, London, WC1V 6RL. 01-242-9964

SUPRANATIONAL RESERVATIONS SERVICE
LONDON: Thistle Hotels Reservations Centre, c/o Kensington Palace Hotel, De Vere Gdns., London, W8 5AF. 01-937-8033

THE TAJ GROUP OF HOTELS, INDIA
LONDON: Utell International, Banda House, Cambridge Grove, London, W6 0LE. 01-741-1588
INDIA: Central Reservation Service, The Taj Mahal Inter-Continental, Apollo Bunder, Bombay 400 039. 243-366

JOHN A. TETLEY CO INC
U.S.A.: 3075 Wilshire Boulevard, Los Angeles, Ca. 90010. (213) 388-1151, tollfree (800) 421-0000 except Ca., (800) 252-0211 (California)

TRUST HOUSE FORTE
LONDON: Paramount House, 71/75 Uxbridge Road, Ealing, London, W5 5SL. 01-567-3444
NEW YORK: 810 Seventh Avenue, New York, N.Y. 10019. (212) 541-4400
and worldwide

UNITED TOURING INTERNATIONAL
LONDON: Blue Star House, Highgate Hill, London, N19 5UT. 01-263-8591

UTELL INTERNATIONAL
LONDON: Banda House, Cambridge Grove, London, W6 0LE. 01-741-1588
NEW YORK: 119 West 57th Street, New York, N.Y. 10019. (212) 757-2981
and worldwide

ROBERT F. WARNER
NEW YORK: 711 Third Avenue, New York, N.Y. 10017. (212) 687-5750
ALSO: Boston, Lausanne, Miami, Toronto and Washington

WESTIN HOTELS RESERVATION SERVICE
LONDON: 7/8 Conduit Street, London, W1R 8QT. 01-408-0636
U.S.A.: The Westin Building, Seattle, Wa. 98121. (206) 447-5022 tollfree U.S.A.
(800) 228-3000, tollfree Canada (800) 268-8383
or any Westin Hotel worldwide

WINDOTEL LTD
LONDON: 149 Sloane Street, London, SW1X 9BZ. 01-730-7144/5

ABOUT THE GUIDE

★ **CLASSIFICATION:** The countries covered are listed in alphabetical order and within these countries the cities in which the hotels are located. The only exceptions are the Caribbean islands which are all grouped under the headings Caribbean, South Pacific and South America.

★ **ENTRIES:** All entries are in two sections – a practical section giving the hotel's vital statistics and a personal comment. The vital statistics have been communicated by the hotels concerned and while it is likely that most of them are accurate, we cannot accept responsibility for those that are not – especially in such matters as the size of bedrooms etc. Every hotel has been visited personally and recently by the Editor or by our own correspondents and opinions have been double-checked against those of others. However, it is possible that changes have occurred in certain hotels due to the length of time taken in producing the Guide.

★ **PRICES:** Much as we would have liked to include prices, in practice this has not proved possible due to inflation, changes in currency rates, seasonal variations etc. Readers will find that worldwide reservations offices quote prices under three headings: CP (Continental Plan) which means room and breakfast; AP (American plan) which means room and all meals; and MAP (Modified American Plan) which means room, breakfast and either lunch or dinner. In holiday resort areas at the height of the season, hotels are often unwilling to quote for anything except AP.

Room prices also vary considerably with orientation and elevation and whether a room is classified as 'standard' or 'de luxe'. A suite is generally accepted to comprise a bedroom and a sitting room – but this is not always the case, especially in Mediterranean countries, and readers are advised to make proper inquiries. Although no rules apply to room service worldwide, it must be understood that this is charged for.

★ **MERIT:** As stated in the Foreword to the Guide, no stars or other emblems of merit are awarded. Hotels included in this Guide cannot therefore be compared one with the other but simply accepted as the best I know in the locality. Neither am I able to rate the standard of food except in a personal way. This Guide being produced by Europeans, naturally comments on hotels and food are those which would be best understood by the average, well-travelled European.

★ **RESERVATIONS:** Most hotels in the Guide are represented by booking agencies which are listed under each entry, with their latest addresses listed on the pages following. Booking agencies make no charge to the client for this service and will supply a confirmation notice.

★ **COMMENTS PLEASE:** As stated in the Foreword, no guide is ever perfect. THE 300 BEST HOTELS IN THE WORLD is not perfect either. The Guide is published every two years and future editions will be only as good and complete as readers of this edition can make it. If you have any complaints, remarks, additions or comments to make, please do so in writing to:

The Travel Editor (Hotel Guide)
HARPERS & QUEEN, NATIONAL MAGAZINE HOUSE,
72 BROADWICK STREET, LONDON W1V 2BP

THE
300 BEST HOTELS
IN THE WORLD

AUSTRALIA
Melbourne

HILTON INTERNATIONAL MELBOURNE, Cnr. Wellington Parade and Clarendon Streets, East Melbourne, Victoria 3002

- ★ TELEPHONE: 419-3311
- ★ CABLES: Hiltels Melbourne
- ★ TELEX: 33057/Himel AA
- ★ IN OPERATION: since December, 1974
- ★ RESERVATIONS: Hilton International
- ★ ROOMS: 78 doubles 316 twins
- ★ SUITES: 22
- ★ RESTAURANTS: 4
- ★ BARS: 3
- ★ DISCOTHEQUE: yes and live piano music in Tapestry Lounge
- ★ SHOPS: 6 – beauty shop/hairdresser, barber, car rental, drugstore/news stand/souvenirs, liquor store and speciality shop
- ★ CONFERENCE ROOMS: 12 (40 to 1,200)
- ★ BANQUETING ROOMS: 12 (40 to 800)
- ★ STANDARD BEDROOM SIZE: 25 m^2
- ★ PRIVATE BALCONIES: no
- ★ SWIMMING POOL: yes – fresh water, 18 × 5 m
- ★ GARDENS: no

- ★ RECREATIONAL ACTIVITIES: health club with sauna and massage, golf and tennis nearby
- ★ NO. OF STAFF: 435
- ★ ROOM SERVICE: around the clock
- ★ ORIENTATION: rooms overlook Melbourne Cricket Ground, Yarra Park and Fitzroy Gardens
- ★ FURTHER DEVELOPMENTS: extra recreation facilities including tennis and squash courts
- ★ CREDIT CARDS: Carte Blanche, American Express, Master Charge, Eurocard, Diners Club, Hilton Hotels, Bankamericard and Air Canada
- ★ OWNING COMPANY: The T. & G. Mutual Life Assurance Society Ltd
- ★ GENERAL MANAGER: Frank D. Christie
- ★ DISTANCE TO BEACH: 5 km
- ★ DISTANCE TO SHOPS: 800 m
- ★ DISTANCE FROM AIRPORT: 24 km

There is always an exception to everything and the Melbourne Hilton is surely an exception to what I have said elsewhere about Australian hotels – it's one of the best and also one which can compete internationally with any big city hotel. Though I don't like the architecture much, the whole hotel, as befits Melbourne, is very gentlemanly and very quiet, despite its size. Rooms are particularly attractive – simple and beautifully furnished in a good international style which does not offend, the lighting is perfect – a rare thing – and items like beds, linen and equipment are of the best. There is one public-room chandelier I don't much care for but the rest is extremely tasteful, spacious, cool and welcoming. Service is well above average for a chain hotel and so is the food which I thought was very appetising.

THE HOTEL WINDSOR, Spring Street, Melbourne, Victoria 3000

- ★ TELEPHONE: (03) 630261
- ★ CABLES: 'Telwindsor' Melbourne
- ★ TELEX: AA30437
- ★ IN OPERATION: 97 years
- ★ RESERVATIONS: R. M. Brooker Ltd, UK

and Europe/Utell International, The Americas and Asia/Loews Representation International, U.S.A., Canada, Mexico, London and Tokyo/Stinnes Touristic

Representations, Frankfurt/Oberoi Hotels Reservation Offices
- ★ ROOMS: 170
- ★ SUITES: 19
- ★ RESTAURANTS: White Hart Grill, Grand Dining Room, Windsor Luncheon Club and Windsor Lounge
- ★ BARS: 3 – Cricketers Bar, Winston Cocktail Lounge and Windsor Corner Bar
- ★ SHOPS: 1 – hairdressing salon
- ★ DISCOTHEQUE: no – live music in Grand Dining Room
- ★ CONFERENCE ROOMS: 3 (70 to 370)
- ★ BANQUETING ROOMS: 3 (50 to 210)
- ★ STANDARD BEDROOM SIZE: 28 m²
- ★ PRIVATE BALCONIES: no
- ★ SWIMMING POOL: no

- ★ RECREATIONAL ACTIVITIES: all facilities are available within a short distance of the hotel
- ★ GARDENS: no
- ★ NO. OF STAFF: 200
- ★ ROOM SERVICE: around the clock
- ★ ORIENTATION: faces Parliament Building
- ★ CREDIT CARDS: American Express, Bankcard, Carte Blanche, Diners Club and Master Charge
- ★ OWNING COMPANY: Federal Hotels
- ★ OPERATING COMPANY: Oberoi Hotels (Australia) Pty Ltd
- ★ GENERAL MANAGER: Mr. Gary Keiseker
- ★ DISTANCE TO BEACH: 5 km
- ★ DISTANCE TO SHOPS: ½ km
- ★ DISTANCE FROM AIRPORT: 20 km

The matrons of Melbourne – the most nose-in-the-air city in Australia – must have had quite a shock when their famous Windsor Hotel was taken over by an Indian company. I mean, it must be rather like having Claridges managed by some Brazilian entrepreneur. I am glad to say that, after many inquiries among the most toffee-nosed people, there has been no revolution and it is to the credit of a company like Oberoi to take over one of the grand hotels of the world and make it their own without anyone batting an eyelid. Knowing them, I never doubted it. So the Windsor remains what it has always been – Australia's most 'Pommie' hotel, lush, plush, a little old fashioned perhaps but with that feeling of grandeur which gets you. Rooms are often enormous and as for public rooms – it's like those old Victorian railway stations: one has to run fast and far to reach the train/reception desk. Service is now far better (it needed to be) and the food more cautious and less given to weekly disasters. The Indian presence is there, behind the scenes, counting the rupees and the figures show that Indians can compete with the best when it comes to running a hotel.

Sydney

SEBEL TOWN HOUSE, 23 Elizabeth Bay Road, Elizabeth Bay, N.S.W. 2011
- ★ TELEPHONE: (02) 358-3244
- ★ CABLES: Sebelhotel
- ★ TELEX: 20067
- ★ IN OPERATION: since 1963
- ★ RESERVATIONS: Hotel Representative Inc, worldwide
- ★ ROOMS: 165 doubles
- ★ SUITES: 23
- ★ RESTAURANTS: 1
- ★ BARS: 1
- ★ DISCOTHEQUE: no
- ★ SHOPS: 2 – gift shop and beauty and hairdressing salon
- ★ CONFERENCE ROOMS: 4 (20 to 250)
- ★ BANQUETING ROOMS: 6 (20 to 500)
- ★ STANDARD BEDROOM SIZE: 47 m²
- ★ PRIVATE BALCONIES: yes

- ★ SWIMMING POOL: yes – fresh water, heated, 10 × 4 m
- ★ RECREATIONAL ACTIVITIES: sauna
- ★ GARDENS: roof garden/sundeck
- ★ NO. OF STAFF: 230
- ★ ROOM SERVICE: around the clock
- ★ ORIENTATION: views of Sydney Harbour
- ★ CREDIT CARDS: Diners Club, American Express, Carte Blanche, Master Charge and Visa
- ★ OWNING COMPANY: Sebel Town House, Mirvac Pty Ltd
- ★ GENERAL MANAGER: Henry Rose
- ★ DISTANCE TO BEACH: 1 km
- ★ DISTANCE TO SHOPS: 300 m
- ★ DISTANCE FROM AIRPORT: 7 km

One American lady tycoon wrote in recently and said that she had just returned from two weeks in the Pacific. 'Apart from Japan and Hong Kong,' she wrote, 'Sebel Town House was the best city hotel I encountered in the whole trip . . .' How nice to have one's own opinions vindicated in such a positive manner (sometimes, it's the other way around . . .). I too like this hotel very much indeed and, at the risk of making enemies, I would suggest it is the best hotel in Australia.

It is not just one of those ever-present concrete blocks. It has personality (that of the genial owner), character, good taste and that hard-to-define feeling of wellbeing which is so rare. One is at home, comfortable, well-cared-for and known by name. Bedrooms are quite large, nicely furnished and with superb views of that incredible city. Service is smiling and efficient – I remember the valet who almost apologised for having replaced a missing button on a shirt. There is a top floor swimming pool, again with fantastic views.

In the restaurant, your table groans with the best things Australia can offer – especially the seafood, the steaks and of course the wines. Definitely a highly civilised hotel in the heart of an exciting city.

WENTWORTH HOTEL, 61–101 Phillip Street, Sydney, N.S.W. 2000

★ TELEPHONE: 230-0700
★ CABLE: Wenthotel Sydney
★ TELEX: AA 21227
★ IN OPERATION: since December, 1966
★ RESERVATIONS: Sheraton Reservations, worldwide
★ ROOMS: 398 doubles 17 singles
★ SUITES: 33
★ RESTAURANTS: 4 – Garden Court International Restaurant, Impressions Grill Room, The Last Train Coffee Shop and the Old Sydney Buttery
★ BARS: 5
★ DISCOTHEQUE: live music with dancing for dinner in the Garden Court Restaurant
★ SHOPS: 16
★ CONFERENCE ROOMS: 13 (10 to 1,000)

★ BANQUETING ROOMS: 13 (10 to 600)
★ STANDARD BEDROOM SIZE: 25 m^2
★ PRIVATE BALCONIES: no
★ SWIMMING POOL: no
★ GARDENS: no
★ NO. OF STAFF: 620
★ ROOM SERVICE: around the clock
★ ORIENTATION: the main facade faces Phillip Street and the city
★ CREDIT CARDS: American Express and Wentworth Hotel
★ OWNING COMPANY: operated by Sheraton Corp
★ GENERAL MANAGER: Peter Thompson
★ DISTANCE TO BEACH: 5 km
★ DISTANCE TO SHOPS: 100 m
★ DISTANCE FROM AIRPORT: 8 km

A 'pommie' (from POHM, prisoner of His Majesty, written on early convicts' clothes, i.e. British) came back from a week at the Wentworth recently with this anecdote: 'They not only took all my telephone messages when I was out but they listed them in order and when I got back, the telephone operator used to ring me and ask "Shall I ring them back in turn, sir?" . . . Not a bad hotel at all – for Australia . . .'. The last convict ship cast anchor here over one hundred years ago – plenty time enough for a tradition of service to lose its flavour of compulsion. It is now untrue to assume that Australians don't know the hotel business. Here, at the Wentworth is ample demonstration of this. Its service is excellent and the food in its several restaurants is far above Australia's admittedly still depressed average. The hotel never seems to sleep and yet, when you are in your room, you hear little noise. Those rooms are average in size but well, if perhaps a little impersonally, furnished. Management is obviously very much on its toes and you will like the Wentworth because it does not pretend to be other than a thoroughly good city hotel.

AUSTRIA

Dürnstein

HOTEL SCHLOSS DURNSTEIN, A-3601 Dürnstein, Donau

- ★ TELEPHONE: 02711 212
- ★ CABLES: Dürnstein
- ★ TELEX: 071 147
- ★ IN OPERATION: since 1970
- ★ RESERVATIONS: Relais et Chateaux
- ★ ROOMS: 27 doubles 4 singles
- ★ SUITES: 2
- ★ RESTAURANTS: 1
- ★ RECREATIONAL ACTIVITIES: sauna
- ★ GARDENS: no
- ★ NO. OF STAFF: 33
- ★ ROOM SERVICE: around the clock
- ★ ORIENTATION: facing Danube River
- ★ FURTHER DEVELOPMENTS: 6 more rooms and a second restaurant
- ★ BARS: 1
- ★ DISCOTHEQUE: no
- ★ SHOPS: none
- ★ CONFERENCE ROOMS: 1 (30)
- ★ BANQUETING ROOMS: 2 (30 and 50)
- ★ STANDARD BEDROOM SIZE: 19–65 m²
- ★ PRIVATE BALCONIES: yes – some rooms
- ★ SWIMMING POOL: yes – fresh water, heated, 72 m²
- ★ CREDIT CARDS: American Express, Diners Club, Eurocard, Visa and Master Charge
- ★ OWNING COMPANY: privately owned
- ★ GENERAL MANAGER: Hans Thiery
- ★ DISTANCE TO SHOPS: 100 m
- ★ DISTANCE FROM AIRPORT: 105 km

Occasionally, one hotel can sum up a country better than all the guidebooks ever written. The view from Dürnstein seen, while sitting on that divine terrace overlooking the Danube at its most beautiful, looking at the riverboats gliding by, could melt an Ayahtollah. Inside, amid the lovely period furnishings were some of those gorgeous enamel stoves which one would love to take home if only the owner was not looking. As for the pastries on the post-lunch trolley, they might get a little stale if one took them home but they would still be better than any one could buy. Bedrooms are often vast and very beautiful – mine had a magnificent carved ceiling of great beauty. Bathrooms are adequate and sometimes very grand. This used to be the country home of the Starhemberg family – as glamorous a name as you could find in Austrian history. Furnishings are splendid, parquet floors shining with the patina of time and the staff are absolutely charming and most helpful. The food is more than one can cope with, as is usually the case in this country, so go easy with each course.

Neumarkt

HOTEL SCHLOSS SIGHARTSTEIN, A-5202 Neumarkt, Salzburg

- ★ TELEPHONE: 06216 251
- ★ CABLES: no
- ★ TELEX: no
- ★ IN OPERATION: since 1935
- ★ RESERVATIONS: direct
- ★ ROOMS: direct
- ★ ROOMS: 5 doubles 3 singles
- ★ SUITES: 1
- ★ RESTAURANTS: 1
- ★ BARS: 1
- ★ DISCOTHEQUE: no
- ★ SHOPS: none
- ★ CONFERENCE ROOMS: 2 (30 to 35)
- ★ BANQUETING ROOMS: 1 (25)
- ★ STANDARD BEDROOM SIZE: 30–40 m²
- ★ PRIVATE BALCONIES: only 2 rooms
- ★ SWIMMING POOL: no
- ★ RECREATIONAL ACTIVITIES: trout fishing
- ★ GARDENS: yes
- ★ NO. OF STAFF: 2–7
- ★ ROOM SERVICE: 07.00–21.00
- ★ ORIENTATION: west
- ★ CREDIT CARDS: none
- ★ OWNING COMPANY: Dr. Martin Palfry (family owned)
- ★ GENERAL MANAGER: François Palfry
- ★ DISTANCE TO BEACH: 1.5 km to Lake Wallersee
- ★ DISTANCE TO SHOPS: 24 km (Salzburg)
- ★ DISTANCE FROM AIRPORT: 22 km (Salzburg) 120 km (Munich)

When is a hotel like a private home? The answer of course is when it is a private home and that certainly applies to Sighartstein. One lady from New York, who wrote about this place before I had had a chance to see it, said: 'Never in my life have I felt more like an honoured guest.' I felt the same way and I very much hope that only a few of us at a time will come to try it for ourselves because this is one of the smallest hotels in the guide.

If you are lucky, the castle's own 'Gräfin' might be on hand to welcome you into this enchanting manor house, a few miles from Salzburg overlooking the beautiful Wallersee. White walls, superb antiques, lovely furniture, heirlooms everywhere and over it all that feeling of upper class Austrian gemütlichkeit which can hardly be described. Rooms are vast and truly baronial and the service is conducted by old family servants. There are fresh flowers everywhere and there is no such thing as cost accounting in this place – you get what your hosts get and that is a way of life evolved over 600 years of occupation by the same family. The gardens are quite lovely and you can go trout fishing nearby or visiting the whole of that heavenly Salzkammergut.

Salzburg
HOTEL OSTERREICHISCHER HOF, Schwarzstrasse 5–7, 5024 Salzburg

- ★ TELEPHONE: 72541
- ★ CABLES: Austriahotel
- ★ TELEX: 633 590
- ★ RESERVATIONS: Steigenberger Reservation Service
- ★ ROOMS: 120
- ★ SUITES: 2
- ★ RESTAURANTS: 5
- ★ BARS: 1
- ★ DISCOTHEQUE: no
- ★ SHOPS: none
- ★ CONFERENCE ROOMS: 4 (10 to 350)
- ★ BANQUETING ROOMS: 4 (10 to 350)
- ★ STANDARD BEDROOM SIZE: 24 m²

- ★ PRIVATE BALCONIES: yes
- ★ SWIMMING POOL: no
- ★ GARDENS: no
- ★ NO. OF STAFF: 230
- ★ ROOM SERVICE: 07.00–22.00
- ★ ORIENTATION: rooms face river
- ★ CREDIT CARDS: American Express, Diners Club and Eurocard
- ★ OWNING COMPANY: Blanckenstein-Segur-Cabanac OHG
- ★ GENERAL MANAGER: Herbert Prinz
- ★ DISTANCE TO SHOPS: walking distance
- ★ DISTANCE FROM AIRPORT: 5 km

The music around this hotel may be Mozart but the food is certainly Wagnerian – I have never seen such fantastic and beautiful portions of everything; I feel sure that if I ate as much as I was given there would be a Hoteleditordämmerung. Obviously, the great musicians who stayed at the Osterreichischer Hof over the years (Bruno Walter, Toscanini, Backhaus, Oistrakh et al.) must have been careful. This, Salzburg's best hotel, is not a grand hotel in the strict sense of the word but it is very good indeed, very comfortable and admirably run and its position across the river Salzbach gives you a chance to see Wolfgang Amadeus' city properly and leave its streets to the trippers. Rooms are good and comfortable, sometimes a little old fashioned but always spotlessly clean and fresh and the service is of a high standard considering that this hotel must have one of the highest occupancy rates in Austria.

HOTEL SCHLOSS FUSCHL, 5322 Hof Bei, Salzburg

- ★ TELEPHONE: 06229/253
- ★ CABLES: Fuschlschloss
- ★ TELEX: 633454
- ★ IN OPERATION: 37 years
- ★ RESERVATIONS: Robert F. Warner, Inc, New York

- ★ ROOMS: 49 doubles 15 singles
- ★ SUITES: 8
- ★ RESTAURANTS: 3
- ★ BARS: 1
- ★ DISCOTHEQUE: no
- ★ SHOPS: none

- ★ CONFERENCE ROOMS: 1 (up to 60)
- ★ BANQUETING ROOMS: 2 (up to 120)
- ★ STANDARD BEDROOM SIZE: 24 m²
- ★ PRIVATE BALCONIES: yes – most rooms
- ★ SWIMMING POOL: yes – fresh water, 4 × 8 m
- ★ RECREATIONAL ACTIVITIES: sauna, massage, 9-hole golf course, boating, surfing, tennis, bowling and rifle range
- ★ GARDENS: yes

- ★ NO. OF STAFF: 150
- ★ ROOM SERVICE: 07.00–01.00
- ★ ORIENTATION: facing east over lake
- ★ CREDIT CARDS: American Express, Diners Club and Eurocard
- ★ OWNING COMPANY: private
- ★ GENERAL MANAGER: Uwe Zeilerbauer
- ★ DISTANCE TO BEACH: 100 m (private)
- ★ DISTANCE TO SHOPS: 15 km
- ★ DISTANCE FROM AIRPORT: 35 km

Standing at the head of the famous lake (The White Horse Inn isn't far away) and surrounded by a truly magnificent park, this is one of the most celebrated castle hotels in the Austrian heartland – a place of such charm, such beauty and such refinement that there is no possible way it could be better. Built during the fifteenth/sixteenth century, Fuschl is a period pearl, vaulted rooms, tortuous passages leading to great vistas of painted ceilings and panelled walls and suddenly emerging into an absolutely divine lakeside terrace where poetic fantasy comes naturally, both on your plate and in your mind. The interior dining room has a caisson ceiling of great beauty and the wintergarden room is one of the most romantic I know. Down below, in the marbled entrails of this fantastic house, the pale green swimming pool is fit for Rhine maidens. Rooms naturally vary in size but not in decor – all quite perfectly furnished, with period pieces beautifully arranged. Service is quiet and dignified and when you sit in one of the Savonarola chairs in the bar sipping some delicious plum brandy, you might be forgiven for thinking that this is the only way to live.

Vienna

HOTEL IMPERIAL, Karntnerring 16, 1015 Vienna

- ★ TELEPHONE: (0222) 65 17 65
- ★ CABLES: Imperialhotel Wien
- ★ TELEX: 01/12630
- ★ IN OPERATION: since 1873
- ★ RESERVATIONS: direct or Hotel Representative Inc, worldwide
- ★ ROOMS: 89 doubles 47 singles
- ★ SUITES: 14
- ★ RESTAURANTS: 2 – Main Dining Room and Viennese Cafe-Restaurant
- ★ BARS: 1
- ★ DISCOTHEQUE: no – but piano music in the restaurants
- ★ SHOPS: none
- ★ CONFERENCE ROOMS: 2 (up to 80)
- ★ BANQUETING ROOMS: 4 (up to 160)

- ★ STANDARD BEDROOM SIZE: 25 m²
- ★ PRIVATE BALCONIES: no
- ★ SWIMMING POOL: no
- ★ GARDENS: no
- ★ STAFF: 260
- ★ ROOM SERVICE: 06.00–23.30
- ★ ORIENTATION: main facade facing the famous Ringstrasse
- ★ CREDIT CARDS: American Express, Diners Club and Eurocard
- ★ OWNING COMPANY: Vereinigte Österreichische Hotel A.G.
- ★ GENERAL MANAGER: Otto N. K. Heinke
- ★ DISTANCE TO SHOPS: walking distance
- ★ DISTANCE FROM AIRPORT: 15 km

Everything about the Imperial is imperial, from the portrait of Franz Josef (larger than life) staring at you from behind his muttonchop whiskers, to the vivacious Austrian baroque of one of the grandest palace hotels in the old world and one which is very dear to all who believe that the first world war killed more than people. Just staying there is like being invited at court. Fantastic marble halls succeed each other like a series of optical illusions, chandeliers glitter and the staff are so marvellously suave and urbane that they could instantly join the diplomatic corps. Rooms and suites are colossal, filled either with gorgeous rococo furniture or the last word in modern. Bathrooms are palatial and admirably equipped and room service, always with a red rose on the tray, is instant. The Imperial has a way of making you feel better, more civilised, more aware of what matters in behaviour and good manners and it also works like a charm thanks to one of the best managements in Europe. The food is superabundant alas, and this is no hotel for the panic-stricken weight-watcher.

HOTEL IM PALAIS SCHWARZENBERG, Schwarzenbergplatz 9, A-1030 Vienna

★ TELEPHONE: (0222) 78-45-15
★ CABLES: Pensionpalais
★ TELEX: 13 61 24
★ IN OPERATION: since 1957
★ RESERVATIONS: direct or Swissair, Austrian Airlines, Air France and British Airways
★ ROOMS: 35 doubles 2 singles
★ STANDARD BEDROOM SIZE: 25 m²
★ PRIVATE BALCONIES: no
★ SWIMMING POOL: no
★ RECREATIONAL ACTIVITIES: tennis and nearby an 18-hole golf course, sauna, horse riding, swimming and sailing
★ GARDENS: yes – 75 acres of private park
★ NO. OF STAFF: 102
★ ORIENTATION: rooms face private gardens – south/west

★ SUITES: 4
★ RESTAURANTS: 1
★ BARS: 1
★ DISCOTHEQUE: no
★ SHOPS: none
★ CONFERENCE ROOMS: 8 (up to 300)
★ BANQUETING ROOMS: 8 (up to 1,000)
★ ROOM SERVICE: around the clock
★ CREDIT CARDS: Diners Club, Eurocard, Master Charge and Visa
★ OWNING COMPANY: Furst Karl Johannes v. Schwarzenberg
★ GENERAL MANAGER: Pierre Roth
★ DISTANCE TO SHOPS: 5 minutes' walking distance
★ DISTANCE FROM AIRPORT: 26 km

As I wrote in the last edition, if you have a weakness for grand palaces, this is the place to stay. It is lodged in a wing of the great Schwarzenberg family's ancestral home, right in the middle of Vienna and with its own 75-acre park. The entrance is so discreet that you have to look hard to find the word 'hotel'.

Once inside, it's a different world. Magnificent public rooms ablaze with history: beautiful panelling, paintings and tapestries and furniture that rightly belongs in a museum. Beds are especially stately – one could hold a new Congress of Vienna in most of them. For myself alas, I always manage to get a crick in the neck in this hotel – the Schwarzenberg's ceilings, all painted caissons, are absolutely magnificent.

The staff are nice, helpful and very, very discreet and some of them look as if they had been there when Franz Josef was on the throne of the Dual Monarchy. The food has improved a little since my last visit but I for one would not travel to Austria for it. It does not much matter – Vienna, with its many gastronomic spots, is all around.

BAHAMAS

Eleuthera

WINDERMERE ISLAND HOTEL AND CLUB, P.O. Box 25, Rock Sound, Eleuthera

★ TELEPHONE: (809) 332-2566
★ CABLES: Windermere Eleuthera Bahamas
★ TELEX: no
★ IN OPERATION: 15 years
★ RESERVATIONS: Windermere Island Club, Greenwich, U.S.A./Robert Reid Associates Ltd, London

★ ROOMS: 21
★ SUITES: 10 and 10 2-bedroomed apartments
★ RESTAURANTS: 1
★ BARS: 1 and a bar at the beach
★ DISCOTHEQUE: no – but live music twice a week by Calypso singer or native band

- ★ SHOPS: tennis house has a shop for club items
- ★ CONFERENCE ROOMS: 1 (35 m²: up to 50)
- ★ BANQUETING ROOMS: 2 (30 to 60)
- ★ STANDARD BEDROOM SIZE: 25 m²
- ★ PRIVATE BALCONIES: all rooms have balcony or terrace
- ★ SWIMMING POOL: yes – fresh water, 10 × 5 m
- ★ RECREATIONAL ACTIVITIES: 6 tennis courts, bicycles, sun fish, windsurfing, waterskiing, snorkelling, canoe, bone-fishing. Shelling and bird watching. Golf about 45 minutes away
- ★ GARDENS: yes
- ★ NO. OF STAFF: 60
- ★ ROOM SERVICE: 08.00–09.30
- ★ ORIENTATION: rooms overlook 2½ mile beach and Atlantic Ocean and face east
- ★ CREDIT CARDS: none
- ★ OWNING COMPANY: Windermere Beach Apartments Ltd
- ★ GENERAL MANAGER: Mr. Allen G. Sawer
- ★ DISTANCE TO BEACH: 30 m
- ★ DISTANCE TO SHOPS: nearest towns 15–30 km
- ★ DISTANCE FROM AIRPORT: 30 km (Rock Sound), 40 km (Governor's Habour)

The trouble with so-called tropical beach resorts is that no sooner have you discovered one than it is no longer worthwhile because travel agents have been there before you and filled it with people you would not wish to meet back home. The charming Bahamas, with some of the clearest seas in the world surrounding them, are, alas, a bit like that. In my opinion if you want the Bahamas and exclusivity, you either take your own yacht or go to Windermere Island, one of the few, very few places which has kept its end up. Let's hope it never becomes really 'popular'. Its beaches are among the finest anywhere, its facilities are great and somehow it never appears overdone and that is obviously because great taste and much fastidiousness have gone into its making. Good-looking simplicity would be my verdict and that, in these days, is difficult enough to find. Service is discreet and smiling and the food nicely Technicolour. What counts however is that here is a small hotel (and club of course) which likes remaining small. This guide, which is known to be very snobbish when it comes to quality, has to acknowledge the fact that some of the nicest people it knows (and does not know) choose Windermere Island regularly. A good reason to go and try it for yourself.

BELGIUM

Bruges

HOTEL DUC DE BOURGOGNE, Huidenvettersplaats 12, 8000 Bruges

- ★ TELEPHONE: 050 33 20 38
- ★ CABLES: Bourgogne-Bruges
- ★ IN OPERATION: 15 years
- ★ RESERVATIONS: direct
- ★ ROOMS: 8 doubles 1 single
- ★ SUITES: none
- ★ RESTAURANTS: 1
- ★ BARS: none
- ★ DISCOTHEQUE: no
- ★ SHOPS: none
- ★ CONFERENCE ROOMS: none
- ★ BANQUETING ROOMS: none – but can cater for small groups of up to 45 persons
- ★ STANDARD BEDROOM SIZE: varied
- ★ PRIVATE BALCONIES: yes – some rooms
- ★ SWIMMING POOL: no
- ★ GARDENS: no
- ★ NO. OF STAFF: 20
- ★ ROOM SERVICE: 07.00–23.00 – breakfast in room
- ★ ORIENTATION: rooms overlook the canal and Tanners Square
- ★ CREDIT CARDS: American Express, Diners Club and Master Charge
- ★ OWNING COMPANY: private
- ★ GENERAL MANAGER: Willy Van de Uyver
- ★ DISTANCE TO BEACH: 13 km
- ★ DISTANCE TO SHOPS: 5 minutes
- ★ DISTANCE FROM AIRPORT: 123 km

With a mere nine rooms this is one of the smallest hotels in the guide – but small is beautiful. Here, in this ravishing old house by the side of the canal in Bruges is miniaturised perfection, a hotel so lovingly furnished and so marvellously kept that it opens your eyes to the finer possibilities of decoration. There are only two reasons to come here – apart from seeing Bruges of course. One is sleeping – in the truly ducal bedrooms, all magnificently furnished in priceless period pieces, lovely great beds and softer-than-soft carpets. The other reason is eating, for the Duc de Bourgogne is one of the most celebrated restaurants in Belgium, a country where they take their sustenance very seriously indeed. You eat in a fantastic tapestried and beamed room, agleam with *objets d'art* and yet the most artistic thing of all is the food on your plate. Quite apart from being Belgian-colossal, it is also extremely choice and lovingly presented as are the wines that go with it. After that it really is a struggle to go out and see this, perhaps the most beautiful city in Flanders.

Brussels

HOTEL AMIGO, Rue de L'Amigo 1/3, B.1000 Brussels

- ★ TELEPHONE: 02.511.59.10
- ★ CABLES: Amigotel
- ★ TELEX: 21618
- ★ IN OPERATION: since 1958
- ★ RESERVATIONS: American Wolfe International, New York/Utell International, London
- ★ ROOMS: 146 doubles 27 singles
- ★ SUITES: 10
- ★ RESTAURANTS: 1
- ★ BARS: 1
- ★ DISCOTHEQUE: no
- ★ SHOPS: 1 – boutique and news stand, etc, and porter's desk
- ★ CONFERENCE ROOMS: 5 (18 to 100)
- ★ BANQUETING ROOMS: 4 (24 to 200)
- ★ STANDARD BEDROOM SIZE: 23 m^2
- ★ PRIVATE BALCONIES: only the presidential suite
- ★ SWIMMING POOL: no
- ★ GARDENS: no
- ★ NO. OF STAFF: 120
- ★ ROOM SERVICE: around the clock
- ★ ORIENTATION: main facade east
- ★ CREDIT CARDS: American Express, Diners Club, Eurocard and Visa
- ★ OWNING COMPANY: Société Hôtelière St. Michel
- ★ GENERAL MANAGER: P. Bouchard
- ★ DISTANCE TO SHOPS: walking distance
- ★ DISTANCE FROM AIRPORT: 20 km

Brussels, this capital of good living and the new Europe, always leaves me in something of a quandary when it comes to hotels. So many have mushroomed to accommodate Eurocrats and their minions that it is hard to avoid the concrete, monolithic leviathans which one can find anywhere these days. This is the principal reason which makes me go for the Amigo, just behind the gothic town hall on the Grand Place. It stands on its own, a fine period building with, inside, quality and individuality. Some of the rooms may not be large enough or palatial enough for some but I infinitely prefer them to the alternative elsewhere. They are well and comfortably furnished in a pleasing way, beautifully kept and serviced. Here one feels like an individual guest – not a transcontinental silicon chip. Besides all this, unless you are one of the above-mentioned Eurocrats, you are where you should be – right in the heart of this very ancient capital. Or, if you are a Eurocrat, you would do well to shift your living allowance to this hotel.

Herbeumont

HOSTELLERIE DU PRIEURÉ DE CONQUES, Route de Florenville 176, B-6803 Herbeumont

★ TELEPHONE: 061-41 14 17
★ CABLES: no
★ TELEX: no
★ IN OPERATION: since March, 1964
★ RESERVATIONS: direct or Relais et Chateaux
★ ROOMS: 11
★ RESTAURANTS: 1
★ BARS: 1
★ DISCOTHEQUE: no – but live music during lunch and dinner times
★ SHOPS: none
★ CONFERENCE ROOMS: 1 (15)
★ BANQUETING ROOMS: none
★ STANDARD BEDROOM SIZE: 18 m²
★ PRIVATE BALCONIES: no

★ SWIMMING POOL: no
★ RECREATIONAL ACTIVITIES: fishing and walking
★ GARDENS: yes
★ NO. OF STAFF: 12
★ ROOM SERVICE: only for breakfast
★ ORIENTATION: all rooms face the south
★ CREDIT CARDS: American Express
★ OWNING COMPANY: Hostellerie du Prieuré de Conques S.A.
★ GENERAL MANAGERS: Mr. and Mrs. F. de Naeyer
★ DISTANCE TO SHOPS: 15 km (Florenville)
★ DISTANCE FROM AIRPORT: 75 km (Luxembourg)

In a small and interesting country which, unfortunately, is not known for the quality of its 'hotels de campagne', here is an exception: a charming eighteenth-century priory deep down in the wooded hills of the Ardennes and so very quiet that a solitary bee at work sounds like an unsilenced motorcycle. The Prieuré is tiny, white-painted and most attractive with handsome lawns and beautiful trees. It is by no means a grand hotel – just a peaceful country place. Rooms are not overlarge but furnished with taste and sensible equipment and the modern bathrooms work very well. There are never more than about twenty people around: interesting people usually – pleasant places attract the best often enough. Take a walk into some of the loveliest countryside in Northern Europe, or just eat – à la Belge – which means a lot and very good.

BERMUDA

CAMBRIDGE BEACHES, Cambridge Road, Somerset 9-08

★ TELEPHONE: 809.294.0331
★ CABLES: Beaches, Bermuda
★ TELEX: 3250 Beach B.A.
★ IN OPERATION: 57 years
★ RESERVATIONS: Robert Reid Associates Inc, New York
★ COTTAGES: 66
★ SUITES: 15
★ RESTAURANTS: 1
★ BARS: 2
★ DISCOTHEQUE: no – but live music
★ SHOPS: none
★ CONFERENCE ROOMS: none
★ BANQUETING ROOMS: none
★ STANDARD BEDROOM SIZE: 40–65 m²
★ PRIVATE BALCONIES: yes

★ SWIMMING POOL: yes – salt water, 50 × 70 ft
★ RECREATIONAL ACTIVITIES: 3 tennis courts, sail boats, power boats and snorkelling
★ GARDENS: yes (25 acres)
★ NO. OF STAFF: 90
★ ROOM SERVICE: breakfast only
★ ORIENTATION: all rooms face the sea
★ CREDIT CARDS: no
★ OWNING COMPANY: Frascati Hotels Ltd
★ GENERAL MANAGER: Hans Fischinger
★ DISTANCE TO BEACH: on the beach
★ DISTANCE TO SHOPS: nearby
★ DISTANCE FROM AIRPORT: 28 km

When people say they are going to Bermuda, I always suggest they should eschew those stupendous palaces dedicated to the pleasures of a certain type of New York weekender and try, instead, something like Cambridge Beaches. This is as near the original Bermuda as you can get – an elegant eighteenth-century mansion in the less frenetic part of the island. Pink and white – the prevailing scheme of decoration – it has a lot of charm, and its cottages have large, airy bedrooms, sitting rooms, terraces and gardens all around.

No fewer than seven beaches, mostly private, await your pleasure. You are on your own in a cosy and charming locality. The staff are friendly but the food tends to be American orientated; however the drinks are tall and frosty. Although not personally bowled over by Bermuda I find Cambridge Beaches highly congenial.

ELBOW BEACH HOTEL, South Shore, Paget

★ TELEPHONE: (809) 295-3535
★ CABLES: Elbobeach
★ TELEX: BA3268
★ IN OPERATION: since 1908
★ RESERVATIONS: Robert F. Warner, New York/Muriel Fleger International, Toronto/Morris Associates, London
★ ROOMS: 296
★ SUITES: 71
★ RESTAURANTS: 3
★ BARS: 4
★ DISCOTHEQUE: yes – and nightclub
★ SHOPS: 2 – gifts and drugstore and beach shop
★ CONFERENCE ROOMS: 3 (20 to 250)
★ BANQUETING ROOMS: 2 (90 to 200)
★ STANDARD BEDROOM SIZE: 30 m²
★ PRIVATE BALCONIES: yes – most rooms
★ SWIMMING POOL: yes – salt water, with children's section

★ RECREATIONAL ACTIVITIES: tennis, children's playground, shuffleboard and golf nearby
★ GARDENS: yes – 28 acres
★ NO. OF STAFF: 400
★ ROOM SERVICE: 08.00–01.00
★ ORIENTATION: most rooms face the ocean
★ FURTHER DEVELOPMENTS: building new rooms in the gardens
★ CREDIT CARDS: none
★ OWNING COMPANY: Elbow Beach Development Co
★ GENERAL MANAGER: John R. Jefferis
★ DISTANCE TO BEACH: 100 m (private)
★ DISTANCE TO SHOPS: 4 km
★ DISTANCE FROM AIRPORT: 15 km

For me this is the best resort hotel in Bermuda. Happily, it combines a cheerful American feeling with a polished and sophisticated continental atmosphere. There is the large hotel building and then, down through the gardens leading to a miraculous pink beach, there are cottages (I'd pick one of those) which offer space and privacy. Bermuda's legendary nine golf courses are all within a cart's drive, there are plenty of beach sports, a very nice swimming pool which you don't need with a beach as good as this. Rooms are fortunately American-sized and beautifully furnished in a quiet, cheerful way with colourful textiles and very good beds plus lots of storage space. You can really swing a no. 3 iron here without danger to anything. The rest of the hotel is both gently dignified and amusingly informal – the evenings are extremely convivial, with music and good company. The beach offers a sensational buffet and at night the main restaurant gleams with silver, glass and good cheer. The food, especially the seafood, is better than average.

LANTANA COLONY CLUB, Somerset Bridge, Sandys 9–20, Bermuda

- ★ TELEPHONE: 809-294-0141
- ★ CABLES: Lantana Bermuda
- ★ TELEX: no
- ★ IN OPERATION: since 1958
- ★ RESERVATIONS: David B. Mitchell & Co Inc, New York/Joyce B. Clarke Associates, Montreal
- ★ ROOMS: 54
- ★ SUITES: Master Suites, Bermuda De Luxe and Lanai Suites and private cottage suites
- ★ RESTAURANTS: 2 – main dining room and attached Solarium and 'La Plage'
- ★ DISCOTHEQUE: no – but dancing to a trio every Tuesday, Thursday and Saturday
- ★ SHOPS: 1
- ★ CONFERENCE ROOMS: none
- ★ BANQUETING ROOMS: none
- ★ STANDARD BEDROOM SIZE: 25–30 m²
- ★ PRIVATE BALCONIES: all suites and cottages
- ★ SWIMMING POOL: yes – fresh water, 6 × 13 m
- ★ RECREATIONAL ACTIVITIES: tennis, with golf and horse riding nearby. Also water skiing, reef and deep sea fishing, putting, croquet and sailing
- ★ GARDENS: yes
- ★ NO. OF STAFF: 81
- ★ ROOM SERVICE: 08.00–10.00 (breakfast only)
- ★ ORIENTATION: fronting upon The Great Sound
- ★ CREDIT CARDS: none
- ★ OWNING COMPANY: Lantana Colony Club Ltd
- ★ GENERAL MANAGER: Paul A. Leseur

For a few years the Lantana Hotel had an off period (it happens to hotels as well as people) but now it is once again one of the most pleasant places in Bermuda. It drapes its pink-washed houses all around some charming, springlike gardens and the whole place has a feeling of cheerful intimacy which is most agreeable. You can have a room in the main house or, much better, one of the cottage suites which are quite splendid with their king- and queen-sized beds, sitting rooms and terraces. Though this is obviously a holiday hotel, the catering is particularly good with culinary efforts that denote a clear understanding of what the art is about. The main restaurant is most attractive as is the wine-list and there is a solarium-garden dining room which gives you the best of the view and the weather.

CARIBBEAN

Antigua

CURTAIN BLUFF HOTEL, P.O. Box 288, Antigua, West Indies

- ★ TELEPHONE: 31115-6
- ★ CABLES: Curb
- ★ TELEX: no
- ★ IN OPERATION: 22 years
- ★ RESERVATIONS: David B. Mitchell & Co Inc, New York
- ★ ROOMS: 52
- ★ SUITES: none
- ★ RESTAURANTS: 2
- ★ BARS: 2
- ★ DISCOTHEQUE: no – live entertainment every evening
- ★ SHOPS: 1
- ★ CONFERENCE ROOMS: none (facilities can be provided for up to 50)
- ★ BANQUETING ROOMS: none (facilities can be provided in split level dining room)
- ★ STANDARD BEDROOM SIZE: 50 m²
- ★ PRIVATE BALCONIES: yes
- ★ SWIMMING POOL: no

★ RECREATIONAL ACTIVITIES: 4 tennis courts and teaching court with professional tuition, and shop. Also sailing, water skiing, aqua lung diving, snorkelling, deep sea trolling and putting
★ GARDENS: yes
★ NO. OF STAFF: 110
★ ROOM SERVICE: 08.00–21.00

★ ORIENTATION: all rooms face the sea
★ CREDIT CARDS: none
★ OWNING COMPANY: Curtain Bluff Ltd
★ GENERAL MANAGER: Edward Sheerin
★ DISTANCE TO BEACH: walking distance
★ DISTANCE TO SHOPS: 20 km
★ DISTANCE FROM AIRPORT: 25 km

If you are Antigua-bound, it is obviously for the beach. Or perhaps one should say beaches since this island has over 300 of them. Two belong to Curtain Bluff which, in these days of Instant Caribbean for so many, strikes one as riches. It drapes its cottages on both sides of a narrow-necked peninsula, with superb sand on each and all the snorkelling, sailing and sun-worshipping you could wish for. It is an American-owned resort hotel but the Bermuda-shorts brigade is not at all overpowering. Rooms are gigantic which is nice in these parts and each one has a handsome terrace. White cane furniture, pretty hangings and extremely good bathrooms complete this Caribbean haven. There are lots of open spaces, lovely gardens and tennis courts and the Antiguan staff have been trained to smile – which is more than one can say elsewhere. Food is not bad for a resort but the winelist is extremely respectable. At a time when the quality of the Caribbean holiday is being fast eroded, Curtain Bluff keeps the flag flying.

Barbados

COBBLERS COVE, St. Peter, Barbados, West Indies

★ TELEPHONE: 22291
★ CABLE: Cobblers
★ TELEX: WB 2314
★ IN OPERATION: 14 years
★ RESERVATIONS: Windotel, London/Robert Reid Associates, New York and Toronto
★ ROOMS: 38 (complete suites with kitchenettes)
★ RESTAURANTS: 1
★ BARS: 1
★ DISCOTHEQUE: no – but live music three or four times a week according to season
★ SHOPS: none
★ CONFERENCE ROOMS: none
★ BANQUETING ROOMS: none
★ STANDARD BEDROOM SIZE: 52 m², including bedroom, bathroom, living room and kitchen

★ PRIVATE BALCONIES: yes
★ SWIMMING POOL: yes – fresh water
★ RECREATIONAL ACTIVITIES: waterskiing, windsurfing, snorkelling, yacht charter, scuba diving and glass-bottom boat. Golf and tennis nearby
★ GARDENS: yes
★ NO. OF STAFF: 60
★ ROOM SERVICE: 07.30–23.00
★ ORIENTATION: some rooms face west overlooking the sea and others overlook the gardens
★ CREDIT CARDS: American Express and Visa
★ OWNING COMPANY: Hayton Ltd
★ GENERAL MANAGER: Richard Williams
★ DISTANCE TO BEACH: walking distance
★ DISTANCE TO SHOPS: 16 km
★ DISTANCE FROM AIRPORT: 22 km

One might say that this hotel is what Barbados is all about – small, intimate, friendly and comfortably laid out in the tropical manner. On the whole it is very nice to know that all the people who would not like Cobblers Cove don't go there and if you like loud pop music, plastic decor and the like, I would respectfully suggest that you should keep away.

Cobblers is like a home – in fact the central mansion used to be one. The rest is made up of handsome two-storey structures and on each floor there is a large, well-furnished bedroom (complete with dressing room next to the bathroom), a semi-outdoor living room also fully furnished and even a little kitchenette should you feel like tossing your own salad. The terrace is handsome indeed, partly shaded by lovely trees and with a swimming pool, of course and, down a few steps, is an incomparable beach. Cobblers is never crowded, never strident, never overdone. Everything is just so – in the British manner of course – simply very relaxing and good-tempered. The staff are among the best and most helpful I have ever encountered anywhere and one feels that the intelligent management's master's eye is everywhere. Food is good and wholesome, the wine list will last your holiday and the drinks are what tropical drinks should be: long and cool.

You can be alone at Cobblers if that's what you want and this is a blessed relief after so much razzmatazz. It's a private place.

COCONUT CREEK CLUB HOTEL, St. James, Barbados, West Indies

★ TELEPHONE: 20803/20804
★ CABLES: Crocreek
★ TELEX: WB 2314
★ IN OPERATION: since 1966
★ RESERVATIONS: Knightsbridge Hotels Ltd, U.S.A.
★ ROOMS: 50 doubles (inc. De Luxe)
★ SUITES: 3–1 bedroom apartments, luxury suite and villa
★ RESTAURANTS: 1
★ BARS: 2 – 'The Cricketers' pub, pool bar
★ DISCOTHEQUE: no – but two live bands a week and one organ player
★ SHOPS: 1
★ CONFERENCE ROOMS: none
★ BANQUETING ROOMS: none
★ STANDARD BEDROOM SIZE: 25 m²
★ PRIVATE BALCONIES: yes
★ SWIMMING POOL: yes – fresh water, 8 × 6 m

★ RECREATIONAL ACTIVITIES: all activities are available on the island
★ GARDENS: yes
★ NO. OF STAFF: 63
★ ROOM SERVICE: available for meals, continental breakfast only between 05.00 and 08.00 and there is a night porter on duty from 23.00–08.00
★ ORIENTATION: most rooms face the sea, others the gardens and the swimming pool
★ CREDIT CARDS: American Express, Visa and Mastercharge
★ OWNING COMPANY: Owen Ellison
★ GENERAL MANAGER: Owen Ellison (Owner)
★ DISTANCE TO BEACH: on the beach
★ DISTANCE TO SHOPS: Bridgetown 5 miles, Holetown 2½ miles
★ DISTANCE FROM AIRPORT: 14 miles

Some people I know (mostly other hoteliers whose business isn't so good) don't like Coconut Creek much. Too-too, they say. Well, maybe. It looks a bit like a Spanish village with an English pub in the middle but it is owner-managed, with constant care and a lot of attention to small details. It has grown bigger since I last saw it but the spirit remains – that of a hotel, small and secluded, which knows how to offer its guests what they want. Rooms are good, fresh and nicely furnished and service everywhere is helpful and smiling. One of Coconut Creek's best points in my judgment is its beaches: not one, not two, but three small, jewel-like strands below the rocks, which cannot be better even along this famed Platinum Coast of Barbados. In terms of holiday value, they are worth every penny or cent.

It can be a cheerful, gregarious place too, especially at night and the owners are past masters at making people welcome. A very good choice.

CORAL REEF CLUB, St. James, Barbados, West Indies

★ TELEPHONE: 22372
★ CABLES: 'Coral' Barbados
★ TELEX: 2407 WB
★ IN OPERATION: 30 years
★ RESERVATIONS: Robert Reid Associates, London/Ralph Locke, New York
★ ROOMS: 68 doubles 10 singles
★ SUITES: none
★ RESTAURANTS: 2
★ BARS: 2
★ DISCOTHEQUE: live music every night
★ SHOPS: 3 – 'The Casual Shop', ladies' hairdressing and water sports shop
★ CONFERENCE ROOMS: 1 (50)
★ BANQUETING ROOMS: none
★ STANDARD BEDROOM SIZE: 16 m²
★ PRIVATE BALCONIES: yes

★ SWIMMING POOL: yes – fresh water, 45,000 gallons, irregular shape
★ RECREATIONAL ACTIVITIES: tennis, scuba diving, sailing, waterskiing and snorkelling
★ GARDENS: yes
★ NO. OF STAFF: 200
★ ROOM SERVICE: around the clock
★ ORIENTATION: rooms face sea
★ CREDIT CARDS: Visa
★ OWNING COMPANY: Trade Winds Hotels Ltd
★ GENERAL MANAGER: Budge O'Hara
★ DISTANCE TO BEACH: walking distance
★ DISTANCE TO SHOPS: 1 km
★ DISTANCE FROM AIRPORT: 30 km

My problem about Coral Reef is trying to find new adjectives to describe it. The best of the great traditional hotels of Barbados? No doubt about that. The most in demand? Just try and get in during the high season. Coral Reef has been one of the finest resort hotels in the world for so long that it knows all the tricks – the cheerful and very tasteful decor, the flowers everywhere, the little touches of luxury, the food which is as good to eat as it is to look at – not always the case in the Caribbean.

Here, amidst twelve acres of gardens, carefully manicured every morning, is a meandering gaggle of divinely conceived cottages, all private, all immaculate, with large airy rooms and splendid private terraces. You are on your own and yet service is there, at the touch of a button. It goes without saying that Coral Reef has a superb beach and a very attractive swimming pool with outdoor furniture designed for the purpose – not something they bought in the sales. The wine list is one of those I would take with me as bedside reading. Coral Reef is intensely civilised in the European manner, well tempered, beautiful to look at and run by a man who knows instinctively that only the best will do. If you are at Coral Reef during the high season you should certainly consider yourself lucky. There are not many places like it.

GLITTER BAY, St. James, Barbados, West Indies

★ TELEPHONE: 24111
★ CABLES: Bayglit
★ TELEX: 2397 WB Glitbay
★ IN OPERATION: since January, 1982
★ RESERVATIONS: Morris Associates, London/Robert Reid Associates, New York, Toronto, Munich/International Travel Co, Rome/Yanou Collart Public Relations, Paris
★ ROOMS: 10 1-bedroom apartments 29 2-bedroom apartments 7 3-bedroom penthouses
★ SUITES: not applicable
★ RESTAURANTS: 1 – Piperade

★ BARS: 2 – Sunset Beach Bar and The Gazebo (which also serves light snacks)
★ DISCOTHEQUE: no – but live music 5 times a week
★ SHOPS: 2 – boutique and a general store
★ CONFERENCE ROOMS: converted suites (up to about 20)
★ BANQUETING ROOMS: none
★ STANDARD BEDROOM SIZE: 1-bedroom apartment 75 m² 2-bedroom apartment 120 m² 3-bedroom penthouse 205 m²
★ PRIVATE BALCONIES: yes
★ SWIMMING POOL: yes – fresh water

★ RECREATIONAL ACTIVITIES: all water sports, golf and tennis nearby
★ GARDENS: yes
★ NO. OF STAFF: 130
★ ROOM SERVICE: 06.30–24.00
★ ORIENTATION: most apartments have sea and garden view, several only garden view
★ CREDIT CARDS: American Express, Visa, Master Charge and En Route
★ OWNING COMPANY: Glitter Bay
★ GENERAL MANAGER: Theo Williams
★ DISTANCE TO BEACH: directly
★ DISTANCE TO SHOPS: Holetown 3 km, Bridgetown 12 km
★ DISTANCE FROM AIRPORT: 16 km

There is always something new in the hotel business – that's what makes it so interesting. I thought I knew every hotel in Barbados – that sweet Caribbean isle which *lives* off its hotels. I did not because when I went back there a little while ago, I found a new one – raised behind my back almost. It's called Glitter Bay, but don't let the ghastly name put you off, it just happens to be the name of the location. Glitter Bay, with its clever and very acceptable modern architecture, does not glitter – it simply shines with good taste, good ideas and one of the ablest managements in the business and I take my hat off to people who really dreamed up something new. At Glitter Bay (sorry) you can have one room, two or three, with living rooms and terraces just as you want them. The layout is almost elastic in its variety. In the centre, facing an extremely acceptable beach, is the central pavilion which houses the bars and a quite remarkable restaurant – Piperade – which gives the lie to all those who maintain that the Caribbean cannot produce civilised, gastronomic food. This one can and does, every day of the week with a handsome menu and splendid touches. I was converted – instantly. If a hotel has to be modern, let it be like this one.

British Virgin Islands

LITTLE DIX BAY, P.O. Box 70, Virgin Gorda

★ TELEPHONE: (809) 495-5555
★ CABLES: Dixbay V6BVI
★ TELEX: 318 916+
★ IN OPERATION: 18 years
★ RESERVATIONS: Rockresorts Reservations
★ ROOMS: 82
★ SUITES: none
★ RESTAURANTS: 2 – Pavilion Terrace and Sugar Mill Terrace
★ BARS: 2
★ DISCOTHEQUE: live music for dancing three nights each week on pavilion terrace
★ SHOPS: 1
★ CONFERENCE ROOMS: none
★ BANQUETING ROOMS: none
★ STANDARD BEDROOM SIZE: 29 m²
★ PRIVATE BALCONIES: yes
★ SWIMMING POOL: no
★ RECREATIONAL ACTIVITIES: tennis, horse riding, snorkelling, scuba diving, sailing and swimming
★ GARDENS: yes
★ NO. OF STAFF: 220
★ ROOM SERVICE: for breakfast only
★ ORIENTATION: facing north-east and directly on the beach
★ CREDIT CARDS: American Express and Diners Club
★ OWNING COMPANY: Rockresorts Inc
★ GENERAL MANAGER: Joel Jennings
★ DISTANCE TO BEACH: 20 m
★ DISTANCE TO SHOPS: 400 m
★ DISTANCE FROM AIRPORT: 800 m

At the risk of being repetitive since the last edition I have absolutely no reason to change my mind about this hotel. Little Dix Bay works on the principle that it takes a rich man to know what a rich man wants when he chooses a holiday. The millionaire in this case is the ubiquitous Laurence Rockefeller and with Little Dix Bay he has succeeded again – here, in 300 acres of one of the most gorgeous tropic isles – Virgin Gorda – are simplicity, quiet and privacy. A series of cone-shaped thatched cottages on stilts, open to the breeze or not, depending on how you feel, blend with the landscape. The simple cane furniture is somehow the happiest choice for the farouche architecture. In the middle of the beach there is the central pavilion with open-air dining rooms and bars. Food is American-style in Vistavision but one gets used to it quite quickly.

A stone's throw away is the beach to end all beaches, unromatically called The Baths. Nothing on earth is as expensive as the simple life when the rich are leading it.

Now, Little Dix also has its own yacht harbour. One sailing friend who blew in recently sent me a card, saying: 'After all you said, I expected champagne on tap when I moored . . .' For all I know they are probably working on it.

PETER ISLAND HOTEL, Box 211, Road Town, Tortola, British Virgin Islands

★ TELEPHONE: (809) 494-2561
★ CABLES: Petertel
★ TELEX: 923 VB
★ IN OPERATION: 10 years
★ RESERVATIONS: David B. Mitchell & Co, New York
★ ROOMS: 32
★ SUITES: 1 – 3-bedroomed villa
★ RESTAURANTS: 2 – one main restaurant and a beach restaurant featuring barbecues
★ BARS: 2
★ DISCOTHEQUE: no – but live music
★ SHOPS: 1
★ CONFERENCE ROOMS: 1 (60)
★ BANQUETING ROOMS: none – only main dining room
★ STANDARD BEDROOM SIZE: 50 m²
★ GARDENS: yes

★ PRIVATE BALCONIES: 16 on upstairs rooms and terraces on 16 downstairs rooms
★ SWIMMING POOL: yes – salt water, 17 m long
★ RECREATIONAL ACTIVITIES: tennis, horse riding, snorkelling and sunfish, also scuba, deep sea fishing, sailing and power boat excursions at a charge
★ NO. OF STAFF: 100
★ ROOM SERVICE: 08.00–10.00 breakfast only
★ ORIENTATION: north-east
★ CREDIT CARDS: American Express
★ OWNING COMPANY: Amway Corp
★ GENERAL MANAGER: Donald Benson
★ DISTANCE TO BEACH: 100 m
★ DISTANCE TO SHOPS: 9 km
★ DISTANCE FROM AIRPORT: 18 km

As everyone knows, the Caribbean – and its hotels – have had their ups and downs in recent years, especially downs. Peter Island is a typical example: I loved it from the very start and then, by and by, complaints began to reach me: food had become 'quelconque', service surly, maintenance doubtful. I was just about to commit another hotel murder when suddenly, other reports came in: 'marvellous', 'new lease of life', 'very expert new management'. Well, I am so glad because Peter Island basically deserves to succeed. It always was an unusual hotel, simple and yet very comfortable with very functional cottage-style bedrooms, modern and very clean. What matters is Peter Island – you have it to yourself, clear seas, superb beaches, total privacy and lots of skin-diving, scuba, fishing and sailing if you want an active time. Now that Peter Island is back on the hotel straight-and-narrow, I have decided to stay the executioner's knife. Besides, I have fond memories of this part of the world: as part of someone's joke, I was once marooned for the day on the desert island next door – only Raquel Welch was missing. It is also comforting to know that there are still British Virgins.

Dominican Republic

CASA DE CAMPO HOTEL, VILLAS AND COUNTRY CLUB, P.O. Box 140, La Romana

★ TELEPHONE: (809) 556-3345
★ CABLES: no
★ TELEX: ITT 346 0398 RCA 326 4360
★ IN OPERATION: 6 years

★ RESERVATIONS: G & W Hotels, New York/Ski Sport Sonne Schwarz, Germany
★ ROOMS: 177

★ SUITES: 6
★ RESTAURANTS: 8
★ BARS: 10
★ DISCOTHEQUE: yes and live music for dancing or listening to in some of the restaurants
★ CONFERENCE ROOMS: 7
★ BANQUETING ROOMS: 6
★ STANDARD BEDROOM SIZE: 30 m²
★ PRIVATE BALCONIES: all rooms
★ SWIMMING POOL: 5 – all fresh water
★ RECREATIONAL ACTIVITIES: golf, tennis, polo, riding club, sailing
★ GARDENS: yes

★ NO. OF STAFF: 800
★ ROOM SERVICE: 07.00–22.00
★ ORIENTATION: rooms face gardens, golf course or ocean
★ CREDIT CARDS: all major credit cards
★ OWNING COMPANY: G & W Hotels
★ GENERAL MANAGER: Anthony Bayarri
★ DISTANCE TO BEACH: on the property – 6 minutes by complimentary shuttle bus
★ DISTANCE TO SHOPS: 12 minutes by complimentary shuttle bus
★ DISTANCE FROM AIRPORT: 95 km

Readers have been telling us for years to go to Casa de Campo and now that we have done so, we wonder how we could have missed it for so long – the ultimate, eye-dazzling resort of resorts in the Caribbean, but not the Caribbean you would expect since this one has a Spanish accent. Our trouble is that we don't know where to begin. With 7,000 acres of glorious, unspoilt countryside? With the eight restaurants and the ten bars? With all the things you can do there from riding to golfing? With the resort's own jet airport? Frankly, the thing that struck us most in all this fantasy of luxurious living was the decor (much of it by Oscar de la Renta), the finished quality, the imagination, the superb colours – everything in such good taste that you fall in love with it at first sight. Then there are the beaches, unsullied and so vast that despite the size of the hotel you can quite easily be on your own. Rooms come in all shapes, sizes and varieties. You can have a suite, a casita, a villa or any combination you care to name – everything superbly furnished and serviced. The food is great but please don't ask us what we ate – we were only there three days and only had time for Continental and Dominican and no opportunity for French, Chinese or American. Of course you won't be alone at Casa de Campo because it's people who make a place like this and here there are only beautiful people. Rich too.

Guadeloupe

HOTEL MERIDIEN GUADELOUPE, BP 37, 97118 St. Francois, Guadeloupe, French West Indies

★ TELEPHONE: 84-4100
★ CABLES: Homer, Pointe-a-Pitre
★ TELEX: 019 774
★ IN OPERATION: 10 years
★ RESERVATIONS: all Air France offices and Meridien hotels worldwide
★ ROOMS: 273
★ SUITES: 8
★ RESTAURANTS: 3 – Le Saint Charles, Le Balaou, Le Cazazoma (beach)
★ BARS: 2
★ DISCOTHEQUE: yes
★ SHOPS: 8 – hairdresser, local handicrafts, perfumery, dress shop
★ CONFERENCE ROOMS: 3 (50 to 250 m²)
★ BANQUETING ROOMS: 3 (25 to 325 m²)
★ STANDARD BEDROOM SIZE: 21 m²
★ PRIVATE BALCONIES: yes – all rooms
★ SWIMMING POOL: yes

★ RECREATIONAL ACTIVITIES: tennis, pedaloes, volley ball, sunfish, sailing boats, waterskiing, windsurfing, golf course. Casino within walking distance
★ GARDENS: yes
★ NO. OF STAFF: 250
★ ROOM SERVICE: around the clock
★ ORIENTATION: north-west and south-west
★ CREDIT CARDS: American Express, Diners Club, Carte Blanche, Master Charge, Eurocard, Access, Visa, Inter-Bank, Carte En Route
★ OWNING COMPANY: Société des Hotels Meridiens
★ GENERAL MANAGER: Gianni Riatsch
★ DISTANCE TO SHOPS: 29 km
★ DISTANCE FROM AIRPORT: 32 km

For any traveller, moving from an Anglophone Caribbean island to a Francophone one is like going from the Moon to Saturn – a different world. Guadeloupe is more West Indian than most and yet it's French with a vengeance and cosmopolitan too. Even Prunier de Paris have a branch-restaurant there and nearby is this splendid, shining Meridien near the little fishing town of St. Francois which, by now, is the St. Tropez of Guadeloupe. I would call the Meridien a hotel a-gogo – there is so much to do, so much activity that one certainly does not have time to get bored. There is a superb and extremely well-equipped beach with bar and a rather nice rustic restaurant where the food is anything but rustic. I only stayed here five days but I counted eleven different kinds of cuisine available. Buffets are Technicolour and, thank goodness, they taste French and the sit-down meals are among the best I have had in a resort hotel. Rooms are large, well furnished if rather international and the public rooms, facing all those tropical gardens are excellently planned. Service is good and smiling and the management is obviously well up to the mark. If you want the Caribbean and Life with a capital 'L', the Meridien Guadeloupe is a very good choice.

Haiti

HABITATION LECLERC RESORT AND CLUB, P.O. Box 2263, Port au Prince, Haiti, West Indies

- ★ TELEPHONE: 20277 (in Port au Prince) or tollfree in U.S.A. (800) 223-56-70
- ★ CABLES: Habiclerc – New York
- ★ TELEX: ITT 42 45 45 – Cler New York
- ★ IN OPERATION: since 1965
- ★ RESERVATIONS: Hotel Representative Inc
- ★ ROOMS: 26
- ★ SUITES: 44 villas
- ★ RESTAURANTS: 2
- ★ BARS: 4
- ★ DISCOTHEQUE: yes
- ★ SHOPS: 1
- ★ CONFERENCE ROOMS: 1 (200)
- ★ BANQUETING ROOMS: terraces with unlimited capacity
- ★ STANDARD BEDROOM SIZE: generous – varies with type of accommodation

- ★ PRIVATE BALCONIES: yes – patios
- ★ SWIMMING POOL: yes – 14, fresh water
- ★ GARDENS: yes
- ★ NO. OF STAFF: 165
- ★ ROOM SERVICE: around the clock
- ★ ORIENTATION: accommodation faces all directions
- ★ CREDIT CARDS: American Express, Diners Club, Carte Bleue, Master Charge and Visa
- ★ OWNING COMPANY: Pyramid Management Inc
- ★ GENERAL MANAGER: Joseph Guardino
- ★ DISTANCE TO BEACH: 20 minutes by car
- ★ DISTANCE TO SHOPS: 10 minutes by car
- ★ DISTANCE FROM AIRPORT: 25 km

In my opinion this is probably the most voluptuous resort hotel in the Western hemisphere. Just the place to read 'The Decline and Fall of the Roman Empire' for this surely is how it must have ended. But the empire that fell was Napoleon's and this place, or at least its older parts, was the creation of his pleasure-loving sister Pauline Bonaparte Leclerc. I don't know just exactly what she got up to here but I do know what you can do now – let yourself be immersed into an atmosphere of incredible luxury tempered with expensive good taste. It's a place for beautiful people for whom money is not a consideration. There are colonnades and balustrades, rooms and suites and cottages à la Marie-Antoinette with acres of bedspace, round bathtubs, fourteen swimming pools, cascades and tropical vegetation left to run riot. There is a magnificent restaurant but the real prize is dinner al fresco on the terrace where, suddenly and mysteriously, the finest food in the world is laid on side by side with the best vintages from everywhere. There is a kind of gold-plated nonchalance about this hotel which is probably without compare. Habitation Leclerc is part of the fourth world – where all the girls are beautiful, all the nights velvety and all that glitters is probably gold. If my ship ever comes home this is one of the places I shall visit to remind myself of what money can buy.

Jamaica

THE HALF MOON CLUB, P.O. Box 80, Montego Bay, Jamaica

★ TELEPHONE: (809) 953-2211
★ CABLES: Halfmoon
★ TELEX: 291 5326
★ IN OPERATION: 29 years
★ RESERVATIONS: Robert Reid Associates Inc, New York/Jamaica Reservation Service, Florida/C.A.I.R.S. Hotel Representatives, Toronto/Princess Reservation Service, Frankfurt/Windotel Ltd, London
★ ROOMS: 191
★ SUITES: 91
★ RESTAURANTS: 2 – Sea Grape Terrace and The Club House Grill
★ BARS: 2
★ DISCOTHEQUE: yes – also live dinner music and live dance music with nightly shows
★ SHOPS: 13 – beauty salon and barber shop, gifts and souvenirs, pharmacy, men's shop, 2 dress shops, crystal, china, jewellery, watches and linen shops
★ CONFERENCE ROOMS: 3 (15 to 150)
★ BANQUETING ROOMS: 3 (15 to 350)
★ STANDARD BEDROOM SIZE: 30 m²

★ PRIVATE BALCONIES: yes
★ SWIMMING POOL: yes – 2 major pools and 17 cottage pools – all fresh water
★ RECREATIONAL ACTIVITIES: 13 tennis courts (4 floodlit), 4 floodlit squash courts, 18-hole golf course, windsurfing, sailing, snorkelling, deep sea fishing, sauna, massage salon, riding, shuffleboard and table tennis
★ GARDENS: yes – 400 acres
★ NO. OF STAFF: 320
★ ROOM SERVICE: 08.00–23.00
★ ORIENTATION: all rooms face directly onto the beach and sea
★ FURTHER DEVELOPMENTS: plans are being drawn up for the construction of golf villas beside the golf course
★ CREDIT CARDS: American Express, Diners Club, Master Charge, Bankamericard, Visa and Barclaycard
★ OWNING COMPANY: Half Moon Bay Ltd
★ MANAGING DIRECTOR: Heinz E. W. Simonitsch
★ DISTANCE TO BEACH: walking distance
★ DISTANCE TO SHOPS: 1 km
★ DISTANCE FROM AIRPORT: 9 km

There are so many overnight hotel experts these days that when you go back to one of your favourite haunts, it's a great relief to get home and find that things are better than ever. That applies to Half Moon which, in my opinion, is an object lesson on how a really great Caribbean hotel should be run. It manages to be everything to everyone – from the honeymooner to the tycoon who is just taking five. Superbly managed by one of the great hotel personalities of the world, it is so successful that the word recession is simply not in its vocabulary. Here, you can have anything you like – from Malossol caviar to Bâtard Montrachet and from one of the finest beaches in Jamaica to one of the greatest golf courses: just go across the road to see it – superb greens sloping down towards the sea, ancient trees, flowers that bloom every night overnight and the kind of clubhouse where you know your dinner is going to be great just by looking at the place. At Half Moon, you can have a room, a suite and any one of a gaggle of absolutely divine 'cottages' if you can call them that, each with its private garden, private swimming pool, living room and gracious decor. The gardener comes every morning and as for the maid, she spends an hour and a half 'doing' every cottage. Now you can have something else too: a choice of marvellous self-catering apartments in a cluster of new buildings next door – with your own delicatessen of course. As for the beach, a mile of it, it's the Caribbean at its best. Half Moon? You can't miss. There is only one like it.

JAMAICA INN, P.O. Box 1, Ocho Rios, Jamaica, West Indies

★ TELEPHONE: 974-2514
★ CABLES: Jamaicainn
★ TELEX: no
★ IN OPERATION: 32 years

★ RESERVATIONS: Ray Morrow Associates, Windotel Ltd, London
★ ROOMS: 50
★ SUITES: 2

★ RESTAURANTS: 1
★ BARS: 2
★ DISCOTHEQUE: no – but small orchestra nightly
★ SHOPS: none
★ CONFERENCE ROOMS: none
★ BANQUETING ROOMS: none
★ STANDARD BEDROOM SIZE: 23 m²
★ PRIVATE BALCONIES: yes
★ SWIMMING POOL: yes – fresh water, 25,000 gallons
★ RECREATIONAL ACTIVITIES: tennis nearby and golf and horse riding 3 miles away

★ GARDENS: yes
★ NO. OF STAFF: 105
★ ROOM SERVICE: 07.30–24.00
★ ORIENTATION: rooms face the sea
★ CREDIT CARDS: American Express
★ OWNING COMPANY: C. P. Morrow and M. P. Archibald
★ GENERAL MANAGER: owner management
★ DISTANCE TO BEACH: walking distance
★ DISTANCE TO SHOPS: 1 km
★ DISTANCE FROM AIRPORT: 90 km (Montego Bay)

Despite changes in management, this is still one of the top hotels of the Caribbean – perhaps not for the young but for all those who have lived and know it all. The first thing you notice is the absence of the showbiz element: Jamaica Inn is just a superbly conceived hotel facing its splendid beach which, everywhere, is only a step away from your outdoor living room, framed with white balustrades and with everything you want at hand. One dines on one of the most famous terraces in the West Indies (it used to be on almost every Jamaican poster) and, there is no doubt about it, this is the good life. People come here year after year and some are lucky (and rich) enough to book the famed White Suite which stands in isolated splendour at the end of the promontory and yes, if you have to ask how much it is, you can't afford it. Jamaica Inn is a legend all right and although it now has stiff competition, I fervently hope that it will know how to keep in step.

PLANTATION INN, P.O. Box 2, Ocho Rios, Jamaica

★ TELEPHONE: 974-2501-3
★ CABLES: Plantation
★ TELEX: 2134
★ IN OPERATION: 26 years
★ RESERVATIONS: David B. Mitchell & Co Inc, New York/Windotel, London/Muriel Fleger International, Toronto
★ ROOMS: 61
★ SUITES: none
★ RESTAURANTS: 1
★ BARS: 2
★ DISCOTHEQUE: resident band
★ SHOPS: 1 (boutique)
★ CONFERENCE ROOMS: 1 (80 m²)
★ BANQUETING ROOMS: 1 (30)
★ STANDARD BEDROOM SIZE: 30 m²

★ PRIVATE BALCONIES: all rooms
★ SWIMMING POOL: 1 – fresh water
★ RECREATIONAL ACTIVITIES: tennis, watersports
★ GARDENS: yes
★ NO. OF STAFF: 120
★ ROOM SERVICE: 07.30–24.00
★ ORIENTATION: all rooms face the ocean
★ CREDIT CARDS: American Express, Master Charge, Visa, Eurocard and Diners Club
★ OWNING COMPANY: Watsons (Off Course Betting) Ltd
★ GENERAL MANAGER: Rudi Schoenbein
★ DISTANCE TO BEACH: on the beach
★ DISTANCE TO SHOPS: 3 km
★ DISTANCE FROM AIRPORT: 100 km

I have long been convinced that hotel general managers are like great vintage wines – unique and unmatcheable, so instead of following hotels themselves, I follow general managers. If they move, I move. And never was this proved more true than during a recent visit to Plantation Inn – once a good but average resort hotel which fell on hard times and was then acquired by some intelligent people who had the wit to choose the best man for the job. It shows. Plantation is now one of the best resort hotels in the Caribbean – all within one season. Quite a miracle.

It always was a good-looking pad of course, graceful, neo-colonial architecture, coolness, charm and space that has been used to best effect. The two beaches are among the best and there is a pretty swimming pool just below the lovely, gracious dining terrace where, at night, only the candelight competes with Jamaica's velvety, starry sky. Rooms are a very handsome size, with balconies or terraces and some have that indispensable extra: a proper closet for your holiday clothes. What matters however, is something entirely different. It is the 'feel' of the place, that 'je ne sais quoi' which filters through to you when you get in and makes you feel that this is going to be some holiday. The staff are superb, cheerful and glad to help and the management's eagle eye is everywhere. They serve English afternoon tea too. Plantation is making it – at last.

ROUND HILL HOTEL, P.O. Box 64, Montego Bay, Jamaica, West Indies

★ TELEPHONE: 809-952-5150-5
★ CABLES: Roundhill
★ TELEX: no
★ IN OPERATION: 28 years
★ RESERVATIONS: Robert F. Warner, Inc, New York/Morris Associates, London/Muriel Fleger, Toronto
★ ROOMS: 36 doubles 5 singles
★ SUITES: 70
★ RESTAURANTS: 3
★ BARS: 2
★ DISCOTHEQUE: no – but dancing nightly with featured entertainers and calypso band
★ SHOPS: 2
★ CONFERENCE ROOMS: 1 (60 to 150)
★ BANQUETING ROOMS: 2 (45 to 200)
★ STANDARD BEDROOM SIZE: 27 m²
★ PRIVATE BALCONIES: yes
★ SWIMMING POOL: yes – 13
★ RECREATIONAL ACTIVITIES: snorkelling, waterskiing, sailing and deep sea fishing and tennis. Golf and horse riding close by
★ GARDENS: yes
★ NO. OF STAFF: 245
★ ROOM SERVICE: 08.00–23.00
★ ORIENTATION: rooms face sea and garden
★ CREDIT CARDS: none
★ OWNING COMPANY: Round Hill Development Ltd
★ MANAGING DIRECTOR: Michael J. Kemp
★ DISTANCE TO BEACH: on the beach
★ DISTANCE TO SHOPS: 15 km
★ DISTANCE FROM AIRPORT: 17 km

Round Hill is not a hotel – more a way of life. Here, on this rounded cape just west of Montego Bay is one of the most original resorts in the business – lots of lush, tropical land, one small but super beach, flowers everywhere and, dotted about, a whole series of absolutely heavenly Jamaican-style cottages, some with their own pools. There are great verandahs, airy rooms with high ceilings and splendid Caribbean resort furniture and very good bathrooms. The rooms in the main buildings are good and acceptable – but not really to be compared with the cottages. At Round Hill, a very private but very convivial place, life gets going at night when you dine on the lovely terrace or even the beach – with Jamaican fireflies dancing above and the moon out. In such a widespread place, service is remarkably good and cheerful and the food ranks high in the Caribbean. Round Hill has had mixed management fortunes in past years but now seems set fair for some time to come.

St. Kitts

THE GOLDEN LEMON, Dieppe Bay, St. Kitts, West Indies

★ TELEPHONE: (809) 465-7260
★ CABLES: Golemon
★ IN OPERATION: 19 years
★ RESERVATIONS: Scott Calder International, New York
★ ROOMS: 11
★ SUITES: 3
★ RESTAURANTS: 1
★ BARS: 1
★ DISCOTHEQUE: local band occasionally
★ SHOPS: 2 – duty free shop with
perfumes, jewellery, clothes and craft shop
★ CONFERENCE ROOMS: none
★ BANQUETING ROOMS: none
★ STANDARD BEDROOM SIZE: 20 m²
★ PRIVATE BALCONIES: most rooms
★ SWIMMING POOL: yes – fresh water
★ RECREATIONAL ACTIVITIES: snorkelling, tennis, golf, riding, mountain climbing and day trips to other islands can be arranged

★ GARDENS: hotel surrounded by walled gardens
★ NO. OF STAFF: 30
★ ROOM SERVICE: 07.00–24.00
★ ORIENTATION: most rooms face the sea
★ CREDIT CARDS: none

★ OWNING COMPANY: Arthur Leaman
★ GENERAL MANAGER: Arthur Leaman
★ DISTANCE FROM BEACH: 150 m
★ DISTANCE FROM SHOPS: 22 km
★ DISTANCE FROM AIRPORT: 22km

In an island which is certainly not known for the quality of its hotels, here is a real find: one of the two or three nicest small hotels in the Caribbean – very chic, very appealing and absolutely gorgeous when it comes to decor. And so it should be since it is the brainchild of a man who used to be decorating editor of *House and Garden*.

Arthur Leaman rescued this 'Great House' from total oblivion and turned it into a place of infinite charm: small, friendly and totally private in its own walled garden and facing an unusual black sand beach. The word here is simple period elegance, with every room done up differently with genuine island furniture, fresh colours, canopied beds and ceiling fans – of course. As your eye roves around, it comes to rest happily on yet one more piece of great artistry. There is a wealth of carefully chosen tropical flora, frequented by finches and hummingbirds and a discreet and charming swimming pool lined with beautiful chaises-longues. The food, served in the elegant, period dining room under candlelight, shows that professional designers sometimes eat too – it is perfection itself, light, different and imaginative and served in great style. If you want the Caribbean away from the obvious, The Golden Lemon it must be.

St. Lucia

ANSE CHASTANET BEACH HOTEL, P.O. Box 216, Soufrière, St. Lucia, West Indies

★ TELEPHONE: (809) 455-7355
★ CABLES: Anchasta, Soufrière, St. Lucia
★ TELEX: 03986370 Anchasta LC
★ IN OPERATION: 12 years
★ RESERVATIONS: direct/Scott Calder International Inc, New York/C.A.I.R.S., Canada
★ ROOMS: 15 doubles
★ SUITES: 2 2-bedroomed and 2-bath and 2 1-bedroomed
★ RESTAURANTS: 2 – one in the main building and one on the beach
★ BARS: 2 – the main bar and one on the beach
★ DISCOTHEQUE: no – but live band at least once a week
★ SHOPS: 1
★ CONFERENCE ROOMS: 1 (up to 25)
★ BANQUETING ROOMS: 3 – available on request
★ STANDARD BEDROOM SIZE: 28 m²

★ PRIVATE BALCONIES: yes
★ SWIMMING POOL: no
★ RECREATIONAL ACTIVITIES: tennis, snorkelling, fishing, sailing, scuba centre and windsurfing
★ GARDENS: no – but hotel is located in the centre of a 500-acre estate with no other buildings
★ NO. OF STAFF: 45
★ ROOM SERVICE: only at breakfast time
★ ORIENTATION: all rooms face sea
★ CREDIT CARDS: American Express, Master Charge, Visa, Barclaycard and Diners Club
★ OWNING COMPANY: Anse Chastanet Hotel Ltd
★ MANAGING DIRECTOR: Nick Troobitscoff
★ GENERAL MANAGER: Peter Pietruszka
★ DISTANCE TO BEACH: on the beach
★ DISTANCE TO SHOPS: 2 km
★ DISTANCE FROM AIRPORT: 30 km

Once upon a time, this most beautiful of all the smaller West Indian islands had quite a few agreeable hotels. Alas, the advent of cheaper mass tourism (plus a little greediness perhaps) has changed all that and I have personally given them all up as not really worthy of St. Lucia's extraordinary beauty. All except Anse Chastanet.

This is no shining luxury hotel but it has so much personality, so much simple niceness that it is almost unique in these parts. The accommodation is simple but comfortable, with splendid views, no noise and a divine beach. Plus the best view of the famous Pitons, the island's trademark.

Most of the people I have sent to Anse Chastanet have been very happy though I did choose them with care because the cottages are spread out on a rather steep hillside and it is quite a hike from the beach when the sun is high. Those cottages are large, with good views and a charming terrace running all the way around. Ceilings are high and the place is never stuffy. Furnishings are fairly simple but in good taste and perfectly adequate and the food is good and natural if not gastronomic. Anse Chastanet has the 'feel' of the old Caribbean and it deserves praise for being itself and different from the obvious lush pads around.

St. Martin

LA SAMANNA, BP 159 Marigot, 97150 St. Martin, French West Indies

★ TELEPHONE: 875122
★ CABLES: Shobal/St. Martin
★ TELEX: 9198292 GL
★ IN OPERATION: 9 years
★ RESERVATIONS: direct or David B. Mitchell, New York
★ ROOMS: 11
★ SUITES: 46
★ RESTAURANTS: 1 – 'Nouvelle Cuisine'
★ BARS: 2
★ DISCOTHEQUE: yes
★ SHOPS: 1 – boutique
★ CONFERENCE ROOMS: none
★ BANQUETING ROOMS: none
★ STANDARD BEDROOM SIZE: 17 m²
★ PRIVATE BALCONIES: yes
★ SWIMMING POOL: yes – fresh water 10 × 20 m

★ RECREATIONAL ACTIVITIES: tennis, snorkelling, windsurfing, scuba, water skiing and sailing
★ GARDENS: yes
★ NO. OF STAFF: 100
★ ROOM SERVICE: continental breakfast only
★ ORIENTATION: east/west – all rooms face the sea
★ CREDIT CARDS: American Express, Master Charge and Visa
★ OWNING COMPANY: Soc. Hôtelière de la Baie Longue
★ GENERAL MANAGER: James Frankel
★ DISTANCE TO BEACH: on the beach
★ DISTANCE TO SHOPS: 15 minutes
★ DISTANCE FROM AIRPORT: 5 km

Tiny St. Martin is two-thirds Dutch and one-third French and therein lies one of the funniest stories of colonial days which, alas, would take half this book to tell. The joke had always been that one slept on the Dutch side because hotels were cleaner and one ate on the French side because the food was better. Now that La Samanna is there, it's the only place really worth going to St. Martin for – one of the most unusual and most attractive small resort hotels anywhere and once again in these latitudes, it took American owners to make this particular dream come true. There is a long low white building and lots of cottages spread along an endless white beach. You can lose your neighbours just by staying on your own divine terrace or by walking a bit further on the beach. It is a deliciously informal and easy-going resort hotel which still manages the right touches when needed. The decor is fresh and quite charming and the food better than that – La Samanna is the only place in the Caribbean which offers 'la nouvelle cuisine' with West Indian overtones. If you are looking for a really unusual place, I don't think you'd be disappointed.

St. Vincent

COTTON HOUSE, Mustique Island, St. Vincent, Grenadines

★ TELEPHONE: 84621/84622
★ CABLES: Mustico St. Vincent
★ TELEX: 549 St. Vincent

★ IN OPERATION: since 1970
★ RESERVATIONS: Utell International, worldwide

★ ROOMS: 19
★ SUITES: none
★ RESTAURANTS: 1
★ BARS: 1
★ DISCOTHEQUE: no – but there is one nearby
★ SHOPS: 2 – toiletries and drugstore and handicrafts and clothes
★ CONFERENCE ROOMS: none
★ BANQUETING ROOMS: none
★ STANDARD BEDROOM SIZE: 25 m²
★ PRIVATE BALCONIES: yes
★ SWIMMING POOL: yes – fresh water
★ RECREATIONAL ACTIVITIES: tennis, fishing, snorkelling

★ GARDENS: no – but 2 private beaches
★ NO. OF STAFF: 30
★ ROOM SERVICE: 07.00–22.00
★ ORIENTATION: ocean view
★ CREDIT CARDS: American Express
★ OWNING COMPANY: Guy de la Houssaye
★ GENERAL MANAGER: Claude and Simon Boye
★ DISTANCE TO BEACH: walking distance
★ DISTANCE TO SHOPS: not applicable
★ DISTANCE FROM AIRPORT: 1 km (private airport)

If you read the social columns anywhere from London to Dallas, you can't very well get away from the privately-owned island of Mustique in those heavenly microdots, the Grenadines. Some of the people who are somebody have been there or own a pad there – and I say this because Mustique is small and very, but very selective and now that it belongs to an eminent Frenchman from nearby Martinique, its services work too. As for the Cotton House, it's really a non-hotel – more of a place where one meets one's friends. There is no noise, no glitter, no cheap sensations, just this gorgeous green Caribbean islet belted with some of the most beautiful beaches in the business. The main house is an old, converted sugarmill, very clubby and quite charming. The rest are the cottages, very fresh and cheerful and all done up in excellent taste. Cotton House may appear rustic. So did Marie Antoinette at times.

Tobago

MOUNT IRVINE BAY HOTEL, P.O. Box 222, Tobago, West Indies

★ TELEPHONE: 639-8871/2/3
★ CABLES: Golfotel, Tobago
★ TELEX: 3463
★ IN OPERATION: since 1972
★ RESERVATIONS: I. Oliver Engebreston Inc, New York/Norma Brodie Cairs, Canada/Morris Associates Ltd, London
★ ROOMS: 110
★ SUITES: none
★ RESTAURANTS: 1
★ BARS: 5
★ DISCOTHEQUE: yes – and live music (combo and steelband)
★ SHOPS: 4 – boutique, art & craft, hairdressing and general
★ CONFERENCE ROOMS: 1 (150 to 200 – theatre style, 75 to 100 seating and tables)
★ BANQUETING ROOMS: 1 (150 to 175)
★ STANDARD BEDROOM SIZE: 28 m²

★ PRIVATE BALCONIES: yes
★ SWIMMING POOL: yes – fresh water, 120,000 gallons
★ RECREATIONAL ACTIVITIES: 18-hole golf course, 2 tennis courts (floodlit), sauna and massage
★ GARDENS: yes
★ NO. OF STAFF: 180
★ ROOM SERVICE: 07.00–21.00
★ ORIENTATION: rooms face west or north, overlooking pool, gardens or golf course
★ CREDIT CARDS: American Express, Diners Club and Visa
★ OWNING COMPANY: Mount Irvine Bay Hotel Ltd
★ GENERAL MANAGER: Stephen Dewick
★ DISTANCE TO BEACH: adjacent
★ DISTANCE TO SHOPS: 13 km
★ DISTANCE FROM AIRPORT: 13 km

In this very beautiful island of Tobago – fortunately untouched by the socio-economic aggro elsewhere in this part of the world – Mount Irvine remains one of the best hotels in the Caribbean. Built somewhat later, and with more good taste, than the average resort in these parts, it has stood the test of time very well and has in fact improved now that West Indian nature, always bountiful, has matured the famous golf course, the gardens and the buildings themselves. Happily too, its new general manager is a man of long experience and it shows in the improvements he has made. It began as a hotel for golfers who liked the beach and it is now a favourite place to stay even for people who don't play. You can have a room in the main building or one in a two-roomed cottage. Both the structure and the decor of the hotel are solid, permanent and well thought out. Furniture is of high quality and great care is taken of the lovely swimming pool and gardens. The centrepiece is the restaurant, built around an original sugar mill, where the food is varied and a good deal of it is local.

U.S. Virgin Islands

CANEEL BAY INC, P.O. Box 120, St. John

- ★ TELEPHONE: 809 776 6111
- ★ CABLES: Caneelbay, St. Thomas VI
- ★ TELEX: 3470019 (via ITT)
- ★ IN OPERATION: 28 years
- ★ RESERVATIONS: Loews Reservations Inc
- ★ ROOMS: 156
- ★ SUITES: none
- ★ RESTAURANTS: 3
- ★ BARS: 3
- ★ DISCOTHEQUE: no – but live music
- ★ SHOPS: 2 – clothing, souvenirs and sundries
- ★ CONFERENCE ROOMS: none
- ★ BANQUETING ROOMS: none
- ★ STANDARD BEDROOM SIZE: 60 m²
- ★ PRIVATE BALCONIES: yes – most rooms

- ★ SWIMMING POOL: no
- ★ RECREATIONAL ACTIVITIES: tennis, sailing, scuba and snorkelling, hiking and bicycling
- ★ GARDENS: yes
- ★ NO. OF STAFF: 350
- ★ ROOM SERVICE: 08.00–10.00 and 19.00–21.00
- ★ ORIENTATION: all rooms face beach
- ★ CREDIT CARDS: American Express, Visa and Master Charge
- ★ OPERATING COMPANY: Rockresorts Inc
- ★ GENERAL MANAGER: E. David Brewer
- ★ DISTANCE TO BEACH: on the beach
- ★ DISTANCE TO SHOPS: 16 km
- ★ DISTANCE FROM AIRPORT: 14 km

Quite apart from the fact that I am sure he is a very nice man, the legendary Mr. Laurence Rockefeller is one of my favourite hotel entrepreneurs. There can seldom be a man who spoils as little and creates as much as he does and Caneel Bay, among his other creations is no exception. It is an entire and absolutely gorgeous Caribbean peninsula – seemingly untouched but cleverly beautiful and there is more space here than anywhere else I know, roughly one acre per guest. One could also measure the rooms by the acre – they are enormous – lovely stone, real timber floors, vistas of windows and nothing but gentle beauty all around. Beds are convention-sized and so are the shining bathrooms. Yet there is nothing showy or vulgar. There are no fewer than seven private beaches, all absolutely superclean, lots of watersports and also some curiosities. I found in the gardens a plant which only grows in the Pacific. On being asked, the manager said: 'Mr. Rockefeller is a very keen botanist, you know.' The food is American – Technicolour and guaranteed safe for any tum. If you are all right for petrodollars or Dubai gold bars, I can't think of a better place to spend them.

DENMARK

Copenhagen

HOTEL KONG FREDERIK, Vester Voldgade 23-27, DK-1552 Copenhagen V

- ★ TELEPHONE: (01) 125902
- ★ CABLES: Frederikhotel
- ★ TELEX: 19702
- ★ IN OPERATION: since 1962; renovated 1978

- ★ RESERVATIONS: Utell International, worldwide
- ★ ROOMS: 127
- ★ SUITES: 5

★ RESTAURANTS: 2 – Queen's Grill and
  Queen's Garden (summer only)
★ BARS: 1
★ DISCOTHEQUE: no
★ SHOPS: none
★ CONFERENCE ROOMS: King's Gallery (up
  to 100)
★ BANQUETING ROOMS: King's Gallery (up
  to 100)
★ STANDARD BEDROOM SIZE: 25 m²
★ PRIVATE BALCONIES: some rooms
★ SWIMMING POOL: no

★ GARDENS: yes
★ NO. OF STAFF: 170
★ ROOM SERVICE: around the clock
★ ORIENTATION: faces west
★ CREDIT CARDS: all major ones
★ OWNING COMPANY: K/S Radhusplasens
  Hoteller
★ GENERAL MANAGER: Jorgen Stampe
★ DISTANCE TO BEACH: 5 km
★ DISTANCE TO SHOPS: hotel located in
  shopping district
★ DISTANCE FROM AIRPORT: 10 km

Having recently returned to Copenhagen – something I forgot to do for so long – I am delighted to be able to add one more address in the lovely Danish capital. Which of the two you choose is your affair but the Kong Frederik struck me as one of the brightest, most cheerful city hotels I have seen in Europe. It's worth going there just for that delightful Queen's Garden courtyard restaurant – they keep your feet warm with a heated floor and aquavit takes care of the rest. The whole hotel is charmingly furnished with good, well-chosen pieces and every room is different as befits such an old building. As usual in Denmark, I found the place so clean that one could eat breakfast off the floor – happily for one's posture one does not have to. The food everywhere is Danish – fabulous and that's enough said. What must be said is that the quality of service is well above the average: nothing is too much trouble in this well-organised multi-lingual hotel. A very good choice.

THE PLAZA HOTEL, 4 Bernstorffsgade, DK-1577 Copenhagen V

★ TELEPHONE: (01) 14 92 62
★ CABLES: Theplaza
★ TELEX: 15330
★ IN OPERATION: 12 years
★ RESERVATIONS: direct
★ ROOMS: 60 doubles   47 singles
★ SUITES: 6
★ RESTAURANTS: 2 – The Baron of Beef and
  Flora Danica
★ BARS: 1
★ DISCOTHEQUE: no
★ SHOPS: none
★ CONFERENCE ROOMS: 1 (50)
★ BANQUETING ROOMS: 1 (50)
★ STANDARD BEDROOM SIZE: 17 m² plus
  bathroom
★ PRIVATE BALCONIES: no

★ SWIMMING POOL: no
★ GARDENS: none
★ NO. OF STAFF: 100
★ ROOM SERVICE: 07.00–22.30
★ ORIENTATION: overlooking Tivoli
  gardens
★ CREDIT CARDS: American Express, Diners
  Club, Master Charge, Eurocard, Visa
  and Access
★ OWNING COMPANY: privately owned –
  Mr. Jorgen Tonnesen
★ GENERAL MANAGER: Mr. Ole Jochumsen
  (Director)
★ DISTANCE TO BEACH: 15 km
★ DISTANCE TO SHOPS: 500 m
★ DISTANCE FROM AIRPORT: 15 km

Copenhagen – that most cheerful and welcoming of capital cities – has had a chequered history where the hotel business is concerned. The quantity is there but often quality is missing – that's why, without hesitation, I have picked the refurbished Plaza as one of the two best hotels in this capital. It started as a kind of station hotel but has very quickly developed into a small but extremely elegant place – I particularly like the rooms and the suites which are quiet, tastefully furnished and beautifully equipped. Decor is sensible – mostly done in the suede-brown range which is most attractive. This hotel has one of the most original bars I have ever seen – in the library – sumptuously decorated with good leather and nice pictures, books and an exceedingly friendly and comfortable feel. The two dining rooms must be visited, not just for the Danish food which is superlative but because they could be object-lessons on how to furnish a restaurant.

Fredensborg

HOTEL STORE KRO, Slotsgade 6, 3480 Fredensborg

★ TELEPHONE: 02-280047
★ CABLES: Store Kro
★ TELEX: none
★ IN OPERATION: since 1723
★ RESERVATIONS: direct
★ ROOMS: 49
★ SUITES: 3
★ RESTAURANTS: 1
★ BARS: 1
★ DISCOTHEQUE: no
★ SHOPS: none
★ CONFERENCE ROOMS: 6 (smallest 20 m², largest 180 m²)
★ BANQUETING ROOMS: 3 (smallest 12 m², largest 180 m²)
★ STANDARD BEDROOM SIZE: 18 m²
★ PRIVATE BALCONIES: some rooms

★ SWIMMING POOL: no
★ RECREATIONAL ACTIVITIES: billiards, table tennis, area suitable for walks
★ GARDENS: yes
★ NO. OF STAFF: 32
★ ROOM SERVICE: around the clock
★ ORIENTATION: some rooms overlook gardens
★ CREDIT CARDS: all major cards except American Express
★ OWNING COMPANY: Dansk Magisterforening
★ GENERAL MANAGER: Bent Petarsen
★ DISTANCE TO BEACH: 12 km
★ DISTANCE TO SHOPS: 150 m
★ DISTANCE FROM AIRPORT: 65 km

Some years ago in Denmark, having discovered the delights of some of the small country hotels I swore I would go back and look for some more. I did and I have and this is the first appearance of Store Kro in this book. I am quite sure it won't be the last because readers will love it. It is basically an old manor house, originally built in 1723 by King Frederik IV (he was probably fed up with putting up so many guests in his own Fredensborg Castle nearby . . .) and since then much renovated and added to, but it has kept the royal touch: splendid public rooms ornamented by priceless furniture, mostly Danish antiques, and a fresh, uncluttered feel that one must appreciate. Everything is in its place. Bedrooms are all individual so you can choose your own and service is gentle, smiling and efficient. There are splendid gardens all around in this particularly royal part of Denmark just a few miles from Copenhagen. Yet undoubtedly, what I will remember best about Store Kro is the food – I got almost as much fun photographing the cold table as I did partaking of it! Scandinavia's (and France's . . .) delicacies are all here: fresh, natural and of the highest quality and they are all so beautifully arranged that it seems a shame to upset the order. Dinners are great too.

Millinge, Fyn

STEENSGAARD HERREGARDS PENSION, D-5642 Millinge, Fyn

★ TELEPHONE: 09-61.94.90
★ CABLES: no
★ TELEX: no
★ IN OPERATION: since 1956
★ RESERVATIONS: direct
★ ROOMS: 13 doubles 2 singles
★ SUITES: none
★ RESTAURANTS: 1
★ BARS: 1
★ DISCOTHEQUE: no
★ SHOPS: none
★ CONFERENCE ROOMS: 1 (15 to 20)
★ BANQUETING ROOMS: sitting rooms can be adapted to banqueting rooms accommodating up to 100
★ STANDARD BEDROOM SIZE: 20–46 m²
★ PRIVATE BALCONIES: no – public terraces

★ SWIMMING POOL: no
★ RECREATIONAL ACTIVITIES: tennis, horse riding and pleasant walks through forests and fields
★ GARDENS: yes – park
★ NO. OF STAFF: 12
★ ROOM SERVICE: 08.00–23.00
★ ORIENTATION: terraces face south
★ CREDIT CARDS: none
★ OWNING COMPANY: Peter Hansen
★ GENERAL MANAGERS: Kirsten Lund & Bent Lillemark
★ DISTANCE TO BEACH: 2 km
★ DISTANCE TO SHOPS: 7 km
★ DISTANCE FROM AIRPORT: 42 km (Beldringe)

A country's hospitality should be judged by hotels away from the big cities, by the small, the remote and the ordinary. Not knowing much about Denmark a sight like Steensgaard makes one feel the standards must be high. I came across it by accident and will surely return; it is a charming little manor house, a fourteenth-century all-timbered building blending carelessly into a great park where generations of cultivated Danes must have had a hand in creating it. Splendid panelled walls, marvellous parquet flooring, extremely pretty furniture combine to ravish the eye. Public rooms are elegantly private – it could be your drawing room if you were lucky enough to own such a place. Being a small place, everybody at Steensgaard knows you, what you like and how you like it within a short time of your arrival.

Nyborg

HOTEL HESSELET, 5800 Nyborg

★ TELEPHONE: 09 31 30 29
★ CABLES: Hesselet
★ TELEX: no
★ IN OPERATION: since 1967
★ RESERVATIONS: direct
★ ROOMS: 43
★ SUITES: 3
★ RESTAURANTS: 1
★ BARS: none
★ DISCOTHEQUE: no – but live music can be arranged if desired
★ SHOPS: none
★ CONFERENCE ROOMS: 1 (120)
★ BANQUETING ROOMS: 3 (20, 60 and 70)
★ STANDARD BEDROOM SIZE: 32 m²
★ PRIVATE BALCONIES: 14 rooms have private terraces
★ SWIMMING POOL: yes – fresh water, 10 × 5 m

★ RECREATIONAL ACTIVITIES: massage, 2 saunas, tennis, horse riding, billiards, table tennis and solarium. International 18-hole golf course
★ GARDENS: yes
★ NO. OF STAFF: 45
★ ROOM SERVICE: 07.00–23.00
★ ORIENTATION: the main facades face west
★ CREDIT CARDS: Eurocard, American Express and Diners Club
★ OWNING COMPANY: Kai Wolhardt and Karl Haustrup
★ GENERAL MANAGER: Zvonko Tresoglavic
★ DISTANCE TO BEACH: directly on the beach
★ DISTANCE TO SHOPS: 2 km
★ DISTANCE FROM AIRPORT: 45 km

This rather unusual hotel, our readers agree, is both different and interesting. It is Scandinavian/Japanese and hyper-modern but not jarringly so – with flowers everywhere and an Eastern attention to small details. Here is an oddity indeed. Rooms are large by European standards and they all have an agreeable sitting area so that you are not forever perched on the edge of the bed. The beds are worth a mention – they are among the most comfortable I have ever rested weary bones on. There is also a marvellous indoor swimming pool where the surroundings are rustic-green. Only an hour away from Copenhagen, this astonishing blend of East and West has certainly captured the attention of some of our most discriminating readers.

DJIBOUTI

DJIBOUTI SHERATON HOTEL, B.P. 1924, Djibouti, République de Djibouti

★ TELEPHONE: 35-04-05
★ CABLES: no
★ TELEX: 5912 DJ SHER
★ IN OPERATION: since December, 1981

★ RESERVATIONS: Sheraton Hotels or Sheraton Reservation Offices
★ ROOMS: 198
★ SUITES: 2

★ RESTAURANTS: 2 and a poolside snack bar
★ BARS: 2 – 1 poolside bar and Khamsin Bar
★ DISCOTHEQUE: yes
★ SHOPS: 2 – boutique and news stand plus a travel agent counter
★ CONFERENCE ROOMS: 1 (up to 150)
★ BANQUETING ROOMS: 1 (up to 150)
★ STANDARD BEDROOM SIZE: 18 m²
★ PRIVATE BALCONIES: none
★ SWIMMING POOL: yes – fresh water, oval shaped, 20 × 15 m
★ RECREATIONAL ACTIVITIES: 1 tennis court, fishing, deep sea fishing, scuba diving – best coral reef and tropical fish viewing

★ GARDENS: yes
★ NO. OF STAFF: 220
★ ROOM SERVICE: around the clock
★ ORIENTATION: all rooms face the sea
★ CREDIT CARDS: yes
★ OWNING COMPANY: Société hotelière d'état
★ GENERAL MANAGER: Franco Laberio Minozzi
★ DISTANCE TO BEACH: hotel by the sea, nearest beach 50 m
★ DISTANCE TO SHOPS: 1 km
★ DISTANCE FROM AIRPORT: 6 km

Another one of those places where only mad dogs and Englishmen used to go – except that in this case, it was Frenchmen, until the locals gained a sort of French-protected independence. Djibouti – a setting fit for Peter Lorre – is right there on the Horn of Africa and now, since the Djibouti Sheraton has opened its 200 rooms you can even drink the water (though the bar is better stocked, especially with French wines). In this part of the world, there has never been anything like it. In any other geographical context, one might perhaps look and pass on. Here you look and stay. It's a friendly hotel too, with nice Gallic touches and quite a lot of life. Decor is international but one can live with it and as for the food, the answer is that whoever it was who said that British imperialists left good policemen behind and the French left good food must have been thinking of Djibouti. Not far away, you can go to the beach, try scuba diving in the Red Sea and shoot off to islands which are hardly marked on the map. Djibouti for your next stopover? That's travelling with a vengeance.

EGYPT
Aswan
HOTEL ASWAN OBEROI, Elephantine Island, Aswan

★ TELEPHONE: 3455
★ CABLES: Obhotel Aswan
★ TELEX: 92120 OBROI
★ IN OPERATION: since 1973
★ RESERVATIONS: Loews Representation International, U.S.A., Canada, Mexico, London and Tokyo/Stinnes Touristic Representations, Frankfurt/Oberoi Hotels Reservation Offices
★ ROOMS: 160
★ SUITES: 38 and 16 villas
★ RESTAURANTS: 'Orangerie', 'Coffee Shop', the 'Nashwah' (night club) and 'Floating Restaurant' (on request)
★ BARS: 'Elephantine Bar'
★ DISCOTHEQUE: yes – and live music
★ SHOPS: 25 – including a bank
★ CONFERENCE ROOMS: 1 (150)
★ BANQUETING ROOMS: 1 (150)

★ STANDARD BEDROOM SIZE: 18 m²
★ PRIVATE BALCONIES: yes
★ SWIMMING POOL: yes – fresh water, 30 × 20 m
★ RECREATIONAL ACTIVITIES: tennis and sailing
★ GARDENS: yes
★ NO. OF STAFF: 415
★ ROOM SERVICE: around the clock
★ FURTHER DEVELOPMENTS: a health spa and 150 additional rooms
★ CREDIT CARDS: American Express, Diners Club and Bankamericard
★ OPERATING COMPANY: Oberoi Hotels International
★ GENERAL MANAGER: Mr. Ibrahim Dessouki
★ DISTANCE TO SHOPS: 10 km
★ DISTANCE FROM AIRPORT: 18 km

One American lady I met in the lobby of the Aswan Oberoi was bubbling over with enthusiasm. 'I just love Egypt,' she cooed. 'It's really quite civilised, isn't it?' Probably the pharaohs would have agreed with her although I must admit that Aswan was never quite like this in the hotel field in the pre-Oberoi days and I remember it buzzing with helicopter-sized mosquitoes. While this hotel cannot be on a par with anything that ancient Egypt has to offer, it is nevertheless a very welcome oasis of peace, coolness and efficiency in a country which, however interesting, is a bit hard on the traveller. Here everything works, smoothly and with commendable efficiency. It's a hotel built for passing tourists of course – the size of the rooms show it – and nobody stays long enough to complain. But the rest certainly makes a change – the telephone works, the moneychanger does not skin you alive and the bellboy's 'yes Mister' comes with a great wide grin. One can drink anything without fear of the Nefertitis and the food, if not distinguished, is perfectly acceptable. Apart from the architecture (happily it won't last as long as Karnak) a good effort it certainly is and one can now brush one's teeth and get a suit pressed in Aswan.

Cairo

CAIRO SHERATON HOTEL & CASINO, P.O. Box 11, Galae Square, Giza, Cairo

- ★ TELEPHONE: 983000
- ★ CABLES: Sheraco Cairo, A.R.E.
- ★ TELEX: (927) 92041 & (927) 382 Shera UN
- ★ IN OPERATION: since March, 1970
- ★ RESERVATIONS: Sheraton Reservation Offices, worldwide
- ★ ROOMS: 396 doubles 10 singles
- ★ SUITES: 50
- ★ RESTAURANTS: 4
- ★ BARS: 3
- ★ DISCOTHEQUE: live music
- ★ SHOPS: 6
- ★ CONFERENCE ROOMS: 1 (400)
- ★ BANQUETING ROOMS: 1 (350)
- ★ STANDARD BEDROOM SIZE: 25 m^2

- ★ PRIVATE BALCONIES: yes
- ★ SWIMMING POOL: yes – fresh water, 11.5 × 10 m
- ★ GARDENS: none
- ★ NO. OF STAFF: 820
- ★ ROOM SERVICE: around the clock
- ★ ORIENTATION: facing Nile and Galae Square
- ★ CREDIT CARDS: Bankamericard, Master Charge, American Express and Diners Club
- ★ OWNING COMPANY: Egyptian Government
- ★ GENERAL MANAGER: A. Basmi
- ★ DISTANCE TO SHOPS: 8 km
- ★ DISTANCE FROM AIRPORT: 26 km

Only a few years ago there was not a single hotel in Cairo where one would have dared to send anyone, not even one's tax collector. Now, the Egyptian capital has four of international standing – two American chains, one French and one Indian and competition is intense. The Cairo Sheraton certainly deserves mention – 25 storeys right on the bank of the Nile facing the old city with the Pyramids in the distance where everything works from the message service to the air-conditioning. The Sheraton silhouette – not unpleasant – simply rather slab-like, must be accepted. What is remarkable in a way is how this chain hotel has been furnished – very elegantly indeed in a kind of periodless Curzon Street Baroque that soon grows on one. Service is fast and attentive and more than willing and the food, in all the varieties offered in the four restaurants, is well up to what one might expect.

HOTEL MENA HOUSE OBEROI, Pyramid Road, Giza, Cairo

- ★ TELEPHONE: 855444 and 856222
- ★ CABLES: Obhotel
- ★ TELEX: 92316 and 93096 OBHTL UN
- ★ IN OPERATION: since 1973

- ★ RESERVATIONS: Loews Representation International, New York, London/Oberoi Hotels, India/Stinnes Touristic Representatives,

Frankfurt/Claude L. C. Duteil,
Paris/Alghanem Travel, Kuwait/Odner
Hotel Representatives, Hong Kong/Utell
International
★ ROOMS: 520
★ SUITES: 15
★ RESTAURANTS: 6 – Khan El Khalili, Al
Rubayyat, The Moghul Room, Oasis,
Abu Nawas and Mena Café
★ BARS: 2 – Mameluke Bar and Lobby Bar
★ DISCOTHEQUE: The Saddle
★ SHOPS: 8
★ CONFERENCE ROOMS: 1 (200)
★ BANQUETING ROOMS: 1 (200)
★ STANDARD BEDROOM SIZE: 21 m^2
★ PRIVATE BALCONIES: yes
★ SWIMMING POOL: yes – fresh water,
40 × 30 m

★ RECREATIONAL ACTIVITIES: 18-hole golf
course, tennis, horse riding and health
spa
★ GARDENS: yes
★ NO. OF STAFF: 1,100
★ ROOM SERVICE: around the clock
★ ORIENTATION: hotel located at the foot of
the Pyramids of Giza
★ CREDIT CARDS: Diners Club, American
Express, Bankamericard and Visa
★ OPERATING COMPANY: Oberoi Hotels
(India) Pvt Ltd
★ GENERAL MANAGER: Mr. Kaval Nain
★ DISTANCE TO SHOPS: 10 km
★ DISTANCE FROM AIRPORT: 30 km

To my way of thinking this hotel is one of the miracles of the Middle East – old and yet
up to date, filled with history and still making it, and restored with such care that it is an
object lesson for hotels of the type around the world.

Once, it was a khedivial weekend place, then the habitual watering place of colonial Brits and then the meeting place of Roosevelt and Churchill and, later, of Anwar Sadat and Menachem Begin. In those days it had a curious, forlorn, Turkish-type decadence and now it is back in all its glory and it took an Indian company to make the changes. Away from the hurly-burly of Cairo (very hurly indeed), Mena House is so near the Pyramids that when I rose in the morning and walked onto my terrace I could almost touch Cheops' great pile – probably the most prestigious location in Egypt. The hotel's fabric has been renewed but not re-made. The old wooden balconies are still there, so are those splendid 'musharabyiah' screens which are so much a part of Arabic art, and everywhere Mena House shines with good taste. Even the Coffee Shop, called Khan el-Khalili after Cairo's great bazaar, is a masterpiece. Elsewhere, amidst gardens and around the pool are the new wings – cool, spacious and elegant.

Above all, this hotel has character and personality. People smile, help and are totally unstinting in the service they give and it is obvious that the excellent management has done its homework. The food runs from good to superb and the Indian restaurant is particularly to be recommended. As in all great hotels, it's being there that counts. Full marks for a great success.

NILE HILTON HOTEL, Tahrir Square, Cairo

★ TELEPHONE: 750666/740777
★ CABLES: Hiltels Cairo
★ TELEX: 92222/92354 Hiltls UN
★ IN OPERATION: since February, 1959
★ RESERVATIONS: Hilton International
★ ROOMS: 382 (all rooms are singles and doubles)
★ SUITES: 47
★ RESTAURANTS: 6 El Nile Rotisserie, Pizzeria, Belvedere Supper Club, Taverne du Champ de Mars, Ibis Coffee Shop and Tropicana
★ BARS: 3
★ DISCOTHEQUE: yes
★ SHOPS: men's wear, ladies' wear, patisserie, silver jewellery and antiques, bazaars, florist, camera shop, book shop, car rental, beauty/hairdressing parlour, barber shop, airlines, travel agent, banks, papyrus
★ CONFERENCE ROOMS: 6 (30 to 800)

★ BANQUETING ROOMS: 6 (30 to 500)
★ STANDARD BEDROOM SIZE: 24 m²
★ PRIVATE BALCONIES: yes – all rooms
★ SWIMMING POOL: yes – fresh water, 22 m
★ RECREATIONAL ACTIVITIES: 2 clay tennis courts, health club with gymnasium, sauna, steam bath and massage; golf, squash and horse riding nearby; water sports and boat rentals by arrangement
★ GARDENS: yes
★ NO. OF STAFF: 950
★ ROOM SERVICE: around the clock
★ ORIENTATION: rooms face Nile and city
★ CREDIT CARDS: Carte Blanche, American Express, Master Charge Eurocard, Diners Club, Bankamericard and Hilton Hotels
★ GENERAL MANAGER: Hugo R. Langer
★ DISTANCE TO SHOPS: walking distance
★ DISTANCE FROM AIRPORT: 24 km

Part of the trinity of great Hiltons in this part of the world (the other two being Athens and Istanbul), the Nile Hilton still deserves every praise. By now, it has to contend with its corporate brother just down the banks of the Nile and this is going to make its success all the more remarkable. The hotel is more than twenty years old which, in Hilton terms, makes it almost an antique and in this space of time it has acquired a patina and a tradition of its own. It has elegance, good looks, just enough bustle and glitter to remind you of where you are. Service is quite superb – instant, smiling and ever present. The swimming pool is one of the best in Cairo and just across the Nile is the Gezira Sporting Club where you can be energetic. The Hilton navy, Isis and Osiris, is moored down below waiting to sail you upstream to the wonders of the land of the Pharaohs. But not, I hope, before you have had time to sample the food in the Rotisserie – one of the two or three best hotel restaurants in Cairo.

Nothing is missing here. The Nile Hilton is a great hotel.

RAMSES HILTON, Corniche El Nil, Cairo

- ★ TELEPHONE: 744400/758000/754999
- ★ CABLES: no
- ★ TELEX: 94260/2
- ★ IN OPERATION: since May, 1981
- ★ RESERVATIONS: direct or Hilton Reservation Service
- ★ ROOMS: 904
- ★ SUITES: 72
- ★ RESTAURANTS: 5 – La Brasserie Coffee Shop, Citadel Grill, La Patisserie, Pool Snack Bar, Two Season Supper Club
- ★ BARS: 3 – Citadel Bar, Garden Bar, Club 36
- ★ DISCOTHEQUE: yes and live music
- ★ SHOPS: 16
- ★ CONFERENCE ROOMS: 10 (from 50 to 500)
- ★ BANQUETING ROOMS: 6 (from 25 to 500)
- ★ STANDARD BEDROOM SIZE: 26 m^2
- ★ PRIVATE BALCONIES: all rooms
- ★ SWIMMING POOL: yes – fresh water
- ★ RECREATIONAL ACTIVITIES: swimming and health club; golf, tennis and riding can be arranged nearby
- ★ GARDENS: yes
- ★ NO. OF STAFF: 1,200
- ★ ROOM SERVICE: around the clock
- ★ ORIENTATION: south-east, overlooking Nile
- ★ CREDIT CARDS: all major credit cards
- ★ OWNING COMPANY: operated by Hilton International
- ★ GENERAL MANAGER: Ahmed El Nahas
- ★ DISTANCE TO SHOPS: walking distance
- ★ DISTANCE FROM AIRPORT: 24 km

As a professional hotel watcher, I have inevitably looked closely at Hilton operations over the years and I must admit that on some occasions in the now distant past, I shook my head in despair. Now, more often than not, I doff my hat to the world's universal host because they have been big enough to learn from their own past mistakes and these days, when a new Hilton opens, one looks carefully.

A case in point is Cairo's second Hilton – a statement of pride – 35 stories rising above this frenetic and absolutely fascinating city, and with even a glass elevator which reveals a new Nile at every touch of the button. So far, so eye-filling. The outside architecture does not thrill me and I must admit that the colossal statue of the old man (Ramses II, I mean . . .) in the lobby fills one with awe. Then you begin to realise the idea behind it all: the vast lobby reminds you of Karnak and Luxor with huge, massive pillars of porphyry rising everywhere like those of a temple. But there is more to it than that. You begin to notice the finish of every item – the edge of the bar, the hinges of a door, the fit of the carpets, the opulent but not disagreable room decor and you finally have to admit that here are people who know how to build a hotel – they have the experience, the knowhow, the values and if the good taste is also there, the results are unmatcheable in the new hotel line. That must be acknowledged. Inevitably, the Ramses has everything: five restaurants (the food is extremely good), three bars, swimming pool, shops galore. One expects that. What is not always quite so automatic is the quality of the management which in this case is of the highest.

Hurghada

HURGHADA SHERATON HOTEL, Hurghada, Red Sea

- ★ TELEPHONE: 785
- ★ CABLES: no
- ★ TELEX: 92750 Un Sherga
- ★ IN OPERATION: 2 years
- ★ RESERVATIONS: Sheraton Hotel or Reservations Offices, Brussels, Cairo, Frankfurt, London, Milan, Paris, Stockholm
- ★ ROOMS: 165
- ★ SUITES: none
- ★ RESTAURANTS: 1
- ★ BARS: 1
- ★ DISCOTHEQUE: no
- ★ SHOPS: 1 – newsagent/giftshop
- ★ CONFERENCE ROOMS: 4 (10 to 35)
- ★ BANQUETING ROOMS: 4 (10 to 35)
- ★ STANDARD BEDROOM SIZE: 25 m^2
- ★ PRIVATE BALCONIES: all rooms
- ★ SWIMMING POOL: 1 – salt water (30 × 20 m)
- ★ RECREATIONAL ACTIVITIES: full range of watersports
- ★ GARDENS: no
- ★ NO. OF STAFF: 75

★ ROOM SERVICE: 07.00–24.00
★ ORIENTATION: all rooms have sea or mountain view
★ CREDIT CARDS: all major credit cards
★ OWNING COMPANY: Egyptian General

Company for Tourism and Hotels
★ GENERAL MANAGER: A. Bakri
★ DISTANCE TO BEACH: on the beach
★ DISTANCE TO SHOPS: 1 km
★ DISTANCE FROM AIRPORT: 5 km

Who on earth goes to the Red Sea coast of Egypt? I do and so will you, I suggest, before very long because this grand and austere desert coast with its fringe along one of the greatest coral reefs in the world is a place of the future. Out there are dozens of beach-girt islands such as you have never seen before. One can fly to Hurghada in 45 minutes from Cairo – which I think is a pity. Do as I did – drive, and you'll feel that you are aiming at the end of the world. You are in fact aiming at the Hurghada Sheraton – one of the most courageous hotel enterprises I have seen recently. All right, I could have done without the drum-like architecture (you know what architects are like . . .). But for what it is, where it is, at the edge of this marine paradise, the Hurghada Sheraton deserves every compliment. It is clean, well planned, quite handsome inside, around its interior garden and the rooms – very, very good indeed – are totally silent. Service is gay and cheerful and the food better than one has any right to expect in this kind of location. And when you have had enough of the pale blue sea, drive on back across the desert and meet the Nile at Luxor. You won't forget the trip.

EIRE
Cong
ASHFORD CASTLE, Cong, Co Mayo

★ TELEPHONE: (094) 22644
★ CABLES: no
★ TELEX: 24749
★ IN OPERATION: since 1973
★ RESERVATIONS: Aer Lingus, Great Britain, Germany, France and U.S.A./Loews Representation International, worldwide/Irish Tourist Board, Central Reservations, London
★ ROÔMS: 72 twin/doubles
★ SUITES: 6
★ RESTAURANTS: 1
★ BARS: 2 – Cocktail Bar and Dungeon Bar
★ DISCOTHEQUE: live music
★ SHOPS: 1
★ CONFERENCE ROOMS: 1 (150)
★ BANQUETING ROOMS: 1 (100)
★ STANDARD BEDROOM SIZE: 30 m²
★ PRIVATE BALCONIES: no
★ SWIMMING POOL: no

★ RECREATIONAL ACTIVITIES: 9-hole golf course and 2 tennis courts, with horse riding nearby
★ GARDENS: yes – 300 acres
★ NO. OF STAFF: 70
★ ROOM SERVICE: 08.00–10.00, afterwards on request
★ ORIENTATION: rooms face Lough Corrib and gardens
★ FURTHER DEVELOPMENTS: a new conference centre within the next two years
★ CREDIT CARDS: all credit cards
★ OWNING COMPANY: John A. Mulcahy Co Ltd
★ GENERAL MANAGER: Rory J. C. Murphy
★ DISTANCE TO BEACH: 40 km
★ DISTANCE TO SHOPS: 40 km
★ DISTANCE FROM AIRPORT: 128 km

If it was not there, Ashford Castle would have to be invented – the kind of Irish stately home where the 'Troubles' never happened. Although it is not all that old, Ashford seems to have been there forever and then some more, a great stone-built pile backed by green fields and woods and facing a beautiful lake. Among other things it has 300 acres of gardens, 4,000 acres of nature reserve and 27,000 acres of shoot. Public rooms are grand, wood-panelled and exceedingly well furnished with much of the eighteenth century's best mahogany. Bedrooms are large and airy, high-ceilinged and very well equipped with good beds and solid, unpretentious Irish country-style furniture, lots of room for your clothes and your luggage and, what is so rare these days, good lighting. In as far as you can see Ireland from a hotel you can see it from this one.

Dublin

FITZPATRICK'S CASTLE HOTEL, Killiney, Co Dublin

★ TELEPHONE: 851533
★ CABLES: no
★ TELEX: 30353
★ IN OPERATION: 12 years
★ RESERVATIONS: American International Hotel Representatives, New York/Muriel Fleger International, Toronto/Aer Lingus/International Hotel Representatives
★ ROOMS: 50
★ SUITES: 2
★ RESTAURANTS: 2
★ BARS: 3
★ DISCOTHEQUE: cabaret, jazz and dixieland in the Dungeon Bar
★ SHOPS: 1
★ CONFERENCE ROOMS: 2 (50 to 200)
★ BANQUETING ROOMS: 2 (up to 300)
★ STANDARD BEDROOM SIZE: 13.5 m²
★ PRIVATE BALCONIES: yes – some rooms

★ SWIMMING POOL: yes – fresh water, 20 m
★ RECREATIONAL ACTIVITIES: tennis, squash and 9-hole mini golf, hairdressing and beauty salons and 3 saunas, an 18-hole championship golf course and horse riding close by
★ GARDENS: yes
★ NO. OF STAFF: 110
★ ROOM SERVICE: around the clock
★ ORIENTATION: rooms face woodlands
★ FURTHER DEVELOPMENTS: the addition of 50 luxury rooms with a rooftop piano bar and speciality restaurant for 150 persons
★ CREDIT CARDS: all major credit cards
★ OWNING COMPANY: Fitzpatrick Hotels Ltd
★ GENERAL MANAGER: Paddy Fitzpatrick
★ DISTANCE TO BEACH: 1.6 km
★ DISTANCE TO SHOPS: 3 km
★ DISTANCE FROM AIRPORT: 22.5 km

When I walked into Fitzpatrick's a few months back for lunch with a French friend, he looked at this incredible pile and said, 'Which lord lives here?' 'You do,' I replied. That's the way it is. One feels that somewhere in the background one of those tweedy, slightly decadent Irish peers will spring out and sell you a racehorse. But the only lordly touch in the place is the superb and intelligent management of the owner and his wife. They know what people want when they go to Ireland and this is it. The rooms come in all shapes and sizes and some of them are in fancy turrets and very fancy indeed, with four-poster beds and the like. The furniture is chosen as if for your own home – comfortable, liveable with and often very classy. Public rooms are endlessly magnificent without being overpowering and I liked the very Irish Grill Bar. And the very Irish food – simple and beautiful, no nonsense about it. Service as usual in the Emerald Isle is beyond compare. There is a great indoor swimming pool, a sauna, lots of lovely parkland and a nine-hole golf course. Only nine miles from Dublin it is the place to go to maintain an intelligent distance from that delightful but confusing capital.

SHELBOURNE HOTEL, St. Stephen's Green, Dublin 2, Ireland

★ TELEPHONE: 7 66 471
★ CABLES: Shelhotel Dublin
★ TELEX: 25184
★ IN OPERATION: over 100 years
★ RESERVATIONS: Trusthouse Forte Hotels Ltd, worldwide – London, New York, Amsterdam, Brussels, Paris, Dublin, Milan, Frankfurt etc
★ ROOMS: 164
★ SUITES: 16
★ RESTAURANTS: 3 – Shelbourne Restaurant, the Saddle Room, the Coffee Shop
★ BARS: 2

★ DISCOTHEQUE: cabaret in summer season/dancing in winter
★ SHOPS: gift shop
★ CONFERENCE ROOMS: 14 (from 6 to 200)
★ BANQUETING ROOMS: 2 (from 100 to 400)
★ STANDARD BEDROOM SIZE: 30 m^2
★ PRIVATE BALCONIES: no
★ SWIMMING POOL: no
★ RECREATIONAL ACTIVITIES: not within hotel
★ GARDENS: no – hotel faces exclusive public park
★ NO. OF STAFF: 225

★ ROOM SERVICE: full service 07.30–23.00. Limited service at other times
★ ORIENTATION: faces St. Stephen's Green
★ CREDIT CARDS: American Express, Diners Club, Barclaycard, Visa, Mastercharge and Eurocard
★ OWNING COMPANY: Trusthouse Forte Hotels Ltd
★ GENERAL MANAGER: Jose C. Borges
★ DISTANCE TO SHOPS: walking distance
★ DISTANCE FROM AIRPORT: 10 km

This was William Makepeace Thackeray's favourite hotel. Of course he's been gone rather a long time but the Shelbourne has never ceased to please except for one or two service hiccups in years gone by. It is a good-looking, well-mannered hotel, dignified and yet not stuffy and worthy of Dublin. The structure is Georgian but most of the decor and furnishings are high Victorian – ample, comfortable, easy to live with and it has the kind of rooms in which you can really move about without bumping into things. They are fresh and clean and well cared for and so are the bathrooms, some of which are as big as the bedrooms. Public rooms are quiet and restful and nobody bothers you. The bars are attractive with a convivial Irish atmosphere and all the liquids you could wish for are there. As for the food, it's great on the best days and perfectly acceptable at all times. From the Shelbourne, you can walk everywhere in the heart of this fair city. Not a bad address.

Newmarket-on-Fergus

DROMOLAND CASTLE, Newmarket-on-Fergus, Co Clare

★ TELEPHONE: 061-71144
★ CABLES: Dromoland Castle, Co Clare
★ TELEX: 6854
★ IN OPERATION: 19 years
★ RESERVATIONS: McDonough Hotels, U.S.A./Relais de Campagne Group, France
★ ROOMS: 67
★ SUITES: none
★ RESTAURANTS: 1
★ BARS: 2
★ DISCOTHEQUE: live entertainment in the bar each evening
★ SHOPS: 1
★ CONFERENCE ROOMS: 2 (75 to 200)
★ BANQUETING ROOMS: 2 (70 to 120)
★ STANDARD BEDROOM SIZE: 28 m²
★ PRIVATE BALCONIES: no – but terrace with seating equipment
★ SWIMMING POOL: no
★ RECREATIONAL ACTIVITIES: tennis, 9-hole golf course, croquet, fishing (both river and lake) with horse riding nearby
★ GARDENS: yes
★ NO. OF STAFF: 90
★ ROOM SERVICE: around the clock
★ ORIENTATION: rooms overlook woods and parkland
★ CREDIT CARDS: American Express, Barclaycard, Visa and Diners Club
★ OWNING COMPANY: Mr. B. P. McDonough (Marmac Corporation)
★ GENERAL MANAGER: Miss Patricia Barry
★ DISTANCE TO SHOPS: 11 km
★ DISTANCE FROM AIRPORT: 13 km (Shannon)

Some people, when they get to Dromoland Castle, don't quite believe it or the rest of Ireland either. Cecil B. de Mille must have been there yesterday afternoon to run it up out of pasteboard and glue. But look closer and it becomes real, even to its root in the distant past when Brian Boru was king of all Ireland. It took an American (naturally) to make Dromoland come true. How he made the plumbing work through walls five feet thick is a major miracle of the art of sanitary engineering. Dromoland is vast – corridors without beginning or end, acres of carpets, walls hung with enough pictures to fill the Louvre, public rooms that look like the nave of Westminster Abbey and, outside, that pervasive green Irishness which is without comparison. Rooms vary greatly in character but they are always well cared for. Service does not vary and the food is Irish from the estate. Here you can play golf or croquet, ride, fish or just sit and dream that you have arrived in a time-zone not yet blown apart by two world wars.

Waterville

WATERVILLE LAKE HOTEL, Waterville, Co Kerry

★ TELEPHONE: Waterville 7 and 066-23100
★ CABLES: no
★ TELEX: 28246
★ IN OPERATION: since 1972
★ RESERVATIONS: Irish Tourist Board/Aer Lingus/Brendan Tours, U.S.A./L.R.I., New York
★ ROOMS: 94 doubles
★ SUITES: 8
★ RESTAURANTS: 1
★ BARS: 2 – Cocktail and Skelligs Bar
★ DISCOTHEQUE: live music
★ SHOPS: 1 – clothing, souvenirs, post cards etc
★ CONFERENCE ROOMS: 1 (100) – suites can be converted to meeting rooms for 25
★ BANQUETING ROOMS: none – but one room can be converted for banqueting purposes, seating 40 persons
★ STANDARD BEDROOM SIZE: 28 m²

★ PRIVATE BALCONIES: yes – 40 rooms
★ SWIMMING POOL: 1 – indoor, heated; also a jacuzzi, sauna and sun-bed
★ RECREATIONAL ACTIVITIES: 2 tennis courts, golf and horse riding nearby
★ GARDENS: yes
★ NO. OF STAFF: 100
★ ROOM SERVICE: 08.00–10.00 for breakfast, afterwards on request
★ ORIENTATION: most rooms face lake and mountains
★ CREDIT CARDS: all credit cards
★ OWNING COMPANY: John A. Mulcahy Co Ltd
★ GENERAL MANAGER: Peter Prendiville
★ DISTANCE TO BEACH: 500 m
★ DISTANCE TO SHOPS: 80 km
★ DISTANCE FROM AIRPORT: 60 km (Cork), 192 km (Shannon)

One American friend sent to Waterville some time back returned agog with enthusiasm for the salmon fishing. 'You know,' he said, 'the fish positively queued up . . .' Those of us who tend to prefer salmon 'à l'oseille' on a plate also feel that way about this hotel. Just right for blowing away the cobwebs of city life. A modern hotel built with respect for the landscape, it drapes itself on the shore of the incomparable Lough Currane, looking to blue waters and green mountains. There is a par 74 golf course and all the riding you could want. What impresses, however, is that here is a perfect example of what a modern country hotel should be like. It is extremely spacious, elegant, free of unnecessary trappings, intelligently furnished and nowhere is one shut off from the Ireland around you. Rooms are large, so are the beds, and bathrooms function perfectly. Service being one of Ireland's best points, here it is even better – people are quite charming. The food, as long as it is local, is superb.

FINLAND
Helsinki

HOTEL HESPERIA, Mannerheimintie 50, 00260 Helsinki 26

★ TELEPHONE: 90-441 311
★ CABLES: Hesperiahotel helsinki
★ TELEX: 12-2117
★ IN OPERATION: since May, 1972
★ RESERVATIONS: Supranational, Omaha, London, Frankfurt, Paris and Milan
★ ROOMS: 262 double   20 single
★ SUITES: 4

★ RESTAURANTS: 3 – Steakhouse, main restaurant and Night Club
★ BARS: 3 – Lobby, Night Club and Sauna Bar
★ DISCOTHEQUE: live music in the Night Club by international top bands and famous singers
★ SHOPS: 5

★ CONFERENCE ROOMS: 9 (6 to 350)
★ BANQUETING ROOMS: 9 (6 to 400)
★ STANDARD BEDROOM SIZE: 22 m²
★ PRIVATE BALCONIES: no
★ SWIMMING POOL: yes – fresh water, indoor, 8 × 14 m with small cold plunge bath
★ RECREATIONAL ACTIVITIES: saunas and solarium
★ GARDENS: no
★ NO. OF STAFF: 280

★ ORIENTATION: overlooks Hesperia Park and Toolo Bay
★ CREDIT CARDS: American Express, Diners Club, Eurocard, Master Charge and Visa
★ OWNING COMPANY: Helsingin Osuuskauppa
★ GENERAL MANAGER: Mr. Frank Moberg
★ DISTANCE TO SHOPS: 1 km
★ DISTANCE FROM AIRPORT: 20 km (Helsinki-Vantaa), air terminal 50 m from hotel and a heli-pad on roof of hotel

Marshal Mannerheim, the great saviour of Finland, would not have cared for the slightly odd-looking submarine Night Club but for the rest of the Hesperia I thought that it fitted very well as a big city hotel. Rooms are scrupulously clean and extremely well maintained in every respect – you feel that someone has been looking around before you checked in. The lobby, very large and straight out of the pages of a design magazine, has real leather, real Italian marble and real timber, which is not always so in modern hotels. The first floor dining room is one of the most comfortable I have ever dined in – I am large and chairs are too often small – and the food is excellent if you stick to the fishy Finnish specialities and, though you won't be able to pronounce their names, the taste will come as a pleasant surprise.

FRANCE
Antibes
HOTEL DU CAP-EDEN ROC, Cap d'Antibes, Boulevard Kennedy, F-06604

★ TELEPHONE: (93) 61 39 01
★ CABLES: Capotel Antibes
★ TELEX: 470763 T

★ IN OPERATION: since 1881
★ RESERVATIONS: Hotel Representative Inc
★ ROOMS: 91

★ SUITES: 8
★ RESTAURANTS: 2
★ BARS: 2
★ DISCOTHEQUE: no
★ SHOPS: none
★ CONFERENCE ROOMS: 2 (25 and 150)
★ BANQUETING ROOMS: 2 (50 and 200)
★ STANDARD BEDROOM SIZE: 25 m²
★ PRIVATE BALCONIES: yes
★ SWIMMING POOL: yes – salt water, heated
★ RECREATIONAL ACTIVITIES: 4 tennis courts, yachting, deep sea fishing and water skiing

★ GARDENS: yes – 15-acre park
★ NO. OF STAFF: 165
★ ROOM SERVICE: around the clock
★ ORIENTATION: main facade faces Mediterranean
★ CREDIT CARDS: no
★ OWNING COMPANY: Eufra, Zurich
★ GENERAL MANAGER: Jean-Claude Irondelle
★ DISTANCE TO BEACH: walking distance
★ DISTANCE TO SHOPS: 4 km
★ DISTANCE FROM AIRPORT: 20 km

When does a hotel become a legend? I suppose it is when it resembles the Cap d'Antibes and, in these days when Riveria real estate is priceless, it has the gall to stand aloof in a 15-acre park and hang the consequences. Its guests are nutty enough to have insisted that a dog's cemetery be included, and they often book, six months ahead, one of the beach cabanas whence you can telephone for your ice-cold Krug. There is a kind of delightful folly about the Cap which never palls. It goes back probably to the Scott Fitzgerald–Tallulah Bankhead–Noel Coward era when those who had what it takes and the money to go with it, could really live it up in style. Behind its balustrades, its chandeliers and its glow, the Cap is quite marvellous – with rooms of all sizes, beautifully kept in an informal way, very discreet, and where the suites really are suites. The staff are among the most experienced in the world – nothing fazes them and the management belongs in the stratosphere of hotelkeeping. Down the gardens is the celebrated Eden Roc with its beautiful bodies and its beautiful food. If you ask for fish, they bring you the whole technicolour platter to choose from. This is a hotel which offers complete privacy and the best of everything. You are either equal to the Cap d'Antibes or you are not.

Avignon

HOSTELLERIE LE PRIEURÉ, 7 Place du Chapitre, B.P. 12, 30400 Villeneuve les Avignon

★ TELEPHONE: (90) 251820
★ CABLES: Prieuré-Avignon
★ TELEX: 431042
★ IN OPERATION: since 1943
★ RESERVATIONS: Relais et Chateaux, Paris
★ ROOMS: 20 doubles 6 singles
★ SUITES: 9
★ RESTAURANTS: 1 – lunch and dinner also served in the garden during the summer
★ BARS: 1
★ DISCOTHEQUE: no
★ SHOPS: none
★ CONFERENCE ROOMS: 2 (each of 40)
★ BANQUETING ROOMS: 2 (20 and 80)
★ STANDARD BEDROOM SIZE: 30 m²
★ PRIVATE BALCONIES: 18 rooms

★ SWIMMING POOL: yes – fresh water, 18 × 8 m
★ RECREATIONAL ACTIVITES: 2 tennis courts
★ GARDENS: yes
★ NO. OF STAFF: 48
★ ROOM SERVICE: 07.00–22.00
★ ORIENTATION: rooms face all sides
★ CREDIT CARDS: Diners Club, American Express, Eurocard, Access, Master Charge and Interbank
★ OWNING COMPANY: Jacques R. Mille
★ GENERAL MANAGER: Jacques R. Mille
★ DISTANCE TO SHOPS: walking distance
★ DISTANCE FROM AIRPORT: 100 km (Marseilles)

The cardinal who, in the fourteenth century, built himself this residence in a lovely village just the other side of the Rhone from Avignon, left it in his will to '12 canons, 12 priests and two deacons'. Without disrespect, I am glad they left because the Prieuré then became a hotel so special, so pretty and so mellow that I always stay there longer than I should. Whether you have a room in the old house, with its serpentine staircases or one in the new wing, you can be certain of comfort. Furniture is mostly of the period, good but very, very expensive; it looks as if it belongs there. The family that runs this hotel knows a great deal about hospitality and it shows in a host of small details. Yet, in the end, two things count most here: the absolutely ravishing, tree-shaded courtyard and the food they serve there – classic French provincial and deserving of the approval of Brillat-Savarin himself.

Barbizon

HÔTELLERIE DU BAS-BREAU, 77630 Barbizon

★ TELEPHONE: (6) 066 40 05
★ CABLES: no
★ TELEX: 690 953
★ IN OPERATION: 45 years
★ RESERVATIONS: Relais et Chateaux, Paris/Jacques de Larsay, New York
★ ROOMS: 12
★ RESTAURANTS: 1
★ BARS: 1
★ DISCOTHEQUE: no
★ SHOPS: none
★ CONFERENCE ROOMS: 2 (10 to 25)
★ BANQUETING ROOMS: 1 (25)
★ STANDARD BEDROOM SIZE: 20 m²
★ PRIVATE BALCONIES: yes
★ SWIMMING POOL: no

★ RECREATIONAL ACTIVITIES: horse riding within walking distance. Golf and saunas 6 km away; indoor tennis court
★ GARDENS: yes
★ NO. OF STAFF: 49
★ ROOM SERVICE: around the clock
★ ORIENTATION: all rooms face gardens, terrace and private courtyard
★ CREDIT CARDS: American Express, Eurocard, Master Charge, Intercard and Access
★ OWNING COMPANY: privately owned
★ GENERAL MANAGER: J.-P. Fava
★ DISTANCE TO SHOPS: walking distance
★ DISTANCE FROM AIRPORT: 35 km (Orly), 75 km (Charles de Gaulle)

Provincials are traditionally the butt of many Parisian jokes but here, in the tranquil green of the great forest of Fontainebleau, tucked away in a village once made famous by the Barbizon painters is a hostelry which I would put among the best in Europe. R. L. Stevenson once lived here for quite a while and I envy him. The gardens are nice and informal and though the rooms vary in size and type, they are all furnished with pleasant country antiques – just right for this place.

One word of warning: when you go to Bas-Bréau, bring your appetite with you. The Fava family, who have owned this hotel for three generations, are known even among their competitors for a fare which can only be described as Rabelaisian. Though notice is taken of 'la nouvelle cuisine' (or what's left of it), this is French gastronomy at its unchanging best. It is served in an elegant restaurant patronised by celebrities from all over the world. As for the wines – you don't even have to look at the impressive list. Just ask Jean-Pierre Fava.

Beaulieu

HOTEL LA RÉSERVE DE BEAULIEU, 06310 Beaulieu sur Mer

★ TELEPHONE: (93) 01 00 01
★ CABLES: Reserve Beaulieu sur Mer
★ TELEX: Reserve 470301 F
★ RESERVATIONS: direct
★ ROOMS: 50
★ SUITES: 3

★ RESTAURANTS: 2 – including one in summer only with direct access by sea
★ BARS: 2
★ DISCOTHEQUE: no
★ SHOPS: none
★ CONFERENCE ROOMS: 2 (30 and 50)

★ BANQUETING ROOMS: 2 (30 and 50)
★ STANDARD BEDROOM SIZE: 20 m²
★ PRIVATE BALCONIES: yes – on second floor
★ SWIMMING POOL: yes – salt water
★ GARDENS: yes
★ STAFF: 96
★ ROOM SERVICE: 07.30–22.00

★ ORIENTATION: most rooms face the sea
★ CREDIT CARDS: no
★ OWNING COMPANY: S.A. Réserve de Beaulieu
★ GENERAL MANAGER: Henri Maria
★ DISTANCE TO BEACH: walking distance
★ DISTANCE TO SHOPS: 80 m
★ DISTANCE FROM AIRPORT: 12 km

The price of quality being what it is, they do not build hotels like this any more so if you wish to see how things were done in great Riviera resorts in days gone by, try La Réserve. Not that there is anything old-fashioned about it for this comparatively small hotel has kept up its vintage very well. It is merely that it manages to blend resort living – beautiful coast views, terraces, swimming pool and such like with, inside, a well-tempered elegance which can hardly be bettered. Most hotels for instance choose darkish upholstery – it lasts longer – but not at La Réserve where chairs, sofas, curtains run the pastel gamut from pale cream to light blues and greens. Rooms are discreet and comfortable and public rooms like the long Grill and its lovely ceiling are so distingué that one feels privileged to be there. Service is exceedingly suave and the food, I feel, deserves far better accolade than its single Michelin star.

Cannes

HOTEL MAJESTIC, P.B., 163, 060403 Cannes

★ TELEPHONE: (93) 68 91 00
★ CABLES: Majesticotel
★ TELEX: 470787
★ IN OPERATION: since 1926
★ RESERVATIONS: Steigenberger Reservation Service/Worldwide Travel Agents/Air France Reservation System
★ ROOMS: 175 doubles 75 singles
★ SUITES: 12
★ RESTAURANTS: 2 – large restaurant and grill room
★ BARS: 1
★ DISCOTHEQUE: no – but night club 'Jackpot' at the Palm Beach Casino
★ SHOPS: 8
★ CONFERENCE ROOMS: 3 (30 to 120)
★ BANQUETING ROOMS: 2 (30 to 250)
★ STANDARD BEDROOM SIZE: 35 m²
★ PRIVATE BALCONIES: yes – in 70 rooms

★ SWIMMING POOL: yes – salt water
★ GARDENS: yes – around the swimming pool
★ NO. OF STAFF: 250
★ ROOM SERVICE: around the clock
★ ORIENTATION: main facade faces the south and the sea, the wings face east and west and the back faces north
★ FURTHER DEVELOPMENTS: it is intended to build a further 20 rooms in a wing along the front of the hotel
★ CREDIT CARDS: Visa, Diners Club, Master Charge and American Express
★ OWNING COMPANY: Chaine Lucien Barrière
★ GENERAL MANAGER: Jaques Bardet
★ DISTANCE TO BEACH: walking distance
★ DISTANCE TO SHOPS: 50 m
★ DISTANCE FROM AIRPORT: 30 km

In the past I have given the Majestic such rave notices that one reader at least accused me of having shares in the company that runs it. Alas, I wish I had. For me the Majestic is that rarest of species – a truly grand hotel in a resort setting. It is smooth, serene, elegant, supremely confident and so well operated that even the 'bagagiste' knows you by name. As for the barman, just walk in there after a couple of years and he knows what your favourite drink is.

Rooms are timeless, spotless and ranging from large to vast and the furniture is what Cesar Ritz might have ordered. From its colonnaded lobby to its vast, chandeliered 'Belle Epoque' restaurant, the Majestic shines with a splendour which is hard to equal. Service is impeccable. In so many hotels these days, one is faced with a multitude of grubby little cards and notices telling you of services which you assume are there anyway. In your Majestic room, there is only the Ericsson telephone. Ask and ye shall be answered – day or night, Sundays or holidays.

The small front garden, with its swimming pool, is unique in Cannes where space costs money and the food in the grillroom is enough to make you forget all other pleasures – or almost all. Sa Majesté le Majestic is what it says – regal.

Chinon

CHÂTEAU DE MARÇAY, 37500 Chinon

★ TELEPHONE: 47 930347
★ CABLES: no
★ TELEX: BOY 750 805 F150
★ IN OPERATION: 11 years
★ RESERVATIONS: Relais et Chateaux
★ ROOMS: 26 doubles
★ SUITES: 4
★ RESTAURANTS: 1
★ BARS: 1
★ DISCOTHEQUE: no
★ SHOPS: none
★ CONFERENCE ROOMS: 2 (10 and 40)
★ BANQUETING ROOMS: 1 (20 to 150)
★ STANDARD BEDROOM SIZE: 30 m²

★ PRIVATE BALCONIES: no
★ SWIMMING POOL: yes – fresh water
★ GARDENS: yes
★ NO. OF STAFF: 30
★ ROOM SERVICE: around the clock
★ FURTHER DEVELOPMENTS: 10 more rooms and another dining room
★ CREDIT CARDS: Visa
★ OWNING COMPANY: M. Mollard
★ GENERAL MANAGER: Mr. Philippe Mollard
★ DISTANCE TO SHOPS: 6 km
★ DISTANCE FROM AIRPORT: Tours (Parcay Meslay) 40 km

It is one of the great attractions of the Loire Valley that one does not have to go far to find a good hotel. This one, a short drive from royal Chinon, is a fine example of what can be done by an individual owner with good ideas and a sense of hospitality. Originally fifteenth century, it still has that white stone of Touraine and those dreamy black-topped towers. There is a swimming pool, a very pretty park extremely well tended and a great feeling of peace and quiet – almost 'un vieux parc solitaire et glacé'. Decor is charmingly muted, with good country-antiques, nice carpets, pretty curtains. Rooms inevitably come in all sizes and some of those in the towers are particularly fine, with high, beamed ceilings and modern bathrooms where one has no right to expect them. Service is quiet and reliable – they do know you as an individual – and the food is above average. A good place from which to take in the Loire Valley.

Deauville

NORMANDY HOTEL, Rue Jean Mermoz, 14800 Deauville

★ TELEPHONE: (31) 88-09-21
★ CABLES: Normanhotel
★ TELEX: 170617 F
★ IN OPERATION: since 1912
★ RESERVATIONS: direct
★ ROOMS: 310
★ SUITES: 20
★ RESTAURANTS: 1
★ BARS: 1

★ DISCOTHEQUE: no
★ SHOPS: none
★ CONFERENCE ROOMS: 13 (12 to 150)
★ BANQUETING ROOMS: 4 (30 to 250)
★ STANDARD BEDROOM SIZE: 25 m²
★ PRIVATE BALCONIES: yes – some rooms
★ SWIMMING POOL: yes – heated, Olympic size

- ★ RECREATIONAL ACTIVITIES: 26 tennis courts and golf 4 km from hotel, horse riding, games room
- ★ GARDENS: no
- ★ NO. OF STAFF: 180
- ★ ROOM SERVICE: around the clock
- ★ ORIENTATION: main facade faces west, others east and north
- ★ CREDIT CARDS: American Express and Diners Club
- ★ OWNING COMPANY: Chaine Lucien Barrière
- ★ GENERAL MANAGER: Michel Crauffon
- ★ DISTANCE TO BEACH: 100 m
- ★ DISTANCE TO SHOPS: adjacent
- ★ DISTANCE FROM AIRPORT: 8 km

Bracing Deauville has long been Paris-by-the-sea and used to be the traditional address for a 'dirty weekend' – a sort of French Brighton. Inflation and a change of moral climate have killed this habit but Deauville remains cheerful and gay and the Normandy is by far its best hotel. It looks like a large Normandy farmhouse – the style is Edwardian Stockbrokers Tudor. Inside, the hotel is one of the most chic in France, very, but very elegant, superbly furnished in the grand manner. It was built just before the first world war when space was not as expensive as it is now and it shows. The Normandy is an unending vista of colossal public rooms which are the perfect mirror for your companion's evening dress. Most bedrooms are colossal too and some have the largest wardrobes I have ever seen – big enough for all those fur coats and mother-in-law too. Service is the best and the food, especially the seafood, is quite excellent. Across the road is the famed Casino and some of the most famous shops in France – just in case you should be lucky.

Eze-sur-Mer

HOTEL CAP ESTEL, 06360 Eze-sur-Mer

★ TELEPHONE: (93) 01 50 44
★ CABLES: Capstel Eze
★ TELEX: 470305 Capstel Eze
★ IN OPERATION: 29 years
★ RESERVATIONS: direct
★ ROOMS: 42
★ SUITES: 7
★ RESTAURANTS: 2 – including one open air by the pool
★ BARS: 2
★ DISCOTHEQUE: no
★ SHOPS: none
★ CONFERENCE ROOMS: 1 (30)
★ BANQUETING ROOMS: 1 (40 to 50) facilities for 80 persons in the garden during summer months
★ STANDARD BEDROOM SIZE: 25 m^2
★ PRIVATE BALCONIES: yes

★ SWIMMING POOL: yes – salt water, one indoor (10 × 5 m) and one outdoor (25 × 8 m) both heated
★ RECREATIONAL ACTIVITIES: sauna, table tennis, water skiing and golf practice
★ GARDENS: yes
★ NO. OF STAFF: 55
★ ROOM SERVICE: around the clock
★ ORIENTATION: all rooms face the sea
★ CREDIT CARDS: Eurocard, Access and Master Charge
★ OWNING COMPANY: Cap Estel, S.A.
★ GENERAL MANAGER: Robert Squarciafichi (Chairman)
★ DISTANCE TO BEACH: on the beach
★ DISTANCE TO SHOPS: 3 km
★ DISTANCE FROM AIRPORT: 18 km

I have yet to meet anyone, but *anyone* who does not love the Cap Estel. Among so many slums of tomorrow – the hotels that are rising on the Côte d'Azur, this hotel really does stand out. No Riviera hotel has a larger, more private garden (it stands on its own little cape all by itself). No hotel of its size has both an indoor and an outdoor swimming pool. None that I know has that graceful Edwardian Baroque architecture. A princess built it in plusher years at a time when, rightly or wrongly, princesses were not pilloried by students' committees and as a hotel it has always been run by Robert Squarciafichi, one of France's best and most individual hoteliers.

This graceful mansion has everything you could possibly wish: large, airy, high-ceilinged bedrooms, quietly and comfortably furnished, good bathrooms, gorgeous balconies, green trees everywhere and blue waters. It has a tiny but very private beach and terraces and quiet spots all around. There is a lively, convivial bar and the public rooms are elegant, late Offenbach. Like a private house belonging to the very rich it makes life worthwhile – the food here is Mediterranean-fresh, good looking and the very sight of it is guaranteed to titillate your tastebuds.

Le Poët-Laval

LES HOSPITALIERS, Le Poët-Laval, 26160 La Bégude de Mazenc, Drôme

- ★ TELEPHONE: (75) 46 22 32
- ★ CABLES: no
- ★ TELEX: no
- ★ IN OPERATION: 12 years
- ★ RESERVATIONS: direct
- ★ ROOMS: 18 doubles 1 single
- ★ SUITES: 1
- ★ RESTAURANTS: 3 – one is on the terrace during the summer only
- ★ BARS: 1
- ★ DISCOTHEQUE: no
- ★ SHOPS: 1 – a boutique, open in summer only
- ★ CONFERENCE ROOMS: 1 (50)
- ★ BANQUETING ROOMS: none
- ★ STANDARD BEDROOM SIZE: 25 m²
- ★ PRIVATE BALCONIES: no – but the suite has a terrace
- ★ SWIMMING POOL: yes – fresh water, 14 × 6.5 m
- ★ RECREATIONAL ACTIVITIES: no – but tennis and horse riding nearby
- ★ GARDENS: terraces
- ★ NO. OF STAFF: 25
- ★ ROOM SERVICE: 07.30–23.00
- ★ ORIENTATION: south, with a view of the valley and the Alps
- ★ CREDIT CARDS: Diners Club, American Express and Eurocard
- ★ OWNING COMPANY: Yvon Morin
- ★ GENERAL MANAGER: Yvon Morin (Proprietor)
- ★ DISTANCE TO SHOPS: 3 km
- ★ DISTANCE FROM AIRPORT: 60 km (Valence), 160 km (Lyon)

Turn east as you drive through Montelimar, drive for half an hour and you are in the gorgeous, sunshiny country of the Drôme. Look left and there, on top of a precipitous hill is one of those half-ruined villages of which there are so many. This one used to belong to the Knights of St. John of Jerusalem. What you do not know and cannot possibly know unless someone tells you is that right up there, among the crumbling stones, is one of France's best and most unusual small country hotels – Les Hospitaliers. It blends so well with its surroundings that one can hardly see it. Its owners, Monsieur and Madame Morin, spent years rebuilding old houses, building new ones out of old stone, digging into solid rock for foundations and plumbing, making a swimming pool where no swimming pool has any right to be. The result is miraculous – a place of poignant beauty and infinite peace. There are terraces everywhere, overlooking twenty miles of paradise. The new rooms are vast, exceedingly well furnished and most comfortable and with bathrooms to match. In the evening, M. Morin presides over two dining rooms where he provides classic French cuisine, agreeably punctuated by unusual personal variations. France's greatest guidebook gives Les Hospitaliers a mere passing glance. They should look closer.

Les Baux de Provence

OUSTAU DE BAUMANIÈRE, 13520 Maussane Les Alpilles, Les Baux de Provence

★ TELEPHONE: (90) 97 33 07
★ CABLES: no
★ TELEX: 420203
★ IN OPERATION: 37 years
★ RESERVATIONS: direct
★ ROOMS: 15
★ SUITES: 11
★ RESTAURANTS: 1
★ BARS: 1
★ DISCOTHEQUE: no
★ SHOPS: 1
★ CONFERENCE ROOMS: 1 (100)
★ BANQUETING ROOMS: 1 (100)
★ STANDARD BEDROOM SIZE: 30 m^2
★ PRIVATE BALCONIES: yes

★ SWIMMING POOL: yes – fresh water, 25 × 15 m
★ RECREATIONAL ACTIVITIES: 1 tennis court and riding
★ GARDENS: yes
★ NO. OF STAFF: 75
★ ROOM SERVICE: 07.00–24.00
★ ORIENTATION: rooms face south
★ CREDIT CARDS: American Express, Visa and Diners Club
★ OWNING COMPANY: R. Thuilier
★ GENERAL MANAGER: R. Thuilier
★ DISTANCE TO BEACH: 50 km
★ DISTANCE TO SHOPS: 18 km
★ DISTANCE FROM AIRPORT: 45 km

By now every gourmet-critic in the world has made the pilgrimage to Monsieur Thuilier's establishment and there is no point in competing. I like good food without making a religion of it but would just say that if you think you know French cuisine, you don't, until you have been to Baumanière. For the purpose of this guide, the interest lies more in the atmosphere and the possibility of staying a night or two in this mellow and gentle manor house in this historic and unusual village which is something one can do if one tries. And try is the word since there are only a few rooms and much in demand at that. As a hotel Baumanière is unostentatious, comfortable and extremely well run – almost like a private house. Rooms are very handsome – solid French country furniture, four-poster beds and great chimney pieces where everything shines with centuries of beeswax and elbow grease. Some very pretty gardens and a pleasant swimming pool provide the correct cadre to digest a famous lunch and the whole of old-fashioned Provence is around you.

Luynes

DOMAINE DE BEAUVOIS, 37230 Luynes

★ TELEPHONE: (47) 55 50 11
★ CABLES: no
★ TELEX: Dombauv 750204 F
★ IN OPERATION: 15 years
★ RESERVATIONS: Relais et Chateaux, Paris
★ ROOMS: 36 doubles 3 singles 1 villa
★ SUITES: 7
★ RESTAURANTS: 3
★ BARS: 1
★ DISCOTHEQUE: no
★ SHOPS: none
★ CONFERENCE ROOMS: 3 (18 to 60)
★ BANQUETING ROOMS: 1 (150 to 180)
★ STANDARD BEDROOM SIZE: 25/30 m^2
★ PRIVATE BALCONIES: no – old castle
★ SWIMMING POOL: yes – fresh water, heated, 22 × 10 m

★ RECREATIONAL ACTIVITIES: tennis, fishing and horse riding. 18-hole golf course 25 km away
★ GARDENS: yes – 380 acres of wooded park
★ NO. OF STAFF: 45/50
★ ROOM SERVICE: 07.00–24.00 (beverage only)
★ ORIENTATION: south-east
★ CREDIT CARDS: Visa
★ OWNING COMPANY: S.A.G.E.I.
★ GENERAL MANAGER: Patrick C. Ponsard
★ DISTANCE TO SHOPS: 13 km
★ DISTANCE FROM AIRPORT: 16 km Tours (Parcay Meslay)

Beauvois is the end-product of what happens when a cultured millionaire (in this case the irrepressible Monsieur Traversac) takes over an old chateau. The place is reborn. Originally fifteenth century (only the central tower now remains), the chateau belonged to a succession of 'grands seigneurs' who built this bit and that bit and so on. Now in the centre of 350 splendid acres of woods and grassland and facing a swimming pool which has to be seen to be believed, Beauvois is one of the nicest country hotels in France, close to all that is worth seeing in the Loire Valley – that avenue of kings. Rooms are very grand (especially those in the tower) but not overpowering and they are intelligently and comfortably furnished and appointed and the plumbing, which must have cost a fortune, works very well. It is all very quiet, very peaceful and elegant. Though we did not care all that much for the decor of the restaurant, we feel that gourmet-critics (which means every Frenchman) have not yet done full justice to this hotel – the food is very good indeed.

Nice

HOTEL NEGRESCO, 37 Promenade des Anglais, 06000 Nice

★ TELEPHONE: (93) 88-39-51
★ CABLES: Negrescotel
★ TELEX: 460 040
★ IN OPERATION: since 1912
★ RESERVATIONS: Hotel Representative Inc, New York/Steigenberger Reservation Service, Frankfurt
★ ROOMS: 100 doubles 60 singles
★ SUITES: 15
★ RESTAURANTS: 2 – La Rotonde and Chantecler
★ BARS: 1 – Le Relais
★ DISCOTHEQUE: no – but piano music in the bar
★ SHOPS: shopping arcade – gifts, perfume, ladies' and men's wear, jewellery, toys etc
★ CONFERENCE ROOMS: 9 (60 to 700)
★ BANQUETING ROOMS: 6 (40 to 1,100)
★ STANDARD BEDROOM SIZE: 35 m²
★ PRIVATE BALCONIES: yes
★ SWIMMING POOL: no – private beach opposite hotel
★ GARDENS: flowered terraces
★ NO. OF STAFF: 200
★ ROOM SERVICE: 07.00–24.00
★ ORIENTATION: facing the sea
★ CREDIT CARDS: American Express, Carte Bleue, Eurocard, Master Charge, Access and Visa
★ OWNING COMPANY: Mrs. J. Augier Mesnage (privately owned)
★ GENERAL MANAGER: Mr. Michel Palmer
★ DISTANCE TO BEACH: walking distance
★ DISTANCE TO SHOPS: walking distance
★ DISTANCE FROM AIRPORT: 3 km

The Negresco is now classed as a French National Monument – and that is the structure only. Inside, it is one of the most beautifully furnished hotels in the world, a symphony of Art Nouveau or Le Modern Style, whichever you prefer, blends marvellously period pieces with great textiles and carpets to make the world safe for Edward VII. Bedrooms are all different, all palatial and more than comfortable and we can hardly bear to leave the often stupendous bathrooms. Public rooms form a whole series of visual delights of which one never tires. Service is on a par – among the best anywhere – they brush your clothes and shine your shoes as a matter of habit. Management is, of course, of the greatest and the owner celebrated the world over. What is new is the Negresco's attitude to cuisine under Jacques Maximin in the Chantecler restaurant which deserves great praise.

Noves

AUBERGE DE NOVES, 13550 Noves

★ TELEPHONE: (90) 941921
★ CABLES: no
★ TELEX: 431312 F Auberno
★ IN OPERATION: 25 years
★ RESERVATIONS: direct or Relais et Chateaux, Paris

★ ROOMS: 20
★ SUITES: 2
★ RESTAURANTS: 1
★ BARS: 1
★ DISCOTHEQUE: no
★ SHOPS: 1 – boutique
★ CONFERENCE ROOMS: 1 (30)
★ BANQUETING ROOMS: 1 (30 to 40)
★ STANDARD BEDROOM SIZE: 30 m²
★ PRIVATE BALCONIES: yes
★ SWIMMING POOL: yes – fresh water, heated, 15 × 7 m
★ GARDENS: yes

★ NO. OF STAFF: 35/40
★ ROOM SERVICE: 07.00–2200
★ ORIENTATION: main facade faces west
★ FURTHER DEVELOPMENTS: more suites and tennis courts
★ CREDIT CARDS: Visa, Master Charge and American Express
★ OWNING COMPANY: Auberge de Noves S.A.
★ GENERAL MANAGER: Lalleman family
★ DISTANCE TO SHOPS: 15 km
★ DISTANCE FROM AIRPORT: 65 km (Marseille)

I have always had a soft spot for this hotel, one of the nicest country pads in France and only a few minutes from Avignon. It is an oldish country house, surrounded by miraculously beautiful gardens and much of Provence at your feet. It is relaxed, run by a family and one feels immediately at home. Rooms are larger than average in France, prettily rustic and very comfortable. The great prize, however, is dinner on the tree-shaded terrace – immaculate tables, a menu that is a work of art and food which is well worth the journey. France, happily, has quite a number of such places and in my opinion the Auberge de Noves is in the front rank.

Paris

HOTEL DE CRILLON, 10 Place de la Concorde, 75008 Paris

★ TELEPHONE: 296 10 81
★ CABLES: Crilonotel
★ TELEX: 290 241
★ IN OPERATION: since 1909
★ RESERVATIONS: direct telex 290 204, Hotel Representative Inc, worldwide
★ ROOMS: 120 double 37 single
★ SUITES: 47
★ RESTAURANTS: 1
★ BARS: 1
★ DISCOTHEQUE: no
★ SHOPS: no – only showcases
★ CONFERENCE ROOMS: 5 (up to 130)
★ BANQUETING ROOMS: 5 (up to 130)
★ STANDARD BEDROOM SIZE: 26 m²

★ PRIVATE BALCONIES: yes
★ SWIMMING POOL: no
★ GARDENS: no – but two inside courtyards
★ NO. OF STAFF: 185
★ ROOM SERVICE: around the clock
★ ORIENTATION: south overlooking Place de la Concorde
★ CREDIT CARDS: American Express, Diners Club, Eurocard, Access, Master Charge, Carte Bleue and Carte Blanche
★ OWNING COMPANY: The Hotel de Crillon
★ GENERAL MANAGER: Mr. Philippe Roche
★ DISTANCE TO SHOPS: 3 minutes
★ DISTANCE FROM AIRPORT: 35 km (Charles de Gaulle) 25 km (Orly)

The Crillon – the hotel with the noblest, grandest facade in Paris right there on the Place de la Concorde – was built as a sumptuous private residence in the eighteenth century (no wonder they had the French Revolution over there) and remains magnificent and stately, with superb marbles, great columns, Gobelins tapestries and priceless carpets. Sipping Pol Roger in your suite at dusk, looking out at Paris, must be one of the greatest indulgences. Rooms, but especially suites, are vast and decorated in superb period style but the great bar is now ultra-modern though the restaurant remains happily ageless which means that you are not put off from looking and tasting the very refined food on your plate. Bathrooms have been refurnished – mostly with his-and-hers, and work excellently. The Crillon is a hotel of enormous presence and dignity and if you stay there, most people know who you are – an American diplomat, an English duke, a German tycoon or Monsieur le Préfet from somewhere.

HÔTEL GEORGE V, 31 Avenue George V, 75008 Paris

- ★ TELEPHONE: 723 54 00
- ★ CABLES: Georgeotel Paris 086
- ★ TELEX: 650082 and 290776
- ★ IN OPERATION: since 1928
- ★ RESERVATIONS: Trust Hotel Forte Ltd/Hotel Representative Inc
- ★ ROOMS: 262 doubles 40 single
- ★ SUITES: 52
- ★ RESTAURANTS: 1
- ★ BARS: 1
- ★ DISCOTHEQUE: no
- ★ SHOPS: 1
- ★ CONFERENCE ROOMS: 9 (25 to 600)
- ★ BANQUETING ROOMS: 9 (20 to 600)

- ★ STANDARD BEDROOM SIZE: 40 m²
- ★ PRIVATE BALCONIES: yes – certain rooms
- ★ SWIMMING POOL: no
- ★ GARDENS: no
- ★ NO. OF STAFF: 430
- ★ ROOM SERVICE: around the clock
- ★ ORIENTATION: east
- ★ CREDIT CARDS: American Express, Diners Club, Carte Blanche, THF and Eurocard
- ★ OWNING COMPANY: Trust House Forte
- ★ GENERAL MANAGER: Christian Falcucci
- ★ DISTANCE TO SHOPS: walking distance
- ★ DISTANCE FROM AIRPORT: 35 km (de Gaulle) 25 km (Orly)

Once rather run down, this hotel is back in the front rank as far as Paris is concerned. A great deal of time, money and effort has been expended on it by the British owning company and it shows in the marvellous tapestries, the expensive carpets and the truly magnificent bathrooms. It is a very civilised hotel, without any of that slight super-ciliousness that one occasionally finds in French palace hotels. The staff are courteous, infinitely knowledgeable about every subject under the sun – including the last reports from the 'Bourse'. Most rooms are huge by continental standards, quiet and very well maintained. The food has improved greatly in recent years and despite the connection with 'perfidious Albion' even the most demanding Parisians eat there – if Monsieur le Président lets them have the expense account.

HÔTEL PLAZA-ATHÉNEÉ, 25 Avenue Montaigne, 75008 Paris

- ★ TELEPHONE: 723-7833
- ★ CABLES: Plazatene Paris
- ★ TELEX: 650092 Plaza
- ★ IN OPERATION: since 1913
- ★ RESERVATIONS: Hotel Representative Inc/Trusthouse Forte Hotels Ltd, worldwide
- ★ ROOMS: 218
- ★ SUITES: 38
- ★ RESTAURANTS: 2 – Regence and Relais
- ★ BARS: 2
- ★ DISCOTHEQUE: yes
- ★ SHOPS: none
- ★ CONFERENCE ROOMS: 6 (30 to 150)
- ★ BANQUETING ROOMS: 6 (30 to 250)
- ★ STANDARD BEDROOM SIZE: 29 m²

- ★ PRIVATE BALCONIES: none
- ★ SWIMMING POOL: no
- ★ RECREATIONAL ACTIVITIES: none
- ★ GARDENS: none
- ★ NO. OF STAFF: 420
- ★ ROOM SERVICE: around the clock
- ★ ORIENTATION: rooms face Avenue Montaigne
- ★ CREDIT CARDS: American Express, Diners Club, Eurocard, THF and Carte Blanche
- ★ OWNING COMPANY: Trusthouse Forte Hotels Ltd
- ★ GENERAL MANAGER: Franco Cozzo
- ★ DISTANCE TO SHOPS: walking distance
- ★ DISTANCE FROM AIRPORT: 35 km

One very elegant and obviously very cosmopolitan New York lady was telling me that she would soon be in Paris. 'Call me there' she said, 'and I'll tell you when I will be getting to London . . .' Thinking that, after all, Paris is a fairly big city and that maybe she had her own private pad there, I asked her for her telephone number. She looked at me as if I had just crawled from under some stone and replied: 'The Plaza Athénée of course – it's the only place to be'. But of course.

Remembering those superb 'petits déjeuners' overlooking the Paris roofs, I must agree with her. The Plaza Athénée is quite a place. It has panache, a 'je ne sais quoi' of quality in everything one sees or touches and an atmosphere that makes you think that you owe it to yourself to be there. The staff are marvellous – roughly two of them to every one of you and there is nothing they do not know about service in the grand manner. As for the food, have no fear: I consider lunch in the garden court restaurant to be one of the great experiences of one's stay in the French capital.

HÔTEL RITZ, 15 Place Vendôme, 75041 Paris

★ TELEPHONE: 260 38 30
★ CABLES: Ritzotel Paris
★ TELEX: 220262
★ IN OPERATION: since 1898
★ RESERVATIONS: Hotel Representative Inc
★ ROOMS: 150 doubles 23 singles
★ SUITES: 46 (some with direct telex)
★ RESTAURANTS: 2 – The Vendôme Restaurant and L'Espadon Grill
★ BARS: 3 – Espadon, Hemingway and Vendôme
★ DISCOTHEQUE: no
★ SHOPS: none – but 120 showcases
★ CONFERENCE ROOMS: 1 (18 to 20)
★ BANQUETING ROOMS: 3 (80 to 100)
★ STANDARD BEDROOM SIZE: 34 m²
★ PRIVATE BALCONIES: yes
★ SWIMMING POOL: no
★ GARDENS: yes – in the summer months

lunch and dinner can be enjoyed in the Vendôme and Espadon gardens
★ NO. OF STAFF: 360
★ ROOM SERVICE: around the clock
★ ORIENTATION: main facade on Place Vendôme – most rooms overlook private gardens
★ FURTHER DEVELOPMENTS: creation of boutiques, a new restaurant with dancing facilities (no discotheque), and a swimming pool within the next two years
★ CREDIT CARDS: Diners Club, American Express, Carte Blanche, Master Charge, Eurocard, Interbank and Access
★ OWNING COMPANY: The Ritz Hotel Ltd
★ MANAGING DIRECTOR: Mr. Frank Klein
★ DISTANCE TO SHOPS: walking distance
★ DISTANCE FROM AIRPORT: 30 km

Most people have noticed how stable the government of France is these days. Yet, two years ago, it nearly fell when Parisians woke up to find that someone, and a foreigner at that, had bought the Ritz. 'Mais, c'est une crime!' The government, which carries out most of its work in the Ritz Bar anyway (the Rue Cambon one of course) deliberated but stayed on. So did the Ritz of course – 'Le Ritz restera toujours le Ritz'. If anything, now that there is solid money behind it, the hotel might even improve which, admittedly, would be extremely difficult since this is the finest old city hotel in the world. Some time ago, the new management decided that it was about time some of those lovely fin de siècle doorhandles should be renewed. Alas, nobody made them quite like that any more. So they went and got a craftsman to make them again – by hand.

There are so many stories about this monument to the great Cesar Ritz that they have filled books – and in this space one cannot compete, except by mentioning personal experiences. It is the only hotel known to me where if you ring room service at two a.m. and ask timidly for scrambled eggs, the order arrives noiselessly on a trolley, with a single rose in a vase and enough gleaming silver for a four-course dinner. The Ritz is discreet, perfect, immaculate. From the great ornate salons to that incredible dining room, the upholstery is renewed as fresh every day, the carpets superbly clean. It is one of the few hotels I know where invisible eyes note when you leave your room – you are never, never disturbed. It is also one of the few hotels where I make a practice of going to bed with the wine list – just so I can drift off into nirvana. As long as the ghosts of Ritz and Escoffier maintain their presence, as long as the Place Vendôme remains, while we wish to have standards to respect, then the Ritz is still living.

LANCASTER HOTEL, 7 Rue de Berri, 75008 Paris

- ★ TELEPHONE: 359.90.43
- ★ CABLES: Otelancast Paris
- ★ TELEX: Loyne 640991
- ★ IN OPERATION: since 1925
- ★ RESERVATIONS: Prestige Hotels, London/Scott Calder International, New York/Zennith, Toronto and Montreal/John Miller, Sydney
- ★ ROOMS: 33 doubles 14 singles
- ★ SUITES: 10
- ★ RESTAURANTS: 1 – meals can be taken outside during fine weather
- ★ BARS: 1
- ★ DISCOTHEQUE: no
- ★ SHOPS: none
- ★ CONFERENCE ROOMS: 1
- ★ BANQUETING ROOMS: 1
- ★ STANDARD BEDROOM SIZE: 14–30 m^2
- ★ PRIVATE BALCONIES: yes – with penthouse suites
- ★ SWIMMING POOL: no
- ★ GARDENS: yes
- ★ NO. OF STAFF: 85
- ★ ROOM SERVICE: 07.00–24.00
- ★ ORIENTATION: south-west
- ★ CREDIT CARDS: American Express, Eurocard, Master Charge and Access
- ★ OWNING COMPANY: S.A. Hotel Lancaster
- ★ GENERAL MANAGER: John Sinclair
- ★ DISTANCE TO SHOPS: walking distance
- ★ DISTANCE FROM AIRPORT: 35 km

The Lancaster, long established and now owned by Britain's Savoy group, is very chic in French terms and for some people it is like having their own Paris town house. It is small, gentle, well bred, intimate and it only impresses those who are no longer easily impressed. Some of the rooms are quite small, others very acceptable in size but what matters is the fact that they are all furnished individually with very fine French furniture and well chosen paintings. They are immaculately kept and the young and intelligent management knows from the records what each guest likes. What I like is the feeling that once in this hotel the world outside can get up to all the capers it wants – the Lancaster remains as an oasis of good living, fate cannot harm me. I also love the restaurant, especially in the good weather months, when it creeps into the sweet and pretty private garden. The food is excellent even for France. A mere gentle stroll away from the Champs Elysees, the Lancaster is indeed a very desirable residence.

Saint Paul de Vence

MAS D'ARTIGNY, 06570 Saint Paul

★ TELEPHONE: (93) 32 84 54
★ CABLES: no
★ TELEX: 470601 Artimas F
★ IN OPERATION: since May, 1973
★ RESERVATIONS: direct
★ ROOMS: 81
★ SUITES: 29
★ RESTAURANTS: 1 – and terrace for lunch in the summer
★ BARS: 1 – and terrace
★ DISCOTHEQUE: on request
★ SHOPS: 1 – also a hairdresser and 2 art galleries
★ CONFERENCE ROOMS: 6 (10 to 250)
★ BANQUETING ROOMS: 1 (150)
★ STANDARD BEDROOM SIZE: 30 m²
★ PRIVATE BALCONIES: yes – most rooms
★ RECREATIONAL ACTIVITIES: tennis

★ SWIMMING POOL: yes – fresh water, 25 m long, and 21 private pools for the apartments, approx. 20 m²
★ GARDENS: yes – also private gardens to each small swimming pool
★ NO. OF STAFF: 100
★ ROOM SERVICE: 07.00–22.00
★ ORIENTATION: most rooms face south
★ FURTHER DEVELOPMENTS: a 7-room villa, sitting room and private pool
★ CREDIT CARDS: none
★ OWNING COMPANY: Sté Grandes Etapes Internationales
★ GENERAL MANAGER: J. C. Scourdel
★ DISTANCE TO BEACH: 9 km
★ DISTANCE TO SHOPS: 9 km
★ DISTANCE FROM AIRPORT: 12 km

It needed guts and a good deal of ready money as well as a lot of imagination to pick a hillside facing St. Paul de Vence and build on it the newest luxury hotel on the Riviera. The French tycoon who created the Mas d'Artigny (and a few others too) had all of these things and that gifted entrepreneurial flair which demands and gets the best. Mas d'Artigny is superb, luxurious and fitted out at great expense, both of money and talent. You can have a suite in the main building or a garden-level suite with your own private swimming pool. Decor is modern-Provençal, and all the rooms are extremely comfortable and facing those scented hills of Provence with the sea in the far distance. Considering the size of the place, service is good and nothing is too much trouble. As for the food, it is superior but in the cheerful, friendly way of the South. In style, space, decor and amenities, Mas d'Artigny is one of the few European hotels which manages to equal the best American resort.

Saint-Péray

CHÂTEAU DU BESSET, Saint-Romain-de-Lerps, 07130 Saint-Péray

★ TELEPHONE: (75) 44-41-63
★ CABLES: no
★ TELEX: no
★ IN OPERATION: since 1974
★ RESERVATIONS: direct
★ ROOMS: 6
★ SUITES: 4
★ RESTAURANTS: 2
★ BARS: 1
★ DISCOTHEQUE: no
★ SHOPS: no
★ CONFERENCE ROOMS: 1 (10 to 60)
★ BANQUETING ROOMS: no
★ STANDARD BEDROOM SIZE: 70 m²
★ PRIVATE BALCONIES: none

★ SWIMMING POOL: heated pool, 15 × 18 m
★ RECREATIONAL ACTIVITIES: tennis, boules, riding and walking in park
★ GARDENS: large park
★ NO. OF STAFF: 21
★ ROOM SERVICE: 7.00–21.30
★ ORIENTATION: views of the park
★ CREDIT CARDS: American Express and Diners Club
★ OWNING COMPANY: Monsieur and Madame Gozlan
★ GENERAL MANAGER: Monsieur Linget
★ DISTANCE TO SHOPS: 10 km
★ DISTANCE FROM AIRPORT: 19 km

As everyone knows, France is not short of chateaux, some of which might just pass off. But not this one. The Château du Besset is not only authentic fifteenth century in structure but its divinely inspired owners have furnished it with treasures which took years to find. It is such a rare place that people come here, having booked months ahead, from all over the world – all that just to stay in one of the ten rooms, each one of which is furnished in a different period: Louis XIV, Napoleonic, Louis XVI, Medici etc. Their windows open on one of France's sweetest landscapes, the Ardèche country just a few miles west of Valence across the Rhone. Le Besset is so discreet, so private, so cleverly hidden away that it almost takes a detective to find it. Some of the greatest hoteliers and chefs in the world have come here and been made speechless at so much good taste, so much beauty, so much good living. There is a vast French-style garden plus a great park. The chef de cuisine, Monsieur Delanné, is as unique as the Château – he cooks the way others paint pictures, with his own brushstrokes. Messrs. Gault and Millau, those high priests of the good (French) life, call the Château du Besset 'la plus belle folie du monde' and although I know of one or two others I am not going to disagree with them.

Saint Tropez

HOTEL BYBLOS, Avenue Paul Signac, 83990 Saint Tropez

- ★ TELEPHONE: (94) 970004
- ★ CABLES: Byblos
- ★ TELEX: 470235
- ★ IN OPERATION: since 1969
- ★ RESERVATIONS: direct and Air France offices, worldwide; also through travel agencies
- ★ ROOMS: 46 doubles 13 singles
- ★ RESTAURANTS: 1 and terraces
- ★ BARS: 1
- ★ DISCOTHEQUE: yes – and 'Les Caves du Roy' Nightclub in the summer
- ★ SHOPS: 3 – fashion and jewellery, beauty parlour and hairdressing salon
- ★ CONFERENCE ROOMS: 1 (130)
- ★ BANQUETING ROOMS: 1 (up to 100)
- ★ STANDARD BEDROOM SIZE: 25 m²
- ★ PRIVATE BALCONIES: yes – some rooms
- ★ GARDENS: yes
- ★ SWIMMING POOL: yes – fresh water, heated, outdoor
- ★ RECREATIONAL ACTIVITIES: sauna and massage in the hotel, with clubs nearby for tennis, golf and horse riding
- ★ NO. OF STAFF: 120
- ★ ROOM SERVICE: around the clock
- ★ ORIENTATION: most rooms face gardens, swimming pool and sea
- ★ CREDIT CARDS: American Express, Diners Club, Visa and Carte Bleue
- ★ OWNING COMPANY: S.A. Byblos
- ★ GENERAL MANAGER: Claude Marret
- ★ DISTANCE TO BEACH: 1 km
- ★ DISTANCE TO SHOPS: walking distance
- ★ DISTANCE FROM AIRPORT: 100 km (Nice)

This hotel that really does not look like a hotel opened a decade ago, to a lot of astonishment and some sneers from the trade. It would never work, they said. Well, try to get in now. The Byblos has succeeded beyond the wildest expectations and for St. Tropez (which never pretended to be Palm Beach) it is also exactly right. Basically, it is a huddle of delicious little Provençal houses around a fine swimming pool. The gardens are lovingly tended. For this kind of holiday hotel, the service is 100 per cent above the average (I have never heard of a single complaint). It is a gay, convivial hotel custom-built for the beautiful people to meet and show off their new husbands/wives/ what have you. Favourable mention must be made of the Provençal cooking – aioli, Bouillabaisse, and the rest.

Talloires

HOTEL L'ABBAYE, 74290 Talloires

- ★ TELEPHONE: (50) 674088
- ★ CABLES: Abbaye Talloires
- ★ TELEX: 385307
- ★ IN OPERATION: since 1885
- ★ RESERVATIONS: direct
- ★ ROOMS: 32

★ SUITES: 2
★ RESTAURANTS: 2
★ BARS: 1
★ DISCOTHEQUE: no
★ SHOPS: none
★ CONFERENCE ROOMS: 2 (12 to 20)
★ BANQUETING ROOMS: 1 (up to 120)
★ STANDARD BEDROOM SIZE: 18 m²
★ PRIVATE BALCONIES: yes
★ SWIMMING POOL: no – but private pontoon on lake
★ GARDENS: yes

★ NO. OF STAFF: 35
★ ROOM SERVICE: around the clock
★ ORIENTATION: rooms face lake
★ CREDIT CARDS: American Express, Diners Club, Eurocard and Visa
★ OWNING COMPANY: Claude Tiffenat
★ GENERAL MANAGER: Jean Tiffenat
★ DISTANCE TO BEACH: on the lake
★ DISTANCE TO SHOPS: 250 m
★ DISTANCE FROM AIRPORT: 45 km (Geneva) 15 km (Annecy)

To sit on a summer's day, on the terrace of this hotel under the centuries-old trees and to look at the white boats silently gliding on the blue waters of the most beautiful lake in France reminds one that this is indeed the land of 'la douceur de vivre'. No doubt the Benedictine monks who began to build the place nearly a thousand years ago must have thought this was a good place to contemplate and praise the Lord. Praise should be reserved for the management too for having preserved this, one of the finest country hotels in France and keeping it as it should be – quiet, serene, beautifully mellow and so smooth that one hardly realises it is a hotel at all. This takes genius, and family genius at that, because strangers would be bound to spoil it. The Abbaye has a gorgeous interior cloister lined with fine antiques, splendidly furnished rooms – in the former monkish cells – and sun-sapped gardens to remove you from unpleasant reality. A spot so beautiful that it has been celebrated in ballads and poems and novels, the Abbaye is what a country hotel should be and yet curiously it is French and not English who claim most often they know what the country is all about. Food here has always been great – and now there is a new and intimate winter restaurant.

Vence

CHÂTEAU DU DOMAINE ST. MARTIN, Route de Coursegoules, 06140 Vence

★ TELEPHONE: (93) 58 02 02
★ CABLES: Domartin
★ TELEX: 470282
★ IN OPERATION: 20 years
★ RESERVATIONS: direct
★ ROOMS: 14 doubles 2 singles
★ SUITES: 11
★ RESTAURANTS: 1
★ BARS: 1
★ DISCOTHEQUE: no
★ SHOPS: none
★ CONFERENCE ROOMS: 1 (15)
★ BANQUETING ROOMS: none
★ STANDARD BEDROOM SIZE: 40 m²
★ PRIVATE BALCONIES: yes

★ SWIMMING POOL: yes – fresh water, heated
★ RECREATIONAL ACTIVITIES: tennis
★ GARDENS: yes
★ NO. OF STAFF: 50
★ ROOM SERVICE: 07.00–21.30
★ ORIENTATION: south
★ CREDIT CARDS: American Express, Carte Bleue and Eurocard
★ OWNING COMPANY: Famille Geneve
★ GENERAL MANAGER: Miss A. Brunet
★ DISTANCE TO BEACH: 15 km
★ DISTANCE TO SHOPS: 25 km
★ DISTANCE FROM AIRPORT: 20 km

To all those who want to stay in the Côte d'Azur but without the company of the Joneses, the Smiths and the Duponts, this hotel must be among the first choices. First of all it does not look like a hotel – more of a Provençal village with houses dotted all over the verdant hillsides. Secondly, it does not cater for the passing trade. Thirdly, it is superbly managed. It has a thirty-five acre park dominating the landscape all the way down to the coast and, above all, it has peace and tranquillity. You will never be crowded here – there aren't enough people! You can have a normal room or, much better, one of the lovely cottages where rooms and suites are charmingly decorated and maintained with great care. The view from the restaurant makes you spend your time looking from the panorama down to your plate and wonder which should come first. The food is delicate and beautifully presented and the service is top class. Domaine St. Martin is a place with personality and charm.

Vonnas

LA MÈRE BLANC, 01540 Vonnas, Ain

- ★ TELEPHONE: (74) 500010
- ★ CABLES: no
- ★ TELEX: 380776
- ★ IN OPERATION: since 1872
- ★ RESERVATIONS: direct
- ★ ROOMS: 21 doubles 4 singles
- ★ SUITES: 4
- ★ RESTAURANTS: 1
- ★ BARS: 1
- ★ DISCOTHEQUE: no
- ★ SHOPS: 1
- ★ CONFERENCE ROOMS: 1 (50)
- ★ BANQUETING ROOMS: 1 (100)
- ★ STANDARD BEDROOM SIZE: 20 m²

- ★ PRIVATE BALCONIES: yes
- ★ SWIMMING POOL: yes – fresh water, 15 × 7.5 m
- ★ RECREATIONAL ACTIVITIES: tennis
- ★ GARDENS: yes
- ★ NO. OF STAFF: 45
- ★ ROOM SERVICE: 07.00–23.00
- ★ ORIENTATION: facing the Veyle River
- ★ CREDIT CARDS: Diners Club and American Express
- ★ OWNING COMPANY: Blanc family
- ★ GENERAL MANAGER: Georges Blanc
- ★ DISTANCE TO SHOPS: immediate
- ★ DISTANCE FROM AIRPORT: 60 km

Don't come here expecting a grand, grand hotel. This is an 'auberge', one of the finest in France, which I only discovered recently and obviously a bit late, since it has been in the hands of four generations of the same country family. It is a delightful, fresh-looking place in this small, flower-decked village and next to a pretty river. Rooms are clean, very well planned (most of them are new) and pleasantly furnished with good country pieces – no Régence, no Boulle. Bathrooms work very well and there is every single small comfort you might wish. Service is fast and efficient and the little interior courtyard where you sit for your pre-lunch champagne-framboise is quite delightful. But it is when you pass the portals of the restaurant that the very special quality of this house strikes you – La Mère Blanc is one of the finest country restaurants in the whole of France, masterminded by fourth-generation Georges Blanc with a long tradition behind him. Being a young man, he has put his own stamp on the food; *nouvelle cuisine* and all that but totally individual. The quality is matchless as is the length of the wine list – I expect to hear much good about this place from satisfied customers.

GERMANY

Assmannshausen

HOTEL KRONE, Rheinuferstrasse 10, 6220 Rud. Assmannshausen

- ★ TELEPHONE: 06722-2236
- ★ CABLES: Krone
- ★ TELEX: no
- ★ IN OPERATION: since 1541
- ★ RESERVATIONS: direct

- ★ ROOMS: 50 doubles 32 singles
- ★ SUITES: 2
- ★ RESTAURANTS: 2
- ★ BARS: 1
- ★ DISCOTHEQUE: no

★ SHOPS: none
★ CONFERENCE ROOMS: 2 (20 to 60)
★ BANQUETING ROOMS: 1 (80)
★ STANDARD BEDROOM SIZE: 30–40 m²
★ PRIVATE BALCONIES: yes – 6 rooms only
★ SWIMMING POOL: yes – fresh water,
6 × 10 m
★ GARDENS: yes
★ NO. OF STAFF: 80

★ ROOM SERVICE: breakfast only
★ ORIENTATION: faces west
★ CREDIT CARDS: American Express, Diners
Club, Eurocard and Barclaycard
★ OWNING COMPANY: privately owned
★ GENERAL MANAGER: Family Hufnagel
★ DISTANCE TO SHOPS: 250 m
★ DISTANCE FROM AIRPORT: 75 km
(Frankfurt)

Four centuries ought to be long enough to create a tradition and when that happens in Germany it augurs good living. That is certainly what one gets at the Krone in the charming little Rheingau town of Assmannshausen. I always like to remember a hotel for one particular thing that no other hotel has got and in this case it must be that quite divine terrace restaurant with its vine roof facing the great river. That and the Rheingau and the food makes this place, as the Michelin people say, 'worth a detour'. It is also a charming place to stay – an old beamed and panelled house of great distinction, good solid country furniture and a feeling of genuine welcome which is a rare thing these days. Rooms are very large, beautifully, one should almost say lovingly, furnished and the service is cheerful. But the things that count most at the Krone are the location and the food and wine.

Baden-Baden

BRENNER'S PARK HOTEL, An der Lichtentaler Allee, D-7570 Baden-Baden

★ TELEPHONE: (07221) 3530
★ CABLES: Parkhotel Baden-Baden
★ TELEX: 781261
★ IN OPERATION: 110 years
★ RESERVATIONS: Hotel Representative Inc,
London and New York/Preferred Hotels
Assoc., Canada
★ ROOMS: 34 doubles 45 singles
★ SUITES: 28
★ RESTAURANTS: 2
★ BARS: 1
★ DISCOTHEQUE: live music
★ SHOPS: none – but the Lancaster Beauty
Farm and Römischer Salon
★ CONFERENCE ROOMS: 5 (10 to 120)
★ BANQUETING ROOMS: 2 (30 to 120)
★ STANDARD BEDROOM SIZE: 40–50 m²

★ PRIVATE BALCONIES: yes
★ SWIMMING POOL: yes – fresh water,
53 × 21 × 5 ft
★ RECREATIONAL ACTIVITIES: sauna, fitness
studio and solarium
★ GARDENS: yes
★ NO. OF STAFF: 210
★ ROOM SERVICE: around the clock
★ ORIENTATION: most rooms face a large
private park and the Lichtentaler Allee
★ CREDIT CARDS: none
★ OWNING COMPANY: Brenner Hotel
★ GENERAL MANAGER: Richard Schmitz
★ DISTANCE TO SHOPS: walking distance
★ DISTANCE FROM AIRPORT: 104 km
(Stuttgart)

Any traveller's list of the six best hotels in the world would certainly contain this one. Where Russian grand dukes used to parade their horses (and their 'cocottes') a better class of person is still to be seen. One American friend recently said to me: 'If that's the way they used to live, no wonder there was a world war . . .'. Egalitarian to the end he then proceeded to stay a month at Brenner's Park. The place gets you. It is so beautiful, so beautifully run, so superbly furnished with elegant dark teak German 1880 furniture, so unbelievably efficient that it is a pleasure every minute of the day. Brenner's Park history needs a book to itself – everyone from Edward VII to Paul Getty stayed there and one understands why, because here luxury is everywhere – in the fork you touch, the pillow on your bed, the carpet in the corridor, the wine you drink. Rooms and suites are so enormous that on my first stay it took me an hour to investigate everything. The indoor swimming pool is the most perfect in Europe and, just in case you should look in the mirror and take fright, the famed Lancaster Beauty Farm is next door. Down in this delicious, wooded little pleasure town is the world-famous Kurhaus and the finest, most ornate casino anywhere. Brenner's Park food is a legend — splendidly conceived — and nowhere does silver gleam more brightly. This is another hotel where I tend to go to bed with the wine list — it's the perfect send-off towards another day.

Badenweiler

HOTEL ROMERBAD, D-7847 Badenweiler, West Germany

- ★ TELEPHONE: 07632-700
- ★ CABLES: Romerbad
- ★ TELEX: 77 29 33
- ★ IN OPERATION: 157 years
- ★ RESERVATIONS: direct and Hotel Representative Inc
- ★ ROOMS: 57 doubles 57 singles
- ★ SUITES: 5
- ★ RESTAURANTS: 1
- ★ BARS: 1
- ★ DISCOTHEQUE: no
- ★ SHOPS: none
- ★ CONFERENCE ROOMS: 3
- ★ BANQUETING ROOMS: 3
- ★ STANDARD BEDROOM SIZE: 24 m^2
- ★ PRIVATE BALCONIES: yes
- ★ GARDENS: yes — large park overlooking Rhine valley
- ★ SWIMMING POOL: yes — fresh water, thermal, 1 indoor 8 × 20 m, and 1 outdoor 9 × 25 m
- ★ RECREATIONAL ACTIVITIES: tennis, sauna, massage, beauty service, boccia, ping pong and children's playhouse
- ★ NO. OF STAFF: 100
- ★ ROOM SERVICE: 07.30–24.00
- ★ ORIENTATION: overlooking Black Forest and Rhine Valley
- ★ CREDIT CARDS: none
- ★ OWNING COMPANY: Family Fellmann-Lauer
- ★ GENERAL MANAGER: Klaus Lauer
- ★ DISTANCE TO SHOPS: 100 m
- ★ DISTANCE FROM AIRPORT: 45 km (Basel/Schweiz)

A century and a half of worldly elegance, a family tradition going back that far and all in the frame of the magnificent Black Forest — that is Romerbad, one of the most unusual and most resplendent country hotels in Europe. The huge park dominates the Rhine Valley and the wine-clad hills — a place of intense beauty and charm. The building itself makes you feel secure — half schloss, half private residence, it has a feeling of having grown over the years, blended in and emerged victorious. It is stately and yet curiously intimate. No two rooms are the same and the only thing they share is a high regard for quality, cleanliness and good taste that seems somehow to borrow nothing from anyone. There are two fantastically beautiful swimming pools — one in and one out — and in the lovely 'Hofsaal' there are music festivals in spring and autumn. The 'Kinder' have a playhouse all to themselves. An aura of good living permeates everything from the food, which is celestially good, to the wine list which is a work of devotion.

Berlin

BRISTOL HOTEL KEMPINSKI BERLIN, Kurfürstendamm 37, 1000 Berlin 15

- ★ TELEPHONE: 030/88 10 91
- ★ CABLES: Kempihotel Berlin
- ★ TELEX: 018-3553
- ★ IN OPERATION: since 1952
- ★ RESERVATIONS: Hotel Representatives Inc, worldwide
- ★ ROOMS: 287 doubles 71 singles
- ★ SUITES: 20
- ★ RESTAURANTS: 3 — Kempinski Restaurant, Grill Room, and Kempinski Eck
- ★ BARS: 3 — Bristol Bar, Grill Bar and Pool Bar
- ★ SHOPS: newspaper stand and flower shop in the main lobby
- ★ CONFERENCE ROOMS: 12 (6 to 600)
- ★ BANQUETING ROOMS: 12 (6 to 600)

★ STANDARD BEDROOM SIZE: 25 m²
★ PRIVATE BALCONIES: 1 suite on the 6th floor overlooking Kurfürstendamm
★ SWIMMING POOL: yes – fresh water, 8 × 16 m
★ RECREATIONAL ACTIVITIES: sauna and solarium
★ GARDENS: no
★ NO. OF STAFF: 450
★ ROOM SERVICE: 06.30–24.00

★ ORIENTATION: facing Fasanenstrasse and Kurfürstendamm
★ CREDIT CARDS: American Express, Diners Club, Eurocard and Americard
★ OWNING COMPANY: Kempinski Corporation
★ GENERAL MANAGER: Hartmut E. Zunk
★ DISTANCE TO SHOPS: walking distance
★ DISTANCE FROM AIRPORT: 15 km

This is Germany at its best, behind a name that has been a Berlin tradition for longer than anyone can remember. I have not been here since the last edition but a friend who arrived, unexpectedly, in mid-morning a while ago told me that the reception manager took her up to her room, asked her to inspect both the bedroom and bathroom to make sure everything was right. Minutes later, piping hot coffee arrived and the housekeeper telephoned to offer her services. I would have expected no less. Everybody seems to speak every language under the sun and nothing is too much trouble. Rooms vary in size but the majority are more than adequate, extremely clean and well kept and no one disturbs you at the wrong time.

The one trouble I find with Kempinski, if trouble it is, is the quantity of food in the two restaurants – one has to be awfully strong-willed to resist the temptation.

I may add that in six years I have not had a single letter of complaint about this hotel – only praise from travellers who know what it is all about.

Bremen

PARK HOTEL, Im Bürgerpark, 2800 Bremen

★ TELEPHONE: 0421/340031
★ CABLES: Parkhotel
★ TELEX: 024-4343
★ IN OPERATION: since 1956
★ RESERVATIONS: Steigenberger Reservation Service
★ ROOMS: 56 doubles 85 singles
★ SUITES: 9
★ RESTAURANTS: 2 – The Park Restaurant and Buten un Binnen Restaurant
★ BARS: 1 – Halai Bar
★ DISCOTHEQUE: live music and dancing in bar
★ SHOPS: 2 – beauty shop and newspaper shop
★ CONFERENCE ROOMS: 7 (up to 400)

★ BANQUETING ROOMS: 7 (up to 400)
★ STANDARD BEDROOM SIZE: 28 m²
★ PRIVATE BALCONIES: yes
★ SWIMMING POOL: no
★ RECREATIONAL ACTIVITIES: bicycling
★ GARDENS: yes
★ NO. OF STAFF: 230
★ ROOM SERVICE: 06.00–2400
★ ORIENTATION: all rooms face park
★ CREDIT CARDS: American Express, Diners Club and Eurocard
★ OWNING COMPANY: Park Hotel GmbH
★ GENERAL MANAGER: Hans-Hermann Rosin
★ DISTANCE TO SHOPS: 1½ km
★ DISTANCE FROM AIRPORT: 4 km

Probably one of the best hotels in Germany, the Park faces the Bürgerpark, an oasis of green beauty, within minutes from the city centre, and consequently the hotel is quiet and almost countryfied. Though it is comparatively new, this hotel has a gracious, ageless quality which shows in every detail. The rooms are quite large, meticulously clean and springlike and there are many different styles – cheerfully chintzy, soberly timbered or modern without madness. Bathrooms are the last word in German efficiency and indeed so is the service – they never, but never forget anything and once you are typed off as a person you need never worry again. It is all very discreet, very comfortable and immensely reassuring. There is a quite superb heated terrace facing the park and all the Mercedes purr to a stop far from your ears. Food is on a par – don't go there if you are on a diet. The Park is just right for the new breed of Hanseatic merchant adventurers and those who come to meet them.

Cologne

EXCELSIOR HOTEL ERNST, Domplatz, 5000 Cologne 1

★ TELEPHONE: 0221/2701
★ CABLES: Excelsior Ernst
★ TELEX: 888 2645
★ IN OPERATION: for 62 years
★ RESERVATIONS: Steigenberger Reservation Service/Preferred Hotels Association/Hotel Representative Inc
★ ROOMS: 58 doubles 73 singles
★ SUITES: 10
★ RESTAURANTS: 2 – 'Hanse Stube' and 'Excelsior Keller'
★ BARS: 1
★ DISCOTHEQUE: no
★ SHOPS: 5 – beauty salon, barber shop, souvenir shop and news stand

★ CONFERENCE ROOMS: 6 (15 to 120)
★ STANDARD BEDROOM SIZE: 20 m^2
★ PRIVATE BALCONIES: no
★ SWIMMING POOL: no
★ GARDENS: no
★ NO. OF STAFF: 165
★ ROOM SERVICE: 06.00–24.00
★ CREDIT CARDS: Diners Club, American Express and Eurocard
★ OWNING COMPANY: Excelsior Hotel Ernst AG
★ GENERAL MANAGER: Siegfried Breunig
★ DISTANCE TO SHOPS: 5 minutes' walking distance
★ DISTANCE FROM AIRPORT: 14 km

Right opposite the famous 'Dom' this is the best hotel in Cologne, well established, well run and not in need of many lessons – it has been home-from-home for a long time to cigar-smoking German tycoons who are not the easiest people to please. It has a tradition of service second to none – everything is there almost before you have time to ask. Decor is nicely timeless – lots of marble and glass – chandeliers and pictures and wood panelling, all of it in solid bourgeois taste (not a bad thing sometimes). The rooms, some of them a little small, cannot be faulted when it comes to comfort and cleanliness and the bathrooms are super-efficient. There is now a very pleasant little patio restaurant while the main restaurant – the Hans Stuben – all dark polished wood and smooth velvet – serves food which would certainly have sustained generations of cardinals/archbishops.

Friedrichsruhe

WALD UND SCHLOSSHOTEL FRIEDRICHSRUHE, 7111 Friedrichsruhe, Württemberg

★ TELEPHONE: 07941/7078
★ CABLES: no
★ TELEX: 074498
★ IN OPERATION: since 1953
★ RESERVATIONS: German National Tourist Office
★ ROOMS: 33 doubles 11 singles
★ SUITES: 4
★ RESTAURANTS: 3
★ BARS: 1
★ DISCOTHEQUE: no
★ SHOPS: none
★ CONFERENCE ROOMS: 4 (20, 20, 40 and 100)
★ BANQUETING ROOMS: 5 (20, 40, 50, 80 and 100)
★ STANDARD BEDROOM SIZE: 18 m^2
★ PRIVATE BALCONIES: yes

★ SWIMMING POOL: 2 – fresh water, indoor and outdoor, 8 × 11 m and 9 × 9 m
★ RECREATIONAL ACTIVITIES: sauna, tennis, golf (9-hole), hunting and guided excursions
★ GARDENS: no – but surrounded by a large park and forest
★ NO. OF STAFF: 70
★ ROOM SERVICE: 06.00–24.00
★ ORIENTATION: all rooms face the park
★ CREDIT CARDS: Master Charge, Diners Club, Visa, American Express, Eurocard and Access
★ OWNING COMPANY: privately owned
★ GENERAL MANAGER: Mr. Lothar Eiermann
★ DISTANCE TO SHOPS: 6 km
★ DISTANCE FROM AIRPORT: 80 km

The original part of this establishment is a hunting lodge built in the early eighteenth century by a well-known German nobleman. Now, there is a new wing with all possible aid to comfort, but of the two we much prefer the former – gabled, roofed with handsome brick and white-walled. The public rooms are stately, tapestried and very beautiful and the bedrooms have great period charm. The new wing is modern, with amply proportioned rooms which are excellently furnished and serviced. There is a swimming pool and a sauna as well as tennis courts and vistas of great parkland. One can go hunting and fishing in the wooded Württemberg hills and it is near enough to places of great interest like Rothenburg and Heidelberg to make Friedrichsruhe a good centre. The staff are charmingly polite in a very well-bred way and the food more than adequate.

Hamburg

ATLANTIC HOTEL, An der Alster 72, 2000 Hamburg 1

- ★ TELEPHONE: 040-24-80-01
- ★ CABLES: Atlantic Hamburg
- ★ TELEX: 21 63 297
- ★ IN OPERATION: since 1909, renovation 1978/79
- ★ RESERVATIONS: HRI – The Leading Hotels of the World/Deutsche Lufthansa, worldwide/J.A.L. Hotel System
- ★ ROOMS: 100 doubles 210 singles
- ★ SUITES: 12
- ★ RESTAURANTS: 1 – Atlantic-Grill
- ★ BARS: 2 – Atlantic Bar, Atlantic-Brücke
- ★ DISCOTHEQUE: no
- ★ SHOPS: 4
- ★ CONFERENCE ROOMS: 18 (5 to 600)
- ★ BANQUETING ROOMS: 18 (5 to 600)
- ★ STANDARD BEDROOM SIZE: 30 m²

- ★ PRIVATE BALCONIES: yes – some rooms
- ★ SWIMMING POOL: yes – fresh water, 9 × 12 m
- ★ GARDENS: courtyard
- ★ NO. OF STAFF: 400
- ★ ROOM SERVICE: around the clock
- ★ ORIENTATION: overlooking the Alster Lake
- ★ CREDIT CARDS: American Express, Diners Club, Bank of America, Eurocard, Access and Master Charge
- ★ OWNING COMPANY: Kempinski-AG
- ★ GENERAL MANAGER: Karl Theodor Walterspiel
- ★ DISTANCE TO SHOPS: 500 m
- ★ DISTANCE FROM AIRPORT: 15 km; bus stop at hotel

One American I met at this hotel not long ago had begun his first visit to Germany in Hamburg. Looking around at the Atlantic, he was rather stunned. 'Do you know,' he told me, 'that the "Trib" came with my breakfast this morning plus a special teleprinter tearout of last night's closing prices in New York . . . Is all Germany like this?' The Atlantic, undoubtedly one of the country's great hotels, has that ability to take care of guests that surprises the hardened traveller. Business is business and only the best will do and the Atlantic is a hotel for large diameter wheeler-dealers. Quite convivial at times too but in the sound-proofed rooms you can hear your watch tick. The food would send any health farm addict back to the shrink – the quality, yes, but ah the quantity. There is here an aura of good living which is unmistakable – a whiff of Havana, the heavenly effluvium of Armagnac, Gucci briefcases everywhere and the cool golden sunshine of the finest German wines. The management, headed by one of the great hotel dynasties of Germany, is superb.

HOTEL VIER JAHRESZEITEN, Neuer Jungfernstieg 9-14, 2000 Hamburg 36

- ★ TELEPHONE: 040/34 94 1
- ★ CABLES: Jahreszeiten
- ★ TELEX: 211 629
- ★ IN OPERATION: since 1897
- ★ RESERVATIONS: Hotel Representative Inc
- ★ ROOMS: 76 doubles 114 singles
- ★ SUITES: 29
- ★ RESTAURANTS: 4 – Gourmet 'Restaurant Haerlin', 'Grill', tearoom 'Condi' and

late dinner restaurant 'Jahreszeiten-Keller'
- ★ BARS: 2 – Simbari and Jahreszeiten Keller bars
- ★ DISCOTHEQUE: live music with international bands
- ★ SHOPS: 5
- ★ CONFERENCE ROOMS: 5 (up to 100)
- ★ BANQUETING ROOMS: 5 (16 to 140)
- ★ STANDARD BEDROOM SIZE: all rooms vary

★ PRIVATE BALCONIES: yes – on the 5th floor

★ SWIMMING POOL: no

★ GARDENS: no

★ NO. OF STAFF: 400

★ ROOM SERVICE: around the clock

★ ORIENTATION: most rooms face the Alster Lake, others face decorated courtyards

★ CREDIT CARDS: American Express, Diners Club, Eurocard, Master Charge, Access and Bankamericard

★ OWNING COMPANY: privately owned by the A. Haerlin family

★ GENERAL MANAGER: Gert Prantner

★ DISTANCE TO SHOPS: walking distance

★ DISTANCE FROM AIRPORT: 11 km

A very fine hotel indeed offering comfort, good taste and the legendary traditions of its owners' three generations' experience. Unlike so many good German hotels elsewhere, the Vier Jahreszeiten does not show off – there is none of that commercial opulence here. It is very quiet, very 'distingué' and sensationally serviced – you have a thermometer for your bath water, they move the telephone to your desk during the day and back to the bedside at night and breakfast standards are of the highest. You get the feeling that the coffee has just been roasted for you. The rooms vary in size but all are absolute perfection when it comes to details and overall furnishing and the bathrooms are unusually good. There are some magnificent tapestries and chandeliers and chairs look as if they had been re-upholstered yesterday. The food is splendidly well served and ranks among the best of any hotel in Germany. Vier Jahreszeiten makes its own chocolates and keeps 185,000 bottles of wine in its superb cellar – the wine-list reads much better than the ninety-five principles Luther nailed to the church door.

Hinterzarten

PARKHOTEL ADLER, 7824 Hinterzarten, Südschwarzwald

★ TELEPHONE: 07652/711-717

★ CABLES: Adlerhotel

★ TELEX: 07-72692

★ IN OPERATION: since first established by the Riesterer family in 1446

★ RESERVATIONS: directly/Hotel Representative Inc/Relais et Chateaux

★ ROOMS: 48 double 15 single

★ SUITES: 19

★ RESTAURANTS: 6; open-air restaurant during the summer

★ BARS: 1

★ DISCOTHEQUE: dancing and musical entertainment by resident house-band

★ SHOPS: Adler Shopping

★ CONFERENCE ROOMS: 2 (40 and 80)

★ BANQUETING ROOMS: 3 (20 to 250)

★ STANDARD BEDROOM SIZE: 28 m^2

★ PRIVATE BALCONIES: yes – and terrace with adequate furnishings

★ SWIMMING POOL: yes – fresh water, 19 × 8 m with underwater massage

★ RECREATIONAL ACTIVITIES: beauty parlour, hairdresser, sauna, solarium, massage, nine-pin bowling, indoor and outdoor tennis, horse riding, all wintersports. Golf and watersports in the vicinity

★ GARDENS: yes – with children's playground, fitness course, deer park; game reserve including private duck pond

★ STAFF: 90

★ ROOM SERVICE: around the clock

★ ORIENTATION: view of the Black Forest

★ CREDIT CARDS: American Express, Diners Club and Eurocard

★ OWNING COMPANY: A. Riesterer KG

★ GENERAL MANAGERS: H. and A. Riesterer

★ DISTANCE TO BEACH: Lake Titisee 4 km

★ DISTANCE TO SHOPS: 200 m

★ DISTANCE FROM AIRPORT: 90 km (Basel or Zürich)

This hotel holds the record for continuous ownership – the same family have owned it for well over 500 years. Sixteenth-century pilgrims and savants have long given way to well-padded tourists – especially at lunchtime when it becomes the focus for Mercedes-borne trenchermen but at other times the Adler remains what it has been for so long – the quintessence of the really superb German country hotel. It's only a few miles from the shining Titisee, has its own sauna and covered swimming pool and charming gardens. All around are those beautiful hills of the Black Forest. The hotel is very, but *very* refined, furnished with pieces which bridge the centuries and staffed by people who really know what service is. Rooms are quite delightful – most of them different – and so comfortable that you might never want to leave. The trouble basically with the Adler is the food – one has to exercise enormous willpower to resist the succession of mouth-watering dishes. This is an hotel for those who don't have to watch their figure, or their wallet, too closely.

Kronberg

SCHLOSSHOTEL KRONBERG, Hainstrasse 25, 6242 Kronberg/Ts

- ★ TELEPHONE: 06173-7011
- ★ CABLES: no
- ★ TELEX: 0415 424
- ★ IN OPERATION: since 1954
- ★ RESERVATIONS: German National Tourist Offices
- ★ ROOMS: 20 doubles 29 singles
- ★ SUITES: 5
- ★ RESTAURANTS: 2
- ★ BARS: 1
- ★ DISCOTHEQUE: no
- ★ SHOPS: none
- ★ CONFERENCE ROOMS: 4 (4 to 50)
- ★ BANQUETING ROOMS: 4 (4 to 250)
- ★ STANDARD BEDROOM SIZE: 22 m²
- ★ SWIMMING POOL: no

- ★ PRIVATE BALCONIES: 3 bedrooms only – large terrace in front of the hotel
- ★ RECREATIONAL ACTIVITIES: 18-hole golf course around the hotel
- ★ GARDENS: yes – large park with old trees
- ★ NO. OF STAFF: 120
- ★ ROOM SERVICE: 06.30–24.00
- ★ ORIENTATION: north and south, built in Tudor style
- ★ CREDIT CARDS: American Express, Diners Club, Eurocard and Visa
- ★ OWNING COMPANY: Kurhessiche Hausstiftung
- ★ GENERAL MANAGER: Klaus Fischer
- ★ DISTANCE TO SHOPS: 2 km
- ★ DISTANCE FROM AIRPORT: 20 km

This is the only hotel I know where Titians and Holbeins look down at you as you are having dinner. This extraordinary piece of mock-Tudor was built by Queen Victoria's daughter when she was German Empress – one supposes to remind her of home. Mama stayed there, of course, plus most of Europe's crowned heads. The place is a monument to a bygone age, filled with Savonarola chairs, Tuscan chests, Flemish tapestries, French Empire chests, priceless oriental carpets and fireplaces so huge it takes two men to carry a log in. Yet one does not feel overawed, probably because Kronberg has relatively few guests (and many staff) and the atmosphere is that of an outstanding country house. Rooms vary a good deal in size and quality but the average is very high on comfort and elegance. The food, once rather nondescript, has improved a lot lately. And it is in the green Taunus Mountains a mere few miles from Frankfurt (Frankfurt is forgettable anyway). One extremely rich English duke I know stayed there once and remarked: 'It's almost like home.' For us ordinary mortals it is a rare treat.

Lohmar

SCHLOSS AUEL, Wahlscheid, 5204 Lohmar 21

- ★ TELEPHONE: Overath (02206) 2041/2/3
- ★ CABLES: no
- ★ TELEX: 0 887 510
- ★ IN OPERATION: since 1951
- ★ RESERVATIONS: direct
- ★ ROOMS: 17 doubles 4 singles
- ★ SUITES: 2
- ★ RESTAURANTS: 4
- ★ BARS: 1
- ★ DISCOTHEQUE: no
- ★ SHOPS: none
- ★ CONFERENCE ROOMS: 7

- ★ BANQUETING ROOMS: 7
- ★ STANDARD BEDROOM SIZE: all very different
- ★ PRIVATE BALCONIES: no
- ★ SWIMMING POOL: yes – fresh water, 5 × 9 m
- ★ RECREATIONAL ACTIVITIES: tennis and sauna
- ★ GARDENS: yes
- ★ NO. OF STAFF: 25
- ★ ROOM SERVICE: 07.00–23.00
- ★ ORIENTATION: east and west

★ CREDIT CARDS: American Express, Diners
  Club and Eurocard
★ OWNING COMPANY: privately owned
★ GENERAL MANAGER: Johann Adolf
  Freiherr (von la Valette St. Georges)

★ DISTANCE TO SHOPS: 45 minutes by car
  to Dusseldorf, 25 km from Cologne and
  25 km from Bonn
★ DISTANCE FROM AIRPORT: 20 km

In this age of the ersatz, authenticity is rare indeed and can only be achieved by people
who are authentic! Schloss Auel, some of which goes back to the fourteenth century,
has been in the hands of the same celebrated family since the eighteenth century and
one would be hard put to find a more charming place than this small, intimate,
white-painted country castle a few Mercedes minutes away from Cologne. In this hotel
there is not a single piece of furniture that looks as if it had not always been there –
marvellous country pieces (including a four poster in which Napoleon once slept),
beautiful chairs, gorgeous tapestries and a real chapel with a magnificent rococo altar.
Most rooms are different but you cannot really go wrong because every one of them is
a gem. People are absolutely charming, in a natural and wellborn way, and service
comes with old fashioned German politeness. Also surprising is the standard of food
and wine – quite stratospheric for a hotel of this size. If an unkind fate decrees that you
have to go to Frankfurt you can take your own revenge and stay here.

Munich

HOTEL BAYERISCHER HOF AND PALAIS MONTGELAS, Promenadeplatz 2-6, 8000 München 2

★ TELÉPHONE: 089/21200
★ CABLES: Bayerhof
★ TELEX: 05/23409
★ IN OPERATION: since 1841, destroyed
  during the second world war and rebuilt
★ RESERVATIONS: HRI (Leading Hotels of
  the World), London and New
  York/Preferred Hotels, Frankfurt and
  U.S.A./SRS (Steigenberger Reservation
  Service), Frankfurt and New York
★ ROOMS: 200 doubles 220 singles
★ SUITES: 20
★ RESTAURANTS: 3 – Grill, Trader Vic's and
  Palais Keller
★ BARS: 3
★ DISCOTHEQUE: night club with live
  music (2 bands)
★ SHOPS: 9 – Christian Dior, Emilio Pucci,
  Paintings, Leder Walter, Rudolph
  Mooshammer, Gallery, Royal Mink,
  Pelzhaus, jewellery etc

★ CONFERENCE ROOMS: 28 (5 to 1,500)
★ BANQUETING ROOMS: 14 (up to 2,000)
★ STANDARD BEDROOM SIZE: 22 m²
★ PRIVATE BALCONIES: no
★ SWIMMING POOL: yes – fresh water,
  16 × 6 × 1.5 m
★ RECREATIONAL ACTIVITIES: sauna,
  massage and solarium
★ GARDENS: grill garden, used in the
  summer for open air meals
★ NO. OF STAFF: 650
★ ROOM SERVICE: 06.00–01.00
★ ORIENTATION: Promenadeplatz, quiet
  back street and courtyard
★ CREDIT CARDS: American Express, Diners
  Club, Carte Blanche and Eurocard
★ OWNING COMPANY: Falk Volkhardt
★ GENERAL MANAGER: Falk Volkhardt
★ DISTANCE TO SHOPS: walking distance
★ DISTANCE FROM AIRPORT: 11 km

The Bayerischer Hof and its aristocratic next-door sister, the Palais Montgelas, are a
legend around the world. Should you feel off colour, don't worry – there is an oxygen
tent in the sauna that will revive you and in one of the suites, there is also a his-and-hers
bathtub. What fun. This hotel is for people who know what they want and don't have
to point to it – quite a lot of those in Germany and Munich, and the Bayerischer Hof is
where they come to get some of the starch off their system.
An exceedingly successful hotel and a very busy one, it manages to be everything to
everyone – convivial in the Bavarian style and the ultimate in peace and quiet if that's
the way you want it. Rooms in the main hotel are elegantly ageless – fresh flowers
everywhere and good, solid furniture that stands the test of ages and in the Palais they
are positively ducal.

In all my several visits, I have never been able to fault the Bayerischer Hof though one German tycoon once complained within my hearing that the morning toast was too hard. He should see his dentist.

HOTEL VIER JAHRESZEITEN, Maximilianstrasse 17, 8000 München 22

★ TELEPHONE: 089/22 88 21
★ CABLES: Jahreszeiten
★ TELEX: 52 38 59
★ IN OPERATION: 63 years
★ RESERVATIONS: Hotel Representatives Inc
★ ROOMS: 365
★ SUITES: 30
★ RESTAURANTS: 2
★ BARS: 1
★ DISCOTHEQUE: no – but dancing in the bar
★ SHOPS: 3
★ CONFERENCE ROOMS: 8 (20 to 500)
★ BANQUETING ROOMS: 8 (20 to 500)
★ STANDARD BEDROOM SIZE: 24 m^2
★ PRIVATE BALCONIES: no

★ SWIMMING POOL: yes – fresh water
★ GARDENS: no
★ NO. OF STAFF: 400
★ ROOM SERVICE: around the clock
★ ORIENTATION: facade faces the Maximilianstrasse
★ CREDIT CARDS: Diners Club, American Express, Bankamericard, Master Charge, Eurocard, Pan Am and Take Off Card
★ OWNING COMPANY: Kempinski Hotels Corporation
★ GENERAL MANAGER: Michael D. Maass
★ DISTANCE TO SHOPS: walking distance
★ DISTANCE FROM AIRPORT: 9 km

This is still one of Germany's great hotel landmarks – I love it and so do many readers. One lady from Seattle wrote: 'When I arrive at the Four Seasons, the whole place really makes me feel that I am back in old Europe . . .' Lovely, dark panelled walls, handsome salons, beautiful antiques and a staff who seem to have been there forever – all this is part of the Vier Jahreszeiten image. There are also the ghosts of the Walterspiel family who once owned it and were the country's greatest gastronomes. Most of the bedrooms have been modernised – if that is the word – with so much intelligent planning and thought for detail that one hardly notices things have changed – apart from the plumbing, of course. It is a very, but very comfortable and aristocratic hotel with a great tradition. The food in the distinguished Walterspiel restaurant attracts Müncheners who, with so much choice around, have a high critical standard.

Oberwesel

BURGHOTEL AUF SCHONBURG, D-6532 Oberwesel/Rhein

★ TELEPHONE: 06744/8198
★ CABLES: no
★ TELEX: no
★ IN OPERATION: 27 years
★ RESERVATIONS: direct
★ ROOMS: 8 doubles
★ SUITES: 1
★ RESTAURANTS: 2
★ BARS: none
★ DISCOTHEQUE: no
★ SHOPS: none
★ CONFERENCE ROOMS: 1 (20)
★ BANQUETING ROOMS: 1 (16)
★ PRIVATE BALCONIES: 1 room only but a large terrace

★ STANDARD BEDROOM SIZE: 42 m^2
★ SWIMMING POOL: no
★ GARDENS: no
★ NO. OF STAFF: 14
★ ORIENTATION: all directions
★ FURTHER DEVELOPMENTS: a further 20 beds and an additional restaurant
★ CREDIT CARDS: American Express and Visa
★ OWNING COMPANY: family Hüttl
★ GENERAL MANAGER: Hüttl family
★ DISTANCE TO SHOPS: 1 km
★ DISTANCE FROM AIRPORT: 90 km (Frankfurt), 120 km (Cologne)

Anyone who goes up or down the Rhine at its noblest can see Auf Schonburg. You can't miss it. It sits up there on its hill like an illustration to a fairy tale, a proud statement in stone going back close on a thousand years. And if you think that it is the home of some great German margrave, you are wrong. It's your home and mine and anyone can get to stay there if he is quick about it because Schonburg, big as it is, has few rooms and only a small number can succeed. Which in a way makes it all the more worthwhile since you can have the great beamed halls, the fantastic corridors and the four-poster beds almost to yourself. The brothers Grimm, one feels, must be somewhere around and Schumann's music goes with it better than Wagner's. Both the management and staff are quite charming and most welcoming and theirs is German hospitality at its finest. Food and wines are excellent too – the latter especially if they come from those glorious local vineyards. Also, watch the Rhine panorama in the early morning or at dusk. You'll never forget it.

Trendelburg

BURGHOTEL TRENDELBURG, D-3526 Trendelburg

★ TELEPHONE: 05675-1021
★ CABLES: no
★ TELEX: 0994812
★ IN OPERATION: 30 years
★ RESERVATIONS: direct
★ ROOMS: 18 doubles 5 singles
★ SUITES: 1
★ RESTAURANTS: 4
★ BARS: none
★ DISCOTHEQUE: no
★ SHOPS: none
★ CONFERENCE ROOMS: 2 (10 to 45)
★ BANQUETING ROOMS: 2
★ STANDARD BEDROOM SIZE: 16–30 m²
★ PRIVATE BALCONIES: no

★ SWIMMING POOL: no
★ RECREATIONAL ACTIVITIES: swimming, tennis and horse riding nearby
★ GARDENS: yes
★ NO. OF STAFF: 24
★ ROOM SERVICE: 07.00–23.00
★ CREDIT CARDS: American Express and Diners Club
★ ORIENTATION: all directions
★ OWNING COMPANY: private
★ GENERAL MANAGER: Mr. V. Stockhausen
★ DISTANCE TO SHOPS: 12 km
★ DISTANCE FROM AIRPORT: 190 km (Hanover), 220 km (Frankfurt)

If your fancy turns to a night or two in a real German castle, you couldn't do better than try Trendelburg – only a few miles from Kassel and yet, it would seem, belonging to a different age. It is beautiful, genuine, totally authentic, gently bucolic and so well run by the baronial family who own it that it has become a legend in Germany. A lot of it dates from the thirteenth century and, like all such places, other centuries added their contribution, making Trendelburg into a residence of immense character and charm. There are old timbers everywhere – even the bathrooms are timbered – lovely floors, delightful country antiques and a magnificent vaulted dining room where the food is simply delicious. If you are lucky you might even get the very romantic Wedding Tower Suite which is the pride of this most unusual and welcoming hotel. The plumbing dates from 1979.

Wiesbaden

HOTEL SCHWARZER BOCK, Kranzplatz 12, D-6200 Wiesbaden

★ TELEPHONE: 06121-3821
★ CABLES: Schwarzerbockhotel
★ TELEX: 04 186 640
★ IN OPERATION: since 1486
★ RESERVATIONS: Utell International, New York/American Wolfe International, New York

★ ROOMS: 60 doubles 100 singles
★ SUITES: 15
★ RESTAURANTS: 2 – Le Capricorne and the Roofgarden Coffee House
★ BARS: 1
★ DISCOTHEQUE: no
★ SHOPS: none – but several show cases

★ **CONFERENCE ROOMS:** 8 (10 to 250)

★ **BANQUETING ROOMS:** 8 (10 to 250)

★ **STANDARD BEDROOM SIZE:** 30 m²

★ **PRIVATE BALCONIES:** yes – 40 rooms

★ **SWIMMING POOL:** yes – indoor, fresh, thermal water, 15 × 8 m

★ **RECREATIONAL ACTIVITIES:** sporting activities by request. Own thermal sparkling springs, Japanese movement bath, massages, sauna, therapeutic exercise bath, solarium, beauty farm

★ **GARDENS:** no – roof garden and terrace

★ **NO. OF STAFF:** 140

★ **ROOM SERVICE:** 07.00–2400

★ **CREDIT CARDS:** Amexco, Diners Club and Eurocard

★ **OWNING COMPANY:** privately owned

★ **GENERAL MANAGER:** H. D. Grube

★ **DISTANCE TO SHOPS:** 5 minutes

★ **DISTANCE FROM AIRPORT:** 25 km from Frankfurt Airport

Frankfurt is a city I can easily forget but I wish I could forget it altogether. The little town of Wiesbaden close to Frankfurt contains the antidote; the Schwarzer Bock. The hotel has been there, on and off, for something like 500 years, but my news of it extends only ten years into the past.

I have no hesitation in saying that this is one of the most pleasant and beautiful city hotels in Germany. Acres of wall panelling, superb wallpapers, furniture that Sotheby's would love to sell and a reception man who looked at his bookings and asked if I preferred baroque or modern! I chose the former and have never regretted it since the furnishings were an unanswerable argument in favour of the Holy Roman Empire. Spotless linen, good lighting, chairs one could sit on – my behind is large and sensitive – in Le Capricorne Restaurant where I spent most of the time just looking at the food and watching the service.

This being Wiesbaden, there is, of course, a thermal swimming pool and lots of massage rooms, saunas etc. I have never felt fit or unfit but at the Schwarzer Bock, I felt good all the time.

GREAT BRITAIN
Ashford

EASTWELL MANOR, Eastwell Park, Ashford, Kent

★ TELEPHONE: Ashford (0233) 35751
★ CABLES: no
★ TELEX: 966281
★ IN OPERATION: since February, 1980
★ RESERVATIONS: direct or Prestige Hotels, London, Amsterdam, Brussels, Frankfurt and Paris/Scott Calder International, U.S.A.
★ ROOMS: 17
★ SUITES: 3
★ RESTAURANTS: 1
★ BARS: 1
★ DISCOTHEQUE: no
★ SHOPS: none – but 2 showcases
★ CONFERENCE ROOMS: 1 (40)
★ BANQUETING ROOMS: 2 (10 to 50)
★ STANDARD BEDROOM SIZE: 29 m²
★ PRIVATE BALCONIES: several terraces around the hotel

★ SWIMMING POOL: no
★ RECREATIONAL ACTIVITIES: tennis, croquet and trout fishing, horse riding, golf and squash nearby
★ GARDENS: yes – 25 acres
★ NO. OF STAFF: 38
★ ROOM SERVICE: around the clock
★ ORIENTATION: country house set in 3,000 acres, formal gardens and rolling downs
★ CREDIT CARDS: American Express, Visa, Barclaycard, Access and Carte Blanche
★ OWNING COMPANY: Eastwell Manor Ltd
★ GENERAL MANAGER: Matthew J. Bates
★ DISTANCE TO SHOPS: 5 km
★ DISTANCE FROM AIRPORT: 65 km (Gatwick)

Several old-style British hoteliers did some tut-tutting when I listed Eastwell Manor in the last edition. After all, though the place itself goes back to the Norman conquest, it had only just opened as a hotel and its general manager was (and still is) in his twenties. Ye men of little faith. I personally had a hunch about it and, though I am not always right (who is?), I had made the right decision in this case. Ever since then I have received a steady trickle of letters about Eastwell Manor – all of them good and full of praise – and I actually know of one top flight French businessman who comes over regularly. '*Un hotel d'une excellence rare*' he writes, which is praise indeed coming from across the English Channel.

Eastwell must be seen, and sampled, to be believed – an extravaganza of English history in mellow stone set amidst no less than 3,000 acres of parkland, with Chaucer's Pilgrim's Way casually within sight. The whole place has been sensibly, and expensively, converted and is now a hotel of such warmth and comfort that it is worth the trip. I expected, or half expected it to fall off slightly on the food front and recently I called there, totally anonymously, for lunch midweek and all I can say is that I wish I could be that lucky every day. Eastwell Manor is a triumph of good training and creative management over experience.

Auchterarder

GLENEAGLES HOTEL, Auchterarder, Perthshire, PH3 1NF, Scotland

★ TELEPHONE: (076 46) 2231
★ CABLES: Glenotel, Auchterarder
★ TELEX: 76105
★ IN OPERATION: since 1924
★ RESERVATIONS: Hotel Representative Inc
★ ROOMS: 154 doubles 35 singles
★ SUITES: 17
★ RESTAURANTS: 3 – The Strathearn, The Eagle's Nest and Dormy House
★ BARS: 2 – Cocktail Bar and Dormy House Bar
★ DISCOTHEQUE: yes – by arrangement – and dancing to live music each evening
★ SHOPS: 7
★ CONFERENCE ROOMS: 6 (50 to 400)
★ BANQUETING ROOMS: 7 (40 to 320)
★ STANDARD BEDROOM SIZE: 28 m^2 (double) 13½ m^2 (single)
★ PRIVATE BALCONIES: yes – some rooms
★ SWIMMING POOL: yes – fresh water, indoor, heated, 10 × 5 × 1–2 m deep

★ RECREATIONAL ACTIVITIES: 4 golf courses, 5 tennis courts, putting green, bowling green, croquet lawn, billiards, fishing, sauna, squash
★ GARDENS: yes – 640-acre estate
★ NO. OF STAFF: 350
★ ROOM SERVICE: around the clock
★ ORIENTATION: facing south
★ FURTHER DEVELOPMENTS: leisure centre with games room, large swimming pool and 2 squash courts
★ OWNING COMPANY: Gleneagles Hotels P.L.C
★ CREDIT CARDS: all major credit cards
★ GENERAL MANAGER: Mr. G. G. Macpherson
★ DISTANCE TO SHOPS: 24 km (Perth), 32 km (Stirling) and 72 km (Edinburgh)
★ DISTANCE FROM AIRPORT: 88 km (Glasgow) and 64 km (Edinburgh)

I don't know what the Scots will say about it but Gleneagles is changing and its new owners are determined to make it great. This vast pile always was that, a place on its own with tremendous aura, where you could arrive by helicopter if you wished. The sort of place where, traditionally, they iron out the creases in The Times before putting it on your breakfast tray. And of course, Gleneagles meant golf-lunatics coming in from all over the world. I once saw an American visitor with tears in his eyes when he caught sight of the courses – King's and Queen's.

But it had to move with the times and from the hotel's 1,000 windows looking over the Perthshire hills to the great pillared hall which I swear is bigger than Piccadilly Circus, the new owners are renovating, initiating, inventing, getting rid of the institutional look and even taking real French food North of the Border (they are spending £40,000 on the kitchens alone). All this plus a huge new leisure complex, an all-year-round affair with squash courts, saunas, jacuzzi pool and solarium (let's hope they import the sun too). I am hoping they won't forget the Gleneagles atmosphere, a blend of grand urbanity and the personal touch which made Gleneagles a much loved place by all those who knew it.

Banbury

WHATELY HALL, Banbury Cross, Banbury, Oxfordshire, OX16 OAN

★ TELEPHONE: (0295) 3451
★ CABLES: no
★ TELEX: 837149
★ IN OPERATION: since the seventeenth century
★ RESERVATIONS: Trust Houses Forte Ltd
★ ROOMS: 17 doubles 36 twins 21 singles
★ SUITES: 1
★ RESTAURANTS: 2
★ BARS: 2

★ DISCOTHEQUE: no – but dancing every other Saturday
★ SHOPS: none
★ CONFERENCE ROOMS: 4 (20 to 120)
★ BANQUETING ROOMS: 4 (16 to 150)
★ STANDARD BEDROOM SIZE: 17 m^2
★ PRIVATE BALCONIES: no
★ SWIMMING POOL: no
★ GARDENS: yes – beautiful lawn where one can play croquet, putting etc
★ NO. OF STAFF: 64

★ ROOM SERVICE: 07.00–22.00

★ ORIENTATION: most rooms overlook the garden

★ CREDIT CARDS: Diners Club, American Express, Barclaycard, Access, Carte Blanche and THF

★ OWNING COMPANY: Trust Houses Forte Ltd

★ GENERAL MANAGER: Bruno Manca

★ DISTANCE TO SHOPS: 200 m

★ DISTANCE FROM AIRPORT: 120 km (Heathrow), 80 km (Birmingham)

Whately Hall is partly seventeenth century. Swift wrote some of 'Gulliver's Travels' here and Benjamin Franklyn also stayed. The centre part is the best – all Cotswold stone, large rooms, solid and comfortable furniture, a strikingly beautiful lawn can be seen through the pretty windows and you can play croquet there. Rooms vary from the vast and comfortable in the old part to the not so vast but efficient in the new wing. The staff are extremely helpful and pleasant and the new management has made a marked difference to the whole atmosphere. The food too has improved greatly and is now unassumingly good and varied. Whately Hall is also most convienient because Banbury is virtually the geographical centre of England.

Bath

ROYAL CRESCENT HOTEL, Royal Crescent, Bath, Avon, BA1 2LS

★ TELEPHONE: (0225) 319090

★ CABLES: Royalguest

★ TELEX: 444251

★ IN OPERATION: 40 years – re-opened in June, 1979, after complete restoration

★ RESERVATIONS: Hotel Representative Inc, London and New York

★ ROOMS: 26 doubles 3 singles

★ SUITES: 4 – 3 have four-poster beds

★ RESTAURANTS: 1

★ BARS: 1

★ DISCOTHEQUE: no

★ SHOPS: none

★ CONFERENCE ROOMS: 2 (up to 30)

★ BANQUETING ROOMS: 2 (up to 20)

★ STANDARD BEDROOM SIZE: 42 m^2

★ PRIVATE BALCONIES: no – but private terrace to one room and terrace outside the bar

★ SWIMMING POOL: no

★ RECREATIONAL ACTIVITIES: tennis, swimming, horse riding, and sauna available nearby. Horse-drawn coach rides by prior appointment

★ GARDENS: yes

★ NO. OF STAFF: 43

★ ROOM SERVICE: around the clock

★ ORIENTATION: faces the private Royal Crescent lawn overlooking the city of Bath

★ FURTHER DEVELOPMENTS: planning additional rooms and guest facilities in the hotel mews

★ CREDIT CARDS: American Express, Access, Barclaycard and Visa

★ OWNING COMPANY: Blakeney Hotels Ltd

★ GENERAL MANAGER: Malcolm J. M. Walker

★ DISTANCE TO SHOPS: walking distance

★ DISTANCE FROM AIRPORT: 30 km

Having recently returned to the Royal Crescent, my affection and admiration for this unique hotel are undimmed – it is still one of the most interesting and remarkable hotels in Europe. The location of course is matchless – right in the middle of that beautiful Georgian Crescent which is possibly one of the six greatest architectural concepts in Europe. Inside, everything is a feast for the eye, a balm for the soul, for this hotel, totally reconditioned in 1979, is absolutely perfect. From the ashtrays to the paintings and from the four poster beds to the magnificent ceiling decorations and the carpets which one would love to roll up and take away, the Royal Crescent is an object lesson on how to present a period hotel.

As for the management and staff, they deserve medals for making this small hotel into a home for its guests – everyone is friendly, helpful, happy to oblige and it is a real pleasure to stay here and stroll around this most handsome of small English towns. The food too is worth travelling for – something deliciously adventurous and yet always within the guidelines of intelligent gastronomy. Full marks to this very rare hostelry.

Broadway

THE LYGON ARMS, Broadway, Worcestershire, WR12 7DU

- ★ TELEPHONE: (0386) 852255
- ★ CABLES: Lygon Broadway
- ★ TELEX: 338260
- ★ IN OPERATION: since the sixteenth century
- ★ RESERVATIONS: direct, Hotel Representative Inc, or Prestige
- ★ ROOMS: 59 doubles 4 singles
- ★ SUITES: 4
- ★ RESTAURANTS: 2 – 1 summer and 1 winter
- ★ BARS: 2
- ★ DISCOTHEQUE: no
- ★ SHOPS: 1 – Inn Shop
- ★ CONFERENCE ROOMS: 4 (10 to 80)
- ★ BANQUETING ROOMS: 5 (10 to 150)
- ★ STANDARD BEDROOM SIZE: 31 m²
- ★ PRIVATE BALCONIES: yes – some rooms
- ★ SWIMMING POOL: no
- ★ RECREATIONAL ACTIVITIES: Tennis, golf close by and horse riding and hunting by arrangement
- ★ GARDENS: yes – secluded formal gardens and orchard
- ★ NO. OF STAFF: 113
- ★ ROOM SERVICE: around the clock
- ★ ORIENTATION: main street, courtyard and garden
- ★ CREDIT CARDS: American Express, Diners Club, Access, Eurocard, Barclaycard and Carte Blanche
- ★ OWNING COMPANY: The Lygon Arms Ltd
- ★ GENERAL MANAGER: Kirk Ritchie
- ★ DISTANCE TO SHOPS: within village
- ★ DISTANCE FROM AIRPORT: 144 km (Heathrow), 55 km (Birmingham), helicopter pad

In the last edition I wrote: 'One of the hardest things in the world to do is to run a good hotel in a location which is invaded twice daily by a gaggle of gawping tourists . . .' And they are still coming to Broadway, one of England's most celebrated villages and a few lucky ones stay at the Lygon Arms, even fewer sleep in the Great Chamber which was built the year the Mayflower sailed. Both Charles I and Cromwell stayed here – though unfortunately not at the same time or the Civil War may have ended differently. Yet, the most remarkable thing of all is that despite its fame, despite the fact that it is in the heart of England's tourist land, the Lygon Arms has managed to remain so good a hotel. One feels that it must take great willpower not to succumb to the temptation of cashing in on the boom. The Lygon Arms remains itself: well-tempered, gentle, beautifully run and totally devoid of razzmatazz. The people who staff it always seem to have time to answer even the tourist's most stupid questions, to help and direct and to make you feel welcome. Now, even the less interesting rooms in the new wing have been given the Lygon look and the food, as before, is very acceptable.

Castle Combe

MANOR HOUSE HOTEL, Castle Combe, Nr Chippenham, Wiltshire, SN14 7HR

- ★ TELEPHONE: (0249) 782206
- ★ CABLES: no
- ★ TELEX: 44220 (Comtel) Manor House
- ★ IN OPERATION: since 1947, but under present management since 1965
- ★ RESERVATIONS: direct
- ★ ROOMS: 29 doubles 4 singles
- ★ SUITES: no
- ★ RESTAURANTS: 1
- ★ BARS: 1
- ★ DISCOTHEQUE: no – but discotheques and bands may be arranged for privately booked functions
- ★ SHOPS: 1 – boutique
- ★ CONFERENCE ROOMS: 4 (15 to 125)
- ★ BANQUETING ROOMS: 4 (15 to 125)
- ★ STANDARD BEDROOM SIZE: all different
- ★ PRIVATE BALCONIES: no
- ★ SWIMMING POOL: yes – fresh water, heated, 11½ × 5½ m
- ★ RECREATIONAL ACTIVITIES: tennis and trout fishing with golf available nearby
- ★ GARDENS: yes – 26½ acres of gardens and parkland bordered by the River Bybrook
- ★ NO. OF STAFF: 70
- ★ ROOM SERVICE: 06.00–02.00

★ ORIENTATION: the hotel mostly faces
  south
★ CREDIT CARDS: Diners Club, American
  Express, Barclaycard and Access
★ OWNING COMPANY: Clegg (Hotels) Ltd

★ GENERAL MANAGER: R. L. Buckley
★ DISTANCE TO SHOPS: 14 km (Bath)
★ DISTANCE FROM AIRPORT: 120 km
  (Heathrow)

In this, truly one of England's most beautiful villages (alas, much trampled on at weekends), is this very beautiful, very remarkable small country hotel which could be a model of the genre. Once it belonged to a certain Sir John Fastolf (Shakespeare borrowed the name but not the character) and it is one of those places you must go to. Despite the sightseers, the Manor House is astonishingly quiet, very well brought up and beautifully managed. It is stone built, spanning three centuries from 1500 to 1800 – a marvellous jumble of handsome wings facing 26 acres of the kind of gardens such as one finds only in England. Bedrooms vary a lot, especially in size, but all of them are period-furnished, attractive and comfortable but do try and insist on being in the main house. Public rooms are country house which is as it should be, as are the staff who cannot do enough for the guest. The food is excellent – certainly good enough to impress even French visitors. And twelve miles away is Bath.

Chelwood

HUNSTRETE HOUSE HOTEL, Chelwood, Nr. Bristol, Avon, BS18 4NS

★ TELEPHONE: (07618) 578
★ CABLES: Hunstrete House Hotel
★ TELEX: 449540
★ IN OPERATION: 4 years
★ RESERVATIONS: direct or David B.
  Mitchell & Co Inc
★ ROOMS: 18
★ SUITES: 2
★ RESTAURANTS: 2
★ BARS: 1
★ DISCOTHEQUE: no
★ SHOPS: no
★ CONFERENCE ROOMS: 1 (5 × 6 m)
★ BANQUETING ROOMS: 1 (30)
★ STANDARD BEDROOM SIZE: 24 m²
★ PRIVATE BALCONIES: none
★ SWIMMING POOL: 1 – outdoor, fresh
  water, heated

★ RECREATIONAL ACTIVITIES: tennis court,
  croquet, swimming. Riding, fishing, golf
  nearby
★ GARDENS: yes
★ NO. OF STAFF: 30
★ ROOM SERVICE: 07.20–23.30
★ ORIENTATION: east, south and west
★ CREDIT CARDS: American Express, Carte
  Blanche, Barclaycard and Visa
★ OWNING COMPANY: Mr. F. J. and Mrs. T.
  Dupays (resident proprietors)
★ GENERAL MANAGER: Sharron Love
★ DISTANCE TO SHOPS: 13 km
  (Bath), 13 km (Bristol)
★ DISTANCE FROM AIRPORT: 140 km
  (London Heathrow)

It is when I find a hotel like Hunstrete House that I realise how lucky foreign visitors are – for them this is the best of England while for us who live in this sceptred isle, a quick weekend is all we can manage. Hunstrete is delightful, totally English and Georgian to boot – a very handsome house with a walled garden, croquet lawn and splendid countryside all around, plus the nearness of such places as Bath and Glastonbury, Longleat, Wilton House and many other stately homes. The house is delightfully individual with most bedrooms done up in a different style and lovingly furnished with good pieces and splendid furnishings. In the public rooms, you feel at home because you could be a guest of the family and the whole atmosphere is just that – a private party for a few fortunate people. Fortunate too because the food, presented here by a chef from Normandy, is one of the high points. Putting Gallic pride aside, he has managed to combine the best of both countries and things like salmon from the Wye for instance are worth the journey. If you are aiming for the West Country, this could well be the right choice.

Dedham

MAISON TALBOOTH, Dedham, Colchester, Essex, CO7 6HN

* ★ TELEPHONE: (0206) 322367
* ★ CABLES: no
* ★ TELEX: no
* ★ IN OPERATION: 13 years
* ★ RESERVATIONS: direct
* ★ ROOMS: 9 doubles
* ★ SUITES: 1
* ★ RESTAURANTS: 1 – Le Talbooth Restaurant, sixteenth-century timbered house
* ★ BARS: 1 – plus private bar in each room
* ★ DISCOTHEQUE: no
* ★ SHOPS: none
* ★ CONFERENCE ROOMS: 2 (20 in each)
* ★ BANQUETING ROOMS: 2 (20 and 50)
* ★ STANDARD BEDROOM SIZE: 25–30 m²
* ★ PRIVATE BALCONIES: yes
* ★ SWIMMING POOL: no
* ★ GARDENS: yes

* ★ NO. OF STAFF: 10 in the hotel and 25 in the restaurant
* ★ ROOM SERVICE: 07.00–24.00
* ★ ORIENTATION: hotel faces north, but suites face all directions
* ★ FURTHER DEVELOPMENTS: construction of tennis court
* ★ CREDIT CARDS: American Express, Barclaycard, Visa, Access and Diners Club
* ★ OWNING COMPANY: Le Talbooth (Dedham) Ltd
* ★ GENERAL MANAGER: G. M. W. Milsom (Proprietor)
* ★ DISTANCE TO BEACH: 30 km
* ★ DISTANCE TO SHOPS: 10 km (Colchester)
* ★ DISTANCE FROM AIRPORT: 80 km (Norwich), 120 km (Heathrow) and 60 km (Southend)

There are twin identities here. One is Le Talbooth, one of England's most celebrated country restaurants lodged in a spectacularly beautiful house which Constable once painted. I like to eat there and discreetly steal the menu to remind me of past delights. Then, half a mile away, is Maison Talbooth – an admirable small country house hotel. Britain's best hotel guide (they are lucky – they only cover one country . . .) gives it the fifth-highest rating in this particular category. Maison Talbooth is a good place to know, largely because it is the creation of one man.

No two rooms are alike. What is similar is the touch – a tremendous effort to lift this once undistinguished Victorian house into something special. Furniture is excellently chosen. The beds are beautiful and wallpapers and colour schemes are exactly what you might pick yourself. Bathrooms are great fun too. There are fresh flowers everywhere and fruit and drinks too and, when breakfast comes, it really makes you feel like facing the new day. Service is impeccable.

All this, with the high gastronomy down the road and the Constable country all around, with its wide skies, great trees and soft, blurry horizons, means that Talbooth is a name to put in your diary.

East Grinstead

GRAVETYE MANOR, Nr East Grinstead, West Sussex, RH19 4LJ

* ★ TELEPHONE: Sharpthorne (0342) 810567
* ★ CABLES: no
* ★ TELEX: 957239
* ★ IN OPERATION: 23 years
* ★ RESERVATIONS: direct
* ★ ROOMS: 12 doubles 2 singles
* ★ SUITES: no
* ★ RESTAURANTS: 1
* ★ BARS: 1
* ★ DISCOTHEQUE: no
* ★ SHOPS: none
* ★ CONFERENCE ROOMS: 1 (14)
* ★ BANQUETING ROOMS: 1 (16)
* ★ STANDARD BEDROOM SIZE: 30 m²

* ★ PRIVATE BALCONIES: no
* ★ SWIMMING POOL: no
* ★ RECREATIONAL ACTIVITIES: trout fishing, croquet, tennis, squash, golf and horse riding can be arranged locally
* ★ GARDENS: yes – 20 acres created by William Robinson, pioneer of the English natural garden
* ★ NO. OF STAFF: 52
* ★ ROOM SERVICE: 07.00–23.30
* ★ ORIENTATION: rooms face garden and forest
* ★ CREDIT CARDS: no credit cards are accepted

★ OWNING COMPANY: Gravetye Manor
   Hotel Ltd
★ GENERAL MANAGER: Peter Herbert
   (Resident Proprietor)

★ DISTANCE TO BEACH: 50 km
★ DISTANCE TO SHOPS: 8 km
★ DISTANCE FROM AIRPORT: 19 km

One of the oddities about writing this book is that when I sit in my study looking over the gentle Sussex Downs, I can almost hear the soft pop of the champagne corks down at Gravetye Manor, a mere two miles away. Alas, this proximity to the finest food in South-East England does me little good (apart from the occasional self-indulgence of course). Trouble is, people ring me up from far and wide accusing me of suggesting temptations in which they have little hope of indulging because they cannnot get into Gravetye. Such is the price of fame for a country house hotel which has a worldwide reputation.

Gravetye, especially in the summertime when you can have your pre-dinner Pol Roger sitting in the superb gardens, is a way of life one can get used to. This lovely, mellow, 400-year-old stone house, beautifully but not ostentatiously furnished, is sheer delight. Rooms are countryfied, gentle and beautifully kept and service is quiet and expert. But what counts here is the food – truly original, beautifully balanced and ecstatically fine. I often take French friends to Gravetye just to show them that Britain too can produce great meals and to a man they remark that, of course, the superb wines are French. Quite. Gravetye is an experience which you owe to yourself but, please, don't telephone me!

Fort William

INVERLOCHY CASTLE, Fort William, Inverness-shire, Scotland

★ TELEPHONE: 0397-2177/8
★ CABLES: Inverlochy Castle
★ TELEX: no
★ IN OPERATION: for 12 years
★ RESERVATIONS: direct
★ ROOMS: 11 doubles 1 single
★ SUITES: 2
★ RESTAURANTS: 2
★ BARS: 1
★ DISCOTHEQUE: no
★ SHOPS: none
★ CONFERENCE ROOMS: none
★ BANQUETING ROOMS: none
★ STANDARD BEDROOM SIZE: variable
★ PRIVATE BALCONIES: no
★ SWIMMING POOL: no

★ RECREATIONAL ACTIVITIES: tennis, trout
   fishing, billiards, horse riding and golf
   nearby
★ GARDENS: yes
★ NO. OF STAFF: 40
★ ROOM SERVICE: around the clock
★ ORIENTATION: rooms face lake or
   mountain
★ CREDIT CARDS: American Express and
   Barclaycard
★ OWNING COMPANY: Mr. & Mrs. J. Hobbs
★ GENERAL MANAGER: Michael Leonard
★ DISTANCE TO BEACH: 40 km
★ DISTANCE TO SHOPS: 5 km
★ DISTANCE FROM AIRPORT: 109 km
   (Inverness) and 160 km (Glasgow)

From Queen Victoria, who once stayed there, down to those lucky enough to get in these days, everybody has been bowled over by this megalomaniac Scottish folly and it is generally thought to be the finest hotel in Scotland. While not disagreeing I must say that the setting itself is worth the journey: overlooked by Ben Nevis and overlooking lovely Loch Linnhe, Inverlochy stands among masses of rhododendrons in the middle of a vast park. The views are stunning. So, in many ways, is the place itself. Far too big it seems for the privileged few guests. From the fantastic great hall with its painted ceiling, one ascends – that's the right word – to bedrooms of ducal magnificence, with lovely fabrics, very comfortable and, does one dare say it, homely furniture (the kind one would like to have) and into bathrooms ankle-deep in carpet and matched with grand plumbing. The public rooms are superb, especially the dining room with its gleaming silver and glass.

What is even more remarkable is the food at Inverlochy of which one must say that it is composed by a lady chef of international fame. Try the local prawns. The local duck too and the wine-list and everything-else – you may not get the chance again. Incidentally, even the water here is special: the owners use it in the making of their own whisky.

Inverness

CULLODEN HOUSE, Inverness

★ TELEPHONE: (0463) 790461

★ CABLES: no

★ TELEX: 75402 Cloden

★ IN OPERATION: 7 years

★ RESERVATIONS: Scott Calder International, New York/Prestige Hotels, Middlesex/John Miller Australia, Sydney

★ ROOMS: 20

★ SUITES: 1

★ RESTAURANTS: 1

★ BARS: 1

★ DISCOTHEQUE: no

★ SHOPS: none

★ CONFERENCE ROOMS: none – but two public rooms can be converted to accommodate up to 30 persons

★ BANQUETING ROOMS: none – dining room used for banquets accommodating up to 50 persons

★ STANDARD BEDROOM SIZE: 27 m²

★ PRIVATE BALCONIES: no

★ SWIMMING POOL: no

★ RECREATIONAL ACTIVITIES: sauna with fishing, shooting, golf and horse riding close by

★ GARDENS: yes – 41 acres

★ NO. OF STAFF: 35

★ ROOM SERVICE: around the clock

★ ORIENTATION: country house situated in peaceful surroundings

★ CREDIT CARDS: American Express, Access, Barclaycard, Diners Club and Master Charge

★ OWNING COMPANY: privately owned and managed by Ian and Marjory McKenzie

★ DISTANCE TO BEACH: 40 km

★ DISTANCE TO SHOPS: 12 km

★ DISTANCE FROM AIRPORT: 20 km

Bonnie Prince Charlie spent a night here. Alas, he could not stay since the day after, in that bitter, bloody battle nearby, he lost all the hopes of the Stuarts and Scotland the finest of its generation. A couple of decades later the house was partly rebuilt in gracious Adam style and today it is undoubtedly one of the finest country hotels in Scotland – largely thanks to the present owner's passion for comfort and hospitality. It is a good-looking, handsomely mellow period piece where people welcome you with genuine warmth and look after you as if you were their personal guest. Bedrooms are elegantly sober and the bathrooms especially good and well looked after. Public rooms are vast and extremely well furnished in the right period. The food, served with quiet pride, is exceedingly good for a country where it is too often pretty awful and in the bar I counted fourteen different kinds of you-know-what. There is a lovely, gracious park and lots of fishing, shooting and golf if you wish. One is also quite near Loch Ness – just in case the monster should show up.

London

THE BERKELEY, P.O. Box 590, Wilton Place, Knightsbridge, London, SW1X 7RL

★ TELEPHONE: 01-235-6000

★ CABLES: Silentium London

★ TELEX: 919252 Berkly G

★ IN OPERATION: since 1972

★ RESERVATIONS: Hotel Representative Inc

★ ROOMS: 127

★ SUITES: 25

★ RESTAURANTS: 2 – 'Le Perroquet' and main hotel restaurant

★ BARS: 1

★ DISCOTHEQUE: yes

★ SHOPS: 4 – hairdressing, bookshop, cinema and flower shop

★ CONFERENCE ROOMS: none

★ BANQUETING ROOMS: 3 (10 to 200)

★ STANDARD BEDROOM SIZE: 24 m²

★ PRIVATE BALCONIES: yes

★ SWIMMING POOL: yes – fresh water, 18 × 30 ft, 4ft deep

★ RECREATIONAL ACTIVITIES: sauna and massage department
★ GARDENS: no, but small roof garden
★ ROOM SERVICE: around the clock
★ ORIENTATION: hotel faces south, west and north with views over Hyde Park
★ CREDIT CARDS: Master Charge, Eurocard, Access and Visa
★ OWNING COMPANY: The Berkeley Hotel Co Ltd
★ GENERAL MANAGER: Mr. Stefano Sebastiani
★ DISTANCE TO SHOPS: walking distance
★ DISTANCE FROM AIRPORT: 30 km

Old Father Time is fast catching up with those, like me, who remember the heyday of the old Berkeley, that gentle bastion of Englishness – Noel Coward, debutantes, country parsons and maiden aunts. Yet when one visits the new Berkeley these days it is strange to see so many characteristics of the progenitor – the almost countryfied decor, the real fireplace, the doorknobs and even the entire Lutyens Room, transported, bit by bit, one would imagine around Hyde Park Corner. Strange too how the present Berkeley, quite apart from being up to date (which the old one certainly was not) has already acquired a face of its own – housing those few people left in Britain one could call gentlemen. I love the mirrors at the Berkeley, each seemingly made for its spot, and the gorgeous carpets and the lightness of the decor. The rooms are very English – much as a gentleman would wish, yet tremendously practical and comfortable. As for the public rooms, there is a lot of marble and crystal around but in no way are they vulgar – vulgarity being the very antithesis of this kind of hotel. Service is like that too – not at all obsequious, just friendly and competent as in a good English club. The food, in Le Perroquet which is almost always full, is an indication that the best Berkeley culinary traditions have been passed on. Country parsons can't afford it now, debs are fewer, but somehow one feels Noel Coward would love it.

CLARIDGE'S HOTEL, Brook Street, London, W1A 2JQ

★ TELEPHONE: 01-629 8860
★ CABLES: Claridges London
★ TELEX: 21872
★ IN OPERATION: since 1855
★ RESERVATIONS: Hotel Representative Inc
★ ROOMS: 205
★ SUITES: 57
★ RESTAURANTS: 2
★ BARS: none – drinks in foyer
★ DISCOTHEQUE: no
★ SHOPS: 4 – theatre agency, travel agency, ladies' and gentlemen's hairdressing and florist shop
★ CONFERENCE ROOMS: none
★ BANQUETING ROOMS: 4 (50 to 250)
★ STANDARD BEDROOM SIZE: 24 m²
★ PRIVATE BALCONIES: no
★ SWIMMING POOL: no
★ GARDENS: no
★ NO. OF STAFF: 450
★ ROOM SERVICE: around the clock
★ ORIENTATION: north and west
★ CREDIT CARDS: Eurocard, Master Charge and Visa
★ OWNING COMPANY: Claridge's Hotel Ltd
★ GENERAL MANAGER: B. Lund Hansen
★ DISTANCE TO SHOPS: walking distance
★ DISTANCE FROM AIRPORT: 30 km

As everyone knows, the wellbred Englishman knows instinctively how to deal with social equals and inferiors and since, in his opinion, he has no superiors, that part of it does not bother him. The same can be said of Claridge's. Never was there a hotel which tried less hard to compete and simply did not bother about publicity. I am not even sure there is such a thing as a reservation service here – Claridge's people just know you are coming. There is no bar – that's vulgar. There is no dial on the room telephone. Just lift, speak and unto you shall be given. Waiters aren't waiters here – they are footmen and share the same elegant detachment with their clientele. To be happy at Claridge's, you must *belong*, and if you do, Claridge's is heaven. Even the four-man orchestra will strike up your favourite tune when you walk into the lounge except, of course, that here it is called the sitting room ('lounge' is non-U). No one ever forgets anything and even if your particular eccentricity is eating fish and chips out of a newspaper (one English marquess I know does it all the time), Claridge's will provide an old copy of the *Daily Mirror*, salt, pepper, and vinegar. A superb hotel, surprisingly modern in its equipment, it is so adept at dealing with any, but any situation, that even the Soviet Prime Minister departed happy in the knowledge that he had seen something of the best of England.

THE CONNAUGHT HOTEL, Carlos Place, Mayfair, London, W1Y 6AL

★ TELEPHONE: 01-499 7070
★ CABLES: Chataigne
★ TELEX: no
★ IN OPERATION: since 1896
★ RESERVATIONS: Hotel Representative Inc
★ ROOMS: 76
★ SUITES: 24
★ RESTAURANTS: 2
★ BARS: 1
★ DISCOTHEQUE: no
★ SHOPS: none
★ CONFERENCE ROOMS: none
★ PRIVATE DINING ROOMS: 2 (10 and 20)
★ STANDARD BEDROOM SIZE: 25 m^2
★ PRIVATE BALCONIES: no

★ SWIMMING POOL: no
★ GARDENS: no
★ NO. OF STAFF: 300
★ ROOM SERVICE: 07.30–23.30
★ ORIENTATION: all rooms face Mayfair location
★ CREDIT CARDS: Eurocard, Master Charge and Access
★ OWNING COMPANY: Connaught Hotel Ltd
★ MANAGING DIRECTOR AND GENERAL MANAGER: Paolo Zago
★ DISTANCE TO SHOPS: walking distance
★ DISTANCE FROM AIRPORT: 30 km

The Connaught is not a hotel. It is home – the kind of house which the management assume you normally live in. It is the most distinctive, the most original, the most select of London's great hotels. Although it does march with the times, it makes quite sure that it is not noticed and just goes serenely on with a kind of half-familiar, half-deferential attitude that is unique. This is its speciality and nobody does it better. It is the kind of hotel where you can be quite sure that if a certain piece of furniture was in this spot last time you came, it will still be there. It shines with refined good living, politeness, old fashioned charm and quite superb service and management. Some people don't like it. Like the young American executive who, at the next table to mine, recently ordered a hamburger. The head waiter looked at him without the slightest hint of patronage and replied: 'I am so very sorry, sir, that is off today.' Rooms are completely dateless and superbly comfortable and the service so highly personalised that once you have been a guest, your tiniest quirk of behaviour or habit is known to all. The Connaught is a club for people who are no longer easily impressed. As for the food (hamburgers apart) it is probably the finest hotel food in London.

THE DORCHESTER HOTEL, Park Lane, London, W1A 2HJ

★ TELEPHONE: 01-629 8888
★ CABLES: Dorchotel
★ TELEX: 887704
★ IN OPERATION: since April, 1931
★ RESERVATIONS: Steigenberger Reservations Service/John Tetley/Robert F. Warner/Preferred Hotels Association
★ ROOMS: 351
★ SUITES: 66
★ RESTAURANTS: 2
★ BARS: 2 – including lobby/lounge
★ DISCOTHEQUE: Piano Bar
★ SHOPS: none – but hairdressers and barbers, with a bookstall and showcases
★ CONFERENCE ROOMS: 2 (90 to 500)
★ BANQUETING ROOMS: 4 (32 to 500)

★ STANDARD BEDROOM SIZE: 30 m^2
★ PRIVATE BALCONIES: yes
★ SWIMMING POOL: no
★ GARDENS: no
★ NO. OF STAFF: 600
★ ROOM SERVICE: around the clock
★ ORIENTATION: south and west overlooking Hyde Park
★ CREDIT CARDS: American Express, Diners Club, Access, Barclaycard, Eurocard and Master Charge
★ OWNING COMPANY: Pageguide Ltd
★ MANAGING DIRECTOR: Udo Schlentrich
★ DISTANCE TO SHOPS: walking distance
★ DISTANCE FROM AIRPORT: 30 km

The selection, once again, of this hotel caused me many heart-searchings, not only because places in one's own parish are the hardest to judge but because I have a built-in feeling against my favourite hotels changing hands or just changing. In this case, having studied the Dorchester closely over the past few months, I am now happy that it deserves a place in this book. Of course it has changed – perhaps, after all, it needed an infusion of new blood (and new money). What is now visible and tangible is perfectly satisfactory – still a great hotel in a marvellous location and, though not all the changes are as happy as the creation of the new Park Lane-side restaurant, a world-travelling stranger should be so lucky. Rooms are good and in many cases decor has been updated. Service is fine except perhaps room service which appears a trifle slow. The food is better than it used to be and has already gained quite a few accolades from the country's top gastronomes. No, don't cross the Dorchester off your address book.

HYATT CARLTON TOWER, 2 Cadogan Place, London, SW1

- ★ TELEPHONE: 01-235 5411
- ★ CABLES: none
- ★ TELEX: 21944 CTOWER G
- ★ IN OPERATION: 21 years
- ★ RESERVATIONS: Hyatt Worldwide Reservations
- ★ ROOMS: 236 (including 17 studies)
- ★ SUITES: 31
- ★ RESTAURANTS: 2 – The Chelsea Room, The Rib Room
- ★ BARS: 2 – The Rib Room Bar, The Chelsea Lounge
- ★ DISCOTHEQUE: no – but piano bar during cocktail hours in both bars
- ★ SHOPS: 4 – newsagent, jeweller, florist, barber
- ★ CONFERENCE ROOMS: 3 (352 m² to 3174 m²)
- ★ BANQUETING ROOMS: 3 (18 to 240)
- ★ STANDARD BEDROOM SIZE: 17 m²
- ★ PRIVATE BALCONIES: most rooms
- ★ SWIMMING POOL: no
- ★ RECREATIONAL ACTIVITIES: health club (sauna and gym), tennis courts, jogging
- ★ GARDENS: yes
- ★ NO. OF STAFF: 390
- ★ ROOM SERVICE: around the clock
- ★ ORIENTATION: south, south-west, west
- ★ CREDIT CARDS: all major credit cards
- ★ OWNING COMPANY: Proteus Ltd Management: Hyatt International Corporation
- ★ GENERAL MANAGER: Bernd Chorengel
- ★ DISTANCE TO SHOPS: walking distance
- ★ DISTANCE FROM AIRPORT: 30 km

Statistics show that more foreign travellers come through London than any other capital city so perhaps I might be forgiven for adding an extra hotel to my listing. In my opinion the Carlton Tower is making it into the big league and now that it has been taken over by a substantial worldwide chain from people who had little interest in the hotel business, I predict a new lease of life.

Its situation, with windows overlooking the green of Cadogan Gardens, could not be better. From here, one can actually walk to Harrods – that Aladdin's Cave of the good life – or to the King's Road – great too but not so good. Carlton Tower rooms are easy on the eye, functional and many have been brought up to date decor-wise. The staff are fine and helpful, the tower suites are highly recommendable. As for the food, don't go near the famed Rib Room unless you want to end up looking like Henry the Eighth! Slimmer, more choosy people should make for the first floor Chelsea Room where the continental menu is fine continental, beautifully balanced and perfect in execution. Welcome to the Carlton Tower.

THE RITZ HOTEL, Piccadilly, London, W1V 9DG

- ★ TELEPHONE: 01-493 8181
- ★ CABLES: Ritzel London
- ★ TELEX: 267200
- ★ IN OPERATION: since 1906
- ★ RESERVATIONS: Cunard, New York/Utell Reservations, worldwide/Loews Reservations International, U.S.A./Swire Travel, Hong Kong/H.R.C., Italy

- ★ ROOMS: 75 doubles 49 singles
- ★ SUITES: 9 with one bedroom and 6 with two bedrooms
- ★ RESTAURANTS: 1 – the Ritz Restaurant, Louis Seize style
- ★ BARS: 2 – The Bar at the Ritz and the Palm Court Lounge
- ★ DISCOTHEQUE: no – but resident trio in restaurant and dancing on Saturday nights
- ★ SHOPS: 6 – menswear, jewellery, leather goods, newsagent, florist and a photographic gallery
- ★ CONFERENCE ROOMS: 2 (26 to 40)
- ★ BANQUETING ROOMS: 2 (26 to 40)
- ★ STANDARD BEDROOM SIZE: 35 m^2
- ★ PRIVATE BALCONIES: yes – some but small
- ★ SWIMMING POOL: no
- ★ GARDENS: yes – the Italian garden, small and private

- ★ NO. OF STAFF: 257
- ★ ROOM SERVICE: around the clock
- ★ ORIENTATION: north facade faces Piccadilly, west facade faces Green Park, south facade faces Westminster Abbey and St Margaret's Church and east facade faces Arlington Street
- ★ FURTHER DEVELOPMENTS: refurbishment of all single rooms designed for the business traveller
- ★ CREDIT CARDS: all major credit cards
- ★ OWNING COMPANY: Trafalgar House Investments
- ★ GENERAL MANAGER: Michael Duffell
- ★ DISTANCE TO SHOPS: walking distance to Bond Street, Jermyn Street, Regent Street and Knightsbridge
- ★ DISTANCE FROM AIRPORT: 30 km (Heathrow)

The top hotel in London according to Britain's most hard-to-please guide and who am I to disagree? I have always loved this hotel, Cesar Ritz's last brainchild, though I must admit that at times in the past my affections took a good deal of buffeting. The Ritz had hard times. Not any more. Its fin de siècle grandeur, its gilt angels and nymphs climbing up the walls, clusters of chandeliers and vast vistas of palatial lobbies plus that incomparable restaurant overlooking the park – they are all still with us. But now the plumbing works, some of the oldest old pensioners have been nicely retired, the management is new and efficient and those great corridors which had not been repainted since Lily Langtry came around the corner are back in their original splendour. It was really like cleaning up an old painting and it has worked – to the point where the most difficult people appear happy and contented. One thing has not changed: the illustrious Ritz wine list, one of the greatest in the world. At the moment the Ritz is going through a culinary revolution (find out for yourself . . .) and I think it is too early to comment on it.

THE SAVOY HOTEL, P.O. Box 189, London, WC2R 0BP

- ★ TELEPHONE: 01-836 4343
- ★ CABLES: Savotel London
- ★ TELEX: 24234
- ★ IN OPERATION: since 1889
- ★ RESERVATIONS: Hotel Representatives Inc
- ★ ROOMS: 200
- ★ SUITES: 46
- ★ RESTAURANTS: 2 – River Restaurant, Savoy Grill
- ★ BARS: 2 – the famous American Bar, new Thames Foyer
- ★ DISCOTHEQUE: no – but music and dancing nightly from Monday to Saturday in River Restaurant
- ★ SHOPS: shopping arcade, florist, news kiosk, ladies' and gentlemen's hairdressing
- ★ CONFERENCE ROOMS: 8 specialising in private parties

- ★ BANQUETING ROOMS: 4 (up to 500)
- ★ STANDARD BEDROOM SIZE: 28 m^2
- ★ PRIVATE BALCONIES: no
- ★ SWIMMING POOL: no
- ★ GARDENS: adjacent Embankment Gardens
- ★ NO. OF STAFF: 550
- ★ ROOM SERVICE: around the clock
- ★ ORIENTATION: rooms face the river, street and courtyard
- ★ CREDIT CARDS: Eurocard, Master Charge, American Express and Visa
- ★ OWNING COMPANY: The Savoy Hotels Ltd plc
- ★ GENERAL MANAGER: Willy B. G. Bauer
- ★ DISTANCE TO SHOPS: adjacent, Covent Garden nearby
- ★ DISTANCE FROM AIRPORT: 29 km

With so many rumours flying about, plus a headline-making financial dogfight, the Savoy has had a bad press in recent years and, in such things as decor, it still has some way to go to recover all its former glory. But things are happening and, staying there recently, I had to admit that it is still one of the great hotels of the world – a place of suave urbanity and continuing tradition as the nursery of great hotel folk. Service simply cannot be faulted: hot coffee and sandwiches at two a.m., a man who is quite willing to park your car (in London?) and a front desk staff for whom nothing is too much trouble. The food, slightly 'off' for a while, is back on top and I thought that, especially in the famous Grill, it could hardly be bettered. In the last edition I wrote: 'Unlike so many London hotels the Savoy is not a club – it's a real hotel, working, buzzing with life, intensely practical and very highborn'. I stick to my guns and as long as financial finagling does not interfere with management, the Savoy is still on.

Moretonhampstead

MANOR HOUSE HOTEL, Moretonhampstead, Devon, TQ13 8RE

★ TELEPHONE: (0647-4) 355
★ CABLES: no
★ TELEX: 42794
★ IN OPERATION: since 1927
★ RESERVATIONS: direct
★ ROOMS: 4 doubles 42 twins 19 singles
★ SUITES: 1
★ RESTAURANTS: 1
★ BARS: 1
★ DISCOTHEQUE: no
★ CONFERENCE ROOMS: 5 (20 to 80)
★ BANQUETING ROOMS: 5 (14 to 250)
★ STANDARD BEDROOM SIZE: 24 m²
★ PRIVATE BALCONIES: 1 only
★ SWIMMING POOL: no
★ GARDENS: yes – 270 acres of gardens, lakes, streams and golf course
★ NO. OF STAFF: 65

★ RECREATIONAL ACTIVITIES: 18-hole golf course, 2 hard tennis courts, 1 squash court, billiard room, fishing, table tennis and horse riding available locally by arrangement
★ ROOM SERVICE: around the clock
★ ORIENTATION: overlooking Dartmoor
★ FURTHER DEVELOPMENTS: proposed swimming pool
★ CREDIT CARDS: Access, Barclaycard, Diners Club, American Express, Carte Blanche and Eurocard
★ OWNING COMPANY: British Transport Hotels Ltd
★ GENERAL MANAGER: Mr. W. Wainright
★ DISTANCE TO BEACH: 45 km
★ DISTANCE TO SHOPS: 25 km
★ DISTANCE FROM AIRPORT: 30 km

High up on Dartmoor, in the middle of 270 acres of some of the most wildly beautiful country in England, the Manor House is one of the country's most stately hotels – striking, beautifully proportioned, extremely well run and cared for and, although it belongs to an institution, it is highly personal and special. The fireplace in the famed Cathedral Lounge is worth the visit in itself and everywhere are fine panelled walls, lovely antiques and beautiful carpets. Rooms vary in quality, but the best are very fine indeed – spacious, shiningly clean and very well equipped. There is a kind of well lived-in feel here – more to be expected in a happy private country house. The parkland is stunningly beautiful, with trout streams, golf course, lovely walks everywhere and views that cannot be better elsewhere because this is Dartmoor and unique. I tried the food again recently and found it much improved and the wine-list long and excellent.

New Milton

CHEWTON GLEN HOTEL, New Milton, Hampshire, BH25 6QS

★ TELEPHONE: Highcliffe (04252) 5341
★ CABLES: no
★ TELEX: 41456
★ IN OPERATION: 14 years
★ RESERVATIONS: Hotel Representative Inc/Scott Calder/Prestige

★ ROOMS: 40 doubles 2 singles
★ SUITES: 7
★ RESTAURANTS: 1
★ BARS: 1
★ DISCOTHEQUE: no
★ SHOPS: 1

★ CONFERENCE ROOMS: 1 (8 to 45)

★ BANQUETING ROOMS: 2 (8 to 90)

★ STANDARD BEDROOM SIZE: 23 m²

★ PRIVATE BALCONIES: 10 on 1st floor and a terrace on the ground floor (7 rooms)

★ SWIMMING POOL: yes – fresh water, outdoor, heated, 40 × 20 ft

★ RECREATIONAL ACTIVITIES: tennis with golf and horse riding nearby

★ GARDENS: yes – 30 acres of parkland

★ NO. OF STAFF: 90

★ ROOM SERVICE: around the clock

★ ORIENTATION: main facade faces south

★ CREDIT CARDS: Diners Club, American Express, Barclaycard, Access and Eurocard

★ OWNING COMPANY: Skan Developments

★ GENERAL MANAGER: David M. Brockett

★ DISTANCE TO BEACH: 2 km

★ DISTANCE TO SHOPS: 2 km

★ DISTANCE FROM AIRPORT: 12 km (Hurn), 170 km (Heathrow)

Drinking alone is not good for the soul. Obviously the Singaporean architect I met in a hotel bar in Dubai thought the same. We chatted. Then he staggered me. 'Do you not think' he said, 'that Chewton Glen is the finest country hotel in England?' The world is obviously getting smaller. We drank a toast to Martin Skan, creator of so much excellence. Just so that some of my friends do not send me a drop of Socrates' last drink, I would add that there are other lovely country hotels in the English countryside. But Chewton Glen is a place apart. For one thing, it looks right – a great period mansion that once belonged to a rich and famous writer, surrounded by acres of parkland, restful terraces (and a swimming pool). Inside, Chewton Glen is both grand and intimate, a rare combination, with well-chosen furniture, lots of flowers everywhere and a welcoming warmth that almost glows. Bedrooms are softly silent and I feel they ought to export their bathroom designs to, say, Zaire or Indonesia. The food is imaginative, superbly produced and served with love and as for the wine list – it is one of those I like for bedside reading. All around is England's lovely New Forest where deer and wild ponies still roam at will. Chewton Glen is an image of England people dream about.

St. Mawes

HOTEL TRESANTON, St. Mawes, Cornwall

★ TELEPHONE: 0326-270544

★ CABLES: no

★ TELEX: no

★ IN OPERATION: since 1944

★ RESERVATIONS: direct

★ ROOMS: 16 doubles 5 singles

★ SUITES: none

★ RESTAURANTS: 1

★ BARS: 2

★ DISCOTHEQUE: no – but pianist in cocktail bar

★ SHOPS: none

★ CONFERENCE ROOMS: none

★ BANQUETING ROOMS: none

★ STANDARD BEDROOM SIZE: 20 m²

★ PRIVATE BALCONIES: yes

★ SWIMMING POOL: no

★ GARDENS: yes

★ NO. OF STAFF: 25

★ ROOM SERVICE: during meal times only

★ ORIENTATION: rooms face south overlooking the sea

★ FURTHER DEVELOPMENTS: plans for a new cocktail bar and suite of rooms

★ CREDIT CARDS: Visa

★ OWNING COMPANY: Col., and Mrs. J. P. Farquharson Oliver (private)

★ GENERAL MANAGER: Miss Margaret McAndrew

★ DISTANCE TO BEACH: adjacent (partly owned by the hotel)

★ DISTANCE TO SHOPS: 300 yd

★ DISTANCE FROM AIRPORT: 50 km (Newquay)

Judging by its popularity with people who count, I am not alone in believing that this is one of the best and most comfortable hotels in England's West Country. Tresanton is a little world of its own – three houses on different levels, gardens filled with interesting flowers and shrubs, patios and terraces, all of them looking over the charming village of St. Mawes (one of the prettiest in Cornwall) and the rugged, beautiful Cornish coastline all around. It is very like a private residence. Indeed, one French traveller wrote from Tresanton saying: 'I still don't know whether I am staying in a hotel or as someone's guest!' That is real praise. It's the kind of place where guests who go fishing bring their catch back to the chef and discuss the dish with him. Rooms are smallish but very pretty in a cottagey kind of way, good beds and well-chosen furniture. There is a good bar and the public rooms are delightfully individual, furnished with some very fine antiques and so comfortable that it is an effort to get out. Food is relatively simple but fresh and very good indeed and service is quiet and efficient. Tresanton is the unchanging face of gracious living.

Taunton

THE CASTLE HOTEL, Castle Green, Taunton, Somerset, TA1 1NF

- ★ TELEPHONE: Taunton (0823) 72671
- ★ CABLES: Castle Hotel
- ★ TELEX: 46488 Castle G
- ★ IN OPERATION: about 300 years
- ★ RESERVATIONS: direct or Prestige Hotel (Tom Eden Associates)/Scott Calder International, U.S.A., Amsterdam, Frankfurt, Brussels, Paris
- ★ ROOMS: 25 doubles 18 singles
- ★ SUITES: 1 – the Bow Suite
- ★ RESTAURANTS: 1
- ★ BARS: 2
- ★ DISCOTHEQUE: no
- ★ SHOPS: none
- ★ CONFERENCE ROOMS: 2 (up to 100)
- ★ BANQUETING ROOMS: 3 (up to 125)
- ★ STANDARD BEDROOM SIZE: variable
- ★ PRIVATE BALCONIES: no
- ★ SWIMMING POOL: no
- ★ RECREATIONAL ACTIVITIES: no – but tennis,

- golf, horse riding etc, easily arranged
- ★ GARDENS: yes – the Norman Garden – featuring remains of ancient Norman keep, moat wall and a unique square Norman well
- ★ NO. OF STAFF: 75
- ★ ROOM SERVICE: around the clock
- ★ ORIENTATION: west over Castle Green, with some rooms overlooking the Norman Garden
- ★ CREDIT CARDS: Diners Club, American Express, Access, Barclaycard, Eurocard and Master Charge
- ★ OWNING COMPANY: The Castle Hotel (Taunton) Ltd (private)
- ★ EXECUTIVE MANAGEMENT: the Chapman family and Mr. David Prior
- ★ DISTANCE TO SHOPS: 2 minutes' walk
- ★ DISTANCE FROM AIRPORT: 217 km (Heathrow), 64 km (Bristol Lulsgate)

Just say 'the Castle' in this part of England's West Country and everybody knows you mean the Castle Hotel in Taunton. Not only is it the best hotel for many miles around but it has somehow managed to be the hub of a special social life – musical evenings, a place for great dinners, first and second time honeymooners and many decorous happenings. Some of the structure is so old that the history books hardly recall its beginnings.

It was not always like that of course, but in the past few years a whole family of hotel geniuses have made the Castle into their own lifestyle and they work hard at it though it hardly shows. Much of the place has been entirely remodelled and refurbished to the point where the rooms are among the finest I know in the English countryside: warm and intimate, yet fairly grand. The food is more-ish – very English and beautifully served: delicious Quantock lamb (the French rave about it . . .) and the hotel's own speciality, Whortleberry Pie; if you have not tasted that, you have not lived.

In the end, it is the atmosphere of the place that counts – urbane, helpful people creating a feeling of well being which is very rare in these hurried days.

Turnberry

TURNBERRY HOTEL, Turnberry, Ayrshire, Scotland, KA26 9LT

- ★ TELEPHONE: 06553 202
- ★ CABLES: Turnberry, Scotland
- ★ TELEX: 777779
- ★ IN OPERATION: 73 years

- ★ RESERVATIONS: British Transport Hotels Ltd, Great Britain/British Transport Hotels Inc, U.S.A.
- ★ ROOMS: 85 doubles 40 singles

★ SUITES: 6
★ RESTAURANTS: 2
★ BARS: 2
★ DISCOTHEQUE: no – music for dancing 2/3 times per week during season
★ SHOPS: 1 – Highland House of Lawrie and 6 showcases
★ CONFERENCE ROOMS: 4 (150, 125, 35 and 20)
★ BANQUETING ROOMS: 4 (300, 150, 30 and 15)
★ STANDARD BEDROOM SIZE: 20–30 m^2
★ PRIVATE BALCONIES: a few
★ SWIMMING POOL: yes – fresh water
★ RECREATIONAL ACTIVITIES: 2 championship 18-hole golf course, tennis, pitch & putt and putting
★ GARDENS: yes – 500 acres

★ NO. OF STAFF: 200
★ ROOM SERVICE: around the clock
★ ORIENTATION: mainly west, but also south and east facing the sea
★ NEW DEVELOPMENTS: an air conditioned conference suite with simultaneous translation facilities and other modern aids
★ CREDIT CARDS: American Express, Diners Club, Barclaycard/Visa, Access, Master Charge
★ OWNING COMPANY: British Transport Hotels Limited
★ GENERAL MANAGER: C. J. Rouse
★ DISTANCE TO BEACH: 1/5 km
★ DISTANCE TO SHOPS: 20 km
★ DISTANCE FROM AIRPORT: 70 km

Burns never played golf – his duties as a cowman did not allow the time, and when fame came he left Ayrshire for Edinburgh. But he might have played golf and if he did it would have been at Turnberry. But should anyone think that this is a tourist trap or a private club, let them go see for themselves. Even if you do not care overmuch for the two star attractions, I believe that Turnberry is a great place to be. It has 366 acres of exhilarating countryside, tennis courts, an indoor pool, some quite stunning silvery beaches and, of course, 'Ailsa' and 'Arran', two of the world's most famous courses. A vast, airy place, well furnished and well appointed, the suites are lovely and one even has a piano – just in case you wish to limber up musically before limbering up in other ways. Public rooms are fairly grand, especially the dining room which serves good, fresh and attractive food. Most of the onetime British Transport-institutional touches have gone for good and this hotel now stands in its own right as a very respectable point of arrival in Scotland.

Upper Slaughter

LORDS OF THE MANOR HOTEL, Upper Slaughter, Bourton-on-the-Water, Nr Cheltenham, Gloucestershire

★ TELEPHONE: (0451) 20243
★ CABLES: no
★ TELEX: Via 83147
★ IN OPERATION: 10 years
★ RESERVATIONS: direct
★ ROOMS: 14 doubles 1 single
★ SUITES: none
★ RESTAURANTS: 1
★ BARS: 1
★ DISCOTHEQUE: no
★ SHOPS: none
★ CONFERENCE ROOMS: none
★ BANQUETING ROOMS: none
★ STANDARD BEDROOM SIZE: all different sizes
★ PRIVATE BALCONIES: no

★ SWIMMING POOL: no
★ RECREATIONAL ACTIVITIES: croquet and fishing
★ GARDENS: yes – with stream and lake
★ NO. OF STAFF: 25
★ ROOM SERVICE: 08.00–23.00
★ ORIENTATION: east
★ CREDIT CARDS: Visa, Access, Diners Club and American Express
★ OWNING COMPANY: Lords of the Manor Hotels Ltd
★ GENERAL MANAGER: Anthony de Trafford
★ DISTANCE TO SHOPS: 15 miles
★ DISTANCE FROM AIRPORT: 110 km (Heathrow)

There has not been a new building erected in Upper Slaughter since the turn of the century. Lovers of English villages know that this is one of the finest and most divinely beautiful. Until ten years ago one went through, stopped a while and passed on. Now you can stay there in this charming and very well reconditioned Cotswold house which is a delight to see since in many ways the combination of the seventeenth century and the Cotswolds produced a type of domestic architecture hardly ever equalled. It is a comfortable, personalised hotel, gentle and mellow and extremely pleasing. There are lovely grounds – England at its best – with a lake and a stream and one could sit there forever. Some Americans I know do just that – they settle in; relax and inspect places like Burford, Broadway, Bourton-on-the-Water, Bilbury and Moreton-in-the-Marsh. Rooms are all different, very nicely furnished and the bathrooms work. Staff and management (it's a family-owned hotel) really make you welcome. The food does not try to be ambitious. It's simply good.

Worcester

THE ELMS HOTEL, Abberley, Nr Worcester, WR6 6AT

★ TELEPHONE: (029 921) 666
★ CABLES: no
★ TELEX: 337105
★ IN OPERATION: since 1946
★ RESERVATIONS: Prestige Hotels, Great Britain/Wandana Travel, Australia/Carte Blanche Tours Ltd, South Africa/Scott Calder International, U.S.A.
★ ROOMS: 17 doubles 3 singles
★ SUITES: none
★ RESTAURANTS: 1 – Regency style, seating 80
★ BARS: 1 – the Library Bar
★ DISCOTHEQUE: no
★ SHOPS: none – 3 show cases
★ CONFERENCE ROOMS: 2 (10 and 40)
★ BANQUETING ROOMS: 2 (10 and 40)
★ STANDARD BEDROOM SIZE: 24–30 m²
★ PRIVATE BALCONIES: no
★ SWIMMING POOL: no

★ RECREATIONAL FACILITIES: tennis, croquet and putting in the grounds. Horse riding, golf and fishing nearby
★ GARDENS: 10 acres of parkland and 10 acres of formal gardens
★ NO. OF STAFF: 45
★ ROOM SERVICE: 07.00–02.00
★ ORIENTATION: the rear of the hotel and the majority of the gardens face south
★ CREDIT CARDS: Barclaycard/Visa, American Express, Diners, Access, Eurocard, Master Charge and Carte Blanche
★ OWNING COMPANY: The Elms Hotel Abberley Ltd
★ GENERAL MANAGER: Donald Crosthwaite (Proprietor)
★ DISTANCE TO SHOPS: 10 miles (Worcester)
★ DISTANCE FROM AIRPORT: 45 km Birmingham (Elmdon)

Beset as they are by urbanisation, instant food and service problems, inhabitants of this sceptred isle often wonder why so many foreign visitors keep coming back. One of the reasons could be our rich heritage of gorgeous country-house hotels. The Elms is one of them, gracious, serene, well brought up and with an air of timelessness. It is near enough to the Cotswolds, the Shakespeare country, Worcester Cathedral and, if you like that sort of thing, the tomb of King John, to offer plenty to see.

Queen Anne did not build the place but the stamp of her times is upon it – handsome facades and noble proportions looking over manicured English lawns. Bedrooms are country-house size, lovingly furnished with period pieces. Public rooms are both stately and comfortable. Above all, this is a hotel with personality – that of the owner who manages it – and the staff really make you welcome. The food is English and very good – there are new dishes every day. The wine selection is better than most.

GREECE
Athens

THE ATHENS HILTON, 46 Vassilissis Sofias Avenue, Athens

★ TELEPHONE: 722-0201 or 722-0301
★ CABLES: Hiltels-Athens

★ TELEX: 21-5808
★ IN OPERATION: since April, 1963

★ RESERVATIONS: Hilton International
★ ROOMS: 28 double 188 twin 240 studio
★ SUITES: 19
★ RESTAURANTS: 5 – Byzantine Cafe, Trattoria, Taverna Ta Nissia, Supper Club and Pool Snack Bar
★ BARS: 2
★ DISCOTHEQUE: no – but live music
★ SHOPS: 14
★ CONFERENCE ROOMS: 5 (5 to 2,000)
★ BANQUETING ROOMS: 5 (5 to 2,000)
★ STANDARD BEDROOM SIZE: 32–35 m^2
★ PRIVATE BALCONIES: yes – all rooms with seating facilities
★ SWIMMING POOL: yes – fresh water, 1 for adults, 12 × 25 m, and 1 for children
★ RECREATIONAL ACTIVITIES: sauna and golf, tennis and other activities by arrangement nearby
★ GARDENS: no
★ NO. OF STAFF: 680
★ ROOM SERVICE: around the clock
★ ORIENTATION: rooms overlook the Acropolis to the west and Mounts Hymettus and Pentelicon to the east
★ CREDIT CARDS: American Express, Carte Blanche and Master Charge
★ OWNING COMPANY: Ioniki Hotel Enterprises Ltd
★ GENERAL MANAGER: Mr. Roman Otto Rickenbacher
★ DISTANCE TO BEACH: 12 km
★ DISTANCE TO SHOPS: walking distance
★ DISTANCE FROM AIRPORT: 10 km

If only all Hiltons were like this one! At least it shows they can do it when they try and here they have succeeded beyond one's wildest expectation. This is, for the moment, the finest city hotel in Greece – extremely well designed on an original plan, imposing without knocking your eye out, with a decor that leaves all other Hiltons in the shade. Everything goes apace. One of my first calls in the Greek capital is always dinner at the Hilton's Taverna Ta Nissia which I think is one of the two or three best hotel restaurants in the Mediterranean. What's more, it is strongly Greek as well as American. Views from the rooms are sensational – Hymettus on one side and the Acropolis on the other.

The hotel has a range of extremely good shops, the staff are friendly and not at all blasé with so many visitors and the service is very well organised. I find the rooms exceptionally pleasing – large, nicely air-conditioned, furnished with easy-going taste. I have never found fault with this very remarkable hotel.

Corfu

ASTIR PALACE CORFU, Kommeno Bay, Corfu

★ TELEPHONE: 91481-490/340
★ CABLES: Koxu GR
★ TELEX: 332169 Koxu GR
★ IN OPERATION: since 1977
★ RESERVATIONS: Astir Hotel Co Inc, Athens, London, Brussels, Rome/Robert F. Warner Inc, New York/Traveline Inc, Toronto/Cruise and Coach Corp Pty, Sydney
★ ROOMS: 274 doubles 26 singles
★ SUITES: 8
★ BUNGALOWS: 124
★ RESTAURANTS: 3
★ BARS: 3
★ DISCOTHEQUE: yes
★ SHOPS: news stand, Beauty parlour
★ CONFERENCE ROOMS: 2 (80 to 350)
★ BANQUETING ROOMS: 2 (60 to 600)
★ STANDARD BEDROOM SIZE: 25 m²

★ PRIVATE BALCONIES: yes
★ SWIMMING POOL: yes – sea water
★ RECREATIONAL ACTIVITIES: water skiing, surfing, sailing, tennis, golf course 16 km from hotel
★ GARDENS: yes
★ NO. OF STAFF: 320
★ ROOM SERVICE: 07.00–23.00
★ ORIENTATION: all rooms and bungalows with sea view
★ CREDIT CARDS: all major credit cards
★ OWNING COMPANY: Astir Hotel Co Inc
★ GENERAL MANAGER: Haralambos Capelles
★ DISTANCE TO BEACH: walking distance to three sandy beaches
★ DISTANCE TO SHOPS: 10 kms Corfu town
★ DISTANCE FROM AIRPORT: 12 km

In an island already over-populated with hotels of all kinds but mostly indifferent, any newcomer had to be special – and the Astir Palace, with its illustrious parentage, is that. The lobby is large enough to hold a presidential convention which is a waste of space on a small island. But Greek niceness overtakes all and I never complained at what I saw. Many of the rooms are in individual cottages with private verandahs decorated in the efficient space style so necessary in a resort. In the main building the rooms are more sober but cool and very pleasant. The hotel stands on a lovely olive-clad hillside, has gardens and a very handsome swimming pool. Over and above this, the genuine Greek charm and hospitality take over – people smile, joke and manage to combine decorum with friendly informality. This would be my choice in Corfu.

Crete

ASTIR PALACE ELOUNDA, Elounda, Crete

★ TELEPHONE: 41580-5
★ CABLES: Starhotel GR
★ TELEX: 262215 Asco GR
★ RESERVATIONS: Astir Hotel Co Inc, Athens, London, Brussels, Rome/Robert F. Warner Inc, New York/Traveline Inc, Toronto/Cruise and Coach Corp Pty, Sydney
★ ROOMS: 210 doubles 10 singles
★ BUNGALOWS: 80 doubles

★ RESTAURANTS: 2
★ BARS: 3
★ DISCOTHEQUE: yes
★ SHOPS: boutique and newsagents
★ CONFERENCE ROOMS: 1 (274 to 450)
★ BANQUETING ROOMS: 2 (400 to 600)
★ STANDARD BEDROOM SIZE: 20 m²
★ PRIVATE BALCONIES: majority of sea view rooms

★ SWIMMING POOLS: 2 sea water, one indoors

★ RECREATIONAL ACTIVITIES: waterskiing, surfing, 2 floodlit tennis courts, table tennis, pedaloes, sailing, cinema

★ GARDENS: yes

★ NO. OF STAFF: 250

★ ROOM SERVICE: 07.00–23.00

★ ORIENTATION: most rooms face the sea

★ CREDIT CARDS: all major ones

★ OWNING COMPANY: Astir Hotel Co Inc

★ GENERAL MANAGER: Panos Skendros

★ DISTANCE TO BEACH: walking distance to 2 small private sandy beaches

★ DISTANCE TO SHOPS: 15 minutes' walk to Elounda and 8 km to Aghios Nicolaos

★ DISTANCE FROM AIRPORT: 64 km

Crete has long been famous as an ante-room to heaven. How it was regarded in antiquity – the centre of the known world – reaffirms one's conviction that all change is bad and that the good old days were best.

There are two beaches at Elounda and innumerable little coves spread over about twenty acres. It is modern without being in the least offensive, good looking, convenient and above all fresh and clean.

The rooms, happily, are cool in hot summers, well designed, with nice, practical Greek furniture and hangings. There is a good-sized balcony which is ideal for breakfast à *deux* and service is fast and reliable. Public rooms are impressive and to have dinner in the arched, al fresco restaurant is to really live a little. Highly recommended by many readers of this guide, this hotel is one of the best of the resort category among the Greek islands.

ELOUNDA BEACH HOTEL, Elounda, Aghios Nikolaos, Crete

★ TELEPHONE: 0841-41412/3

★ CABLES: Elotel

★ TELEX: 0262192 EL GR

★ IN OPERATION: 11 years

★ RESERVATIONS: direct

★ ROOMS: 226 doubles 30 singles

★ SUITES: 45

★ RESTAURANTS: 4

★ BARS: 3

★ DISCOTHEQUE: nightclub

★ SHOPS: 5

★ CONFERENCE ROOMS: 5 (40 to 250)

★ BANQUETING ROOMS: 5 (30 to 250)

★ STANDARD BEDROOM SIZE: 15–18 m²

★ PRIVATE BALCONIES: yes

★ SWIMMING POOL: yes – salt water, 36 × 12 m

★ RECREATIONAL ACTIVITIES: 2 floodlit tennis courts, water skiing, sailing, pedaloes, canoes, day trips and fishing trips in the hotel kaiki, ping-pong, billiards, T.V. lounge, card room and sauna

★ GARDENS: yes

★ NO. OF STAFF: 300

★ ROOM SERVICE: 07.00–23.00

★ ORIENTATION: most rooms face the sea

★ CREDIT CARDS: American Express and Diners Club

★ OWNING COMPANY: Ilios S.A.

★ GENERAL MANAGER: Peter T. Palashis

★ DISTANCE TO BEACH: walking distance

★ DISTANCE TO SHOPS: 3 km

★ DISTANCE FROM AIRPORT: 60 km

In a most scenic island – Crete – the Gulf of Mirabello is the most scenic spot, great craggy mountains going down to a sea so blue you cannot credit it. And there, not far from Aghios Nikolaos is the Elounda Beach, a very modern hotel which not long ago won the first prize as Greece's most beautiful new hotel. It is certainly handsome and very well thought out. What I like most are the charming, Cretan-style bungalows spread along the shore – each one very private, very rustic in a charming way and extremely comfortable. There is a good, if rather small beach, a splendid poolside restaurant and a very amusing open-air Greek nightclub. For a holiday hotel, service is above the average and so is the food.

Lemnos

AKTI MYRINA HOTEL, Island of Lemnos

★ TELEPHONE: (0276) 22681/2/3/4
★ CABLES: Aktimyr Lemnos
★ TELEX: 0297173 Myri GR
★ IN OPERATION: since 1964
★ RESERVATIONS: Robert F. Warner, New York/The Best of Greece, Great Britain
★ ROOMS: 125
★ SUITES: 15
★ RESTAURANTS: 4
★ BARS: 3
★ DISCOTHEQUE: yes
★ SHOPS: 1 – boutique
★ CONFERENCE ROOMS: 1 (up to 80)
★ BANQUETING ROOMS: 1 (up to 80)
★ STANDARD BEDROOM SIZE: 20 m²
★ PRIVATE BALCONIES: yes – terraces with small gardens
★ SWIMMING POOL: yes – open air, heated, sea water

★ RECREATIONAL ACTIVITIES: tennis, volleyball, table tennis, mini-golf, waterskiing, sailing, windsurfing, pedaloes, canoes, fishing boats and excursions to other islands by hotel-owned caique
★ GARDENS: yes
★ NO. OF STAFF: 130
★ ROOM SERVICE: 07.00–23.00
★ ORIENTATION: south-west, facing the sea
★ CREDIT CARDS: American Express, Diners Club and Visa
★ OWNING COMPANY: Akti Myrina S.A.
★ GENERAL MANAGER: George Papadam
★ DISTANCE TO BEACH: on the beach
★ DISTANCE TO SHOPS: 2 km
★ DISTANCE FROM AIRPORT: 23 km

This hotel has been listed in the book once before and then fell out of favour with a number of readers who complained about indifferent service. Now so many people have complained at its disappearance that I think it is perhaps time to re-instate it. After all, there are not that many good hotels in the Greek islands and this is not meant to be patronising towards Akti Myrina which is perfectly good by itself. It has a vague Costa Smeralda feel – a gaggle of stone cottages leading to a very pretty sandy beach, lots of terraces and private places where one can sit in the sun. Rooms are cool, very well kept and simply but comfortably furnished and on this truly lovely island of Lemnos one could not hope for better. On the whole, the food is excellent, fresh and interesting and comes largely from the sea which is right and proper. It is not a grand, grand hotel in the traditional manner but a very pleasant place to spend a holiday. On the whole, it deserves to return to our pages.

Nauplion

HOTEL XENIA COMPLEX, Nauplion

★ TELEPHONE: 0752/28981-2-3
★ CABLES: Hotel Xenia, Nauplion
★ TELEX: no
★ IN OPERATION: since 1962
★ RESERVATIONS: Greek Tourist Offices
★ ROOMS: 88 doubles 18 singles
★ SUITES: 3 and 54 bungalows
★ RESTAURANTS: 2
★ BARS: 3
★ DISCOTHEQUE: yes
★ SHOPS: 5
★ CONFERENCE ROOMS: 1 (150)
★ BANQUETING ROOMS: 2 (200 and 250)
★ STANDARD BEDROOM SIZE: 20 m²
★ PRIVATE BALCONIES: yes

★ SWIMMING POOL: yes – fresh water, 180 m²
★ GARDENS: yes
★ NO. OF STAFF: 150
★ ROOM SERVICE: 07.00–23.00
★ ORIENTATION: facing the sea
★ CREDIT CARDS: Diners Club
★ OWNING COMPANY: National Tourist Organisation of Greece
★ GENERAL MANAGER: Nikolaos Smyrniotakis
★ DISTANCE TO BEACH: 300 m
★ DISTANCE TO SHOPS: 200 m
★ DISTANCE FROM AIRPORT: 150 km (Athens)

The Government-run Xenia chain in Greece went into business to provide good, clean, utilitarian hotels where commercial operators feared to tread but I have a feeling that in the new, hilltop part of the Nauplion Xenia, it has also been trying to show off what it could achieve. The result is extremely impressive. Up the road from the old Xenia is this luxury cottages-and-suites complex, right by the ancient fortress and the care taken with the planning on this august site is remarkable. Rooms are modern – in fact the last word – and done up with a very high sense of quality – good timber, fine textiles, functional furniture that is a pleasure to see. Very good design everywhere and a good deal of privacy, with superb terraces overlooking this gorgeous little city, once the first capital of independent Greece. Everything is cool, gently understated and yet very carefully organised. The staff as usual in Greece are friendliness personified and the food, if not great, is very acceptable. The above of course applies only to the Xenia Palace part of the complex.

Rhodes

GRAND HOTEL ASTIR PALACE, Akti Miaouli, Rhodes

- ★ TELEPHONE: 26284 (20 lines)
- ★ CABLES: Grandrhodes
- ★ TELEX: 292121 GHSP GR
- ★ IN OPERATION: since 1962
- ★ RESERVATIONS: Astir Hotel Co Inc, Athens, London, Brussels, Rome/Robert F. Warner Inc, New York/Traveline Inc, Toronto/Cruise and Coach Corp Pty, Sydney
- ★ ROOMS: 320 doubles 56 singles
- ★ SUITES: 12
- ★ RESTAURANTS: 4
- ★ BARS: 3
- ★ DISCOTHEQUE: Night Club Isabella
- ★ SHOPS: shopping arcade, news stand, tailors, gifts and beauty parlour
- ★ CONFERENCE ROOMS: 3 (75 to 450)
- ★ BANQUETING ROOMS: 3 (100 to 500)
- ★ STANDARD BEDROOM SIZE: 20 m^2
- ★ PRIVATE BALCONIES: yes
- ★ GARDENS: yes
- ★ SWIMMING POOLS: 2 outdoor sea water, 1 indoor fresh water
- ★ RECREATIONAL ACTIVITIES: floodlit tennis court, sauna, gym, table tennis, casino
- ★ NO. OF STAFF: 300
- ★ ROOM SERVICE: 07.00–23.00
- ★ ORIENTATION: majority of rooms face the sea
- ★ CREDIT CARDS: all major ones
- ★ OWNING COMPANY: Astir Hotel Co Inc
- ★ GENERAL MANAGER: George Louisidis
- ★ DISTANCE TO BEACH: across the road
- ★ DISTANCE TO SHOPS: 1 km
- ★ DISTANCE FROM AIRPORT: 15 km

Like starlings, tourists only spoil their own perch and its vicnity and the splendidly beautiful island of Rhodes still has much to offer to those who are willing to go off the track. Yet, after trying the obvious holiday haunts it is always a great pleasure to return to the Astir Palace which, in my view, is the most civilised hotel in Rhodes. In the Greek islands the best hotels are usually close to the water. Here is a hotel that maintains a grand hotel style translated into an unlikely location. Rooms are good, fairly simple but perfectly comfortable and kept beautifully clean. There is a nightclub and a casino and two swimming pools, one in and one out, both of which are unusually well looked after. What is more the food here is well above the average standard for hotels in Greece.

Vouliagmeni

ASTIR PALACE HOTEL AND BUNGALOWS, Vouliagmeni Beach

- ★ TELEPHONE: 8960211-8960311/9
- ★ CABLES: Bungotel Vouliagmeni
- ★ TELEX: 215013-215913 GR ASPA
- ★ IN OPERATION: since 1967
- ★ RESERVATIONS: Astir Hotel Co Inc, Athens, London, Brussels, Rome/Robert F. Warner Inc, New York/Traveline Inc, Toronto/Cruise and Coach Co Pty, Sydney
- ★ ROOMS: 255 doubles 11 singles

★ SUITES: 23
★ APARTMENTS: 8
★ BUNGALOWS: 77
★ RESTAURANTS: 3
★ BARS: 4
★ DISCOTHEQUE: yes
★ SHOPS: 6
★ CONFERENCE ROOMS: 4 (33 to 500)
★ BANQUETING ROOMS: 6 (60 to 450)
★ STANDARD BEDROOM SIZE: old building 20 m² new building 39 m²
★ PRIVATE BALCONIES: all rooms
★ SWIMMING POOL: 2 outdoor sea water, 1 indoor fresh water
★ RECREATIONAL ACTIVITIES: tennis, mini

golf, water skiing, surfing, sauna, health care, yachting harbour, golf course 5 km away
★ GARDENS: yes
★ NO. OF STAFF: 600
★ ROOM SERVICE: around the clock
★ ORIENTATION: majority of the rooms face the sea
★ CREDIT CARDS: all major ones
★ OWNING COMPANY: Astir Hotel Co
★ GENERAL MANAGER: Chronis Stergiopoulos
★ DISTANCE TO BEACH: walking distance
★ DISTANCE TO SHOPS: 3 km
★ DISTANCE FROM AIRPORT: 15 km

Apart from the city itself this is by far the best hotel in the vicinity of the Greek capital – so you can have the best of both worlds, a super resort, extremely well run and very sophisticated and a quick visit to the immortal city when you want it. It is a large and busy hotel, one never gets bored here because there is so much to do, but it is also a very elegant, cool and dignified place where one is treated as a guest and not a day tripper and the staff are quite charming and very experienced. If you can obtain one of the top floor suites, do – there is nothing to touch them – superb space and furnishings, great views and complete privacy. The food is Greek and international; you also have a large choice of eating places. Weekends, of course, see rather a lot of noisy Athenian children but since they all look like baby gods it does not matter too much. When they have moved Athens' airport away to its new location, this hotel should be even better.

HONG KONG

THE HONG KONG MANDARIN, 5 Connaught Road, Central, G.P.O. Box 2623

★ TELEPHONE: 5-220111
★ CABLES: Mandarin Hongkong
★ TELEX: HX 73653
★ IN OPERATION: since 1963
★ RESERVATIONS: Hotel Representative Inc, worldwide
★ ROOMS: 442 doubles 51 singles
★ SUITES: 58
★ RESTAURANTS: 5 – Mandarin Grill, Man Wah Chinese Restaurant, Pierrot, Clipper Lounge and The Mandarin Coffee Shop
★ BARS: 3 – Captains, Chinnery and Harlequin Bar
★ DISCOTHEQUE: no – but dancing to a live band in the Captains Bar
★ SHOPS: 28
★ CONFERENCE ROOMS: 4 (60 to 400)
★ BANQUETING ROOMS: 4 (30 to 300)
★ STANDARD BEDROOM SIZE: 26.4 m²
★ PRIVATE BALCONIES: yes – most rooms

★ SWIMMING POOL: yes – fresh water, 10 × 5 × 2.5 m
★ RECREATIONAL ACTIVITIES: sauna, solarium, massage and whirlpools at the Mandarin Health Centre. Arrangements can be made for golf, tennis and waterskiing
★ GARDENS: no
★ NO. OF STAFF: 1,200
★ ROOM SERVICE: around the clock
★ ORIENTATION: best rooms face north and east harbour, others south and west
★ CREDIT CARDS: Amexco, Visa, Diners Club, Carte Blanche and Master Charge
★ OWNING COMPANY: Mandarin International Hotels Ltd
★ GENERAL MANAGER: Peter French
★ DISTANCE TO BEACH: 10 km
★ DISTANCE TO SHOPS: walking distance
★ DISTANCE FROM AIRPORT: 9 km

The best hotel in Asia and one of the six best in the world. That is what I wrote about the Mandarin in the last edition and I have a feeling that if I pass any more flowery compliments readers will become suspicious – and yet I must because the Mandarin always manages to surprise me by getting even better. In big things and little things. Take ashtrays for instance. On my last visit, I suddenly noticed that here, any ashtray resting on a glass or marble table holds little rubber pads underneath, to avoid noise and scratching. Somebody had to think of that one and this is the Mandarin all over – here hotelkeeping becomes an art form and the interested guest is always a student.

In this miraculous city where fortunes are made overnight, this hotel remains utterly civilised, totally unperturbed by the noise and bustle and becomes in a way the very image of Hong Kong as it should be – the place where the finest in the West meets the best in the East.

Rooms and suites are truly magnificent and even if you are only a modest VIP you reach them from Kaitak in the hotel's Rolls. The famous Grill is the most polished international restaurant in the East and as for the Chinese Man Wah Room, with its superb decor, you simply cannot know what Chinese food is like until you have tried it. Now, the Pierrot Restaurant brings a delicate French touch to the gastronomic round. Yet, in the end, it is the service that counts: at the Mandarin you never see a dirty ashtray, never carry a parcel, never wait for a lift – it's that kind of a place. In the last edition, I wrote that when a Mandarin general manager leaves, there is only one place for him to go: heaven. I was wrong. The dear man has only been promoted. May all his future Mandarins be of such celestial excellence.

THE PENINSULA HOTEL, Salisbury Road, Kowloon

★ TELEPHONE: 3-666251
★ CABLES: Penhote Hong Kong
★ TELEX: 43821 PEN HX
★ IN OPERATION: since 1928
★ RESERVATIONS: Cathay Pacific Airways, worldwide/Steigenberger Reservation Service/Preferred Hotels Association, worldwide/HORIS Hotel Reservation and Information System (Swissair)
★ ROOMS: 320
★ SUITES: 20
★ RESTAURANTS: 4
★ BARS: 1
★ DISCOTHEQUE: yes and live music in Gaddi's and The Verandah
★ SHOPS: 80 – a variety of boutiques, leatherware, jewellery, antiques, airline and travel agent counters, book shop etc
★ CONFERENCE ROOMS: 2 (60 to 200)
★ BANQUETING ROOMS: 3 (90 to 170)

★ STANDARD BEDROOM SIZE: 43 m^2
★ PRIVATE BALCONIES: none
★ SWIMMING POOL: no
★ GARDENS: none
★ NO. OF STAFF: 775
★ ROOM SERVICE: around the clock
★ ORIENTATION: main facade faces harbour
★ CREDIT CARDS: American Express, Bankamericard, Diners Club, Master Charge, Carte Blanche and OTB
★ OWNING COMPANY: The Hongkong & Shanghai Hotels Ltd
★ GENERAL MANAGER: Urs Aeby
★ DISTANCE TO BEACH: 10 km
★ DISTANCE TO SHOPS: walking distance
★ DISTANCE FROM AIRPORT: 6.5 km
★ TRANSPORTATION: by reservation. The hotel maintains a fleet of Rolls Royce Silver Shadow II saloons

Before it vanished into the history books, the British Empire invented the Pen which remains one of the great landmarks of the hotel world, standing with dignified hauteur on the edge of Kowloon overlooking that fantastic Hong Kong Island skyline. People often ask me how it is that I can have such affection and admiration for two hotels in the same city. The answer is simple – I like Asprey's and Tiffany's too. The Peninsula is a special place and my heart warms to it when one of those tiny bellboys in a white uniform ushers me into that holy of holies, the Pen's world famous lobby. It takes your breath away – latterday Victoriana with frills – and the place where 'taipans', Swiss bankers and Hollywood stars rub shoulders.

Rooms at the Pen are enormous and stately and when one thinks of what they used to be like, they are surely the most successful hotel rebirth in the world. Service is matchless – carried out by people and not computers – and even the return of your laundry is a ceremony. Another ceremony of course is Gaddi's which many believe is the finest continental restaurant East of Suez, with traditional cuisine in the grand manner.

The Peninsula has enormous style and great personality. Of course I know people who, in Hong Kong, would never even think of staying anywhere else while some Mandarins would never move from the other shore. That's human nature. For myself as a perennial traveller, the fact that these two great hotels face each other across the water and speak a different language is one of the miracles of Hong Kong.

HUNGARY

Budapest

BUDAPEST HILTON, 1014 Budapest, Hess Andras Ter 1-3

★ TELEPHONE: 853-500
★ CABLES: Hiltels – Budapest
★ TELEX: 225984/BPHI H
★ IN OPERATION: since January, 1977
★ RESERVATIONS: Hilton International
★ ROOMS: 295
★ SUITES: 28
★ RESTAURANTS: 4 – Kalocsa Dining Room, Coffee Shop, Margareta Espresso, Fishermen's Bastion wine cellar and restaurant
★ BARS: 2
★ DISCOTHEQUE: no
★ SHOPS: 10 – boutique, beauty parlour, barber, florist, gift shop, news stand, optical shop, tourist offices, photo shop and airline office
★ CONFERENCE ROOMS: 8 (12 to 700)
★ BANQUETING ROOMS: 8 (12 to 400)

★ STANDARD BEDROOM SIZE: 27.6 m^2
★ PRIVATE BALCONIES: no
★ SWIMMING POOL: no
★ RECREATIONAL ACTIVITIES: casino, tennis and swimming nearby
★ GARDENS: yes
★ NO. OF STAFF: 600
★ ROOM SERVICE: around the clock
★ ORIENTATION: all directions
★ CREDIT CARDS: Carte Blanche, American Express, Master Charge, Eurocard, Diners Club, Hilton Hotels, Bankamericard
★ OWNING COMPANY: Danubius Hotel & Spa Co
★ GENERAL MANAGER: Dr. Karoly Biro
★ DISTANCE TO SHOPS: walking distance
★ DISTANCE FROM AIRPORT: 21 km

If I had not seen it with my own eyes I would not have believed it – the Hilton Corporation have taken over a few old walls and a baroque facade in the heart of old Buda, digging it out, building with great discretion and coming up with a magnificent hotel. I doff my deerstalker in salute. This is about the only hotel I like on the dark side of Europe. It shines with good taste, intelligent planning, respect for the past and, so rare in chain hotels, an eye for real beauty. Sit in the elegant lobby and through the glass wall you can see a 700-year-old Dominican church with a marvellous, partly reconstructed cloister. The Codex Bar has been dug out of a fifteenth-century printing shop. Then, miracle of miracles, the rooms are Hilton-sized, fresh and clean and done up in a way which makes you admire ingenuity. There is surely nothing old fashioned about the Budapest Hilton and yet its architectural roots are so deep in the past that there is not a single jarring note. This hotel is enough to make the government of Hungary rejoin the Austro-Hungarian Empire.

INDIA

Agra

HOTEL MUGHAL SHERATON, Taj Ganj, Agra 282 001

- ★ TELEPHONE: 64701
- ★ CABLE: WELCOTEL AGRA
- ★ TELEX: 0565 – 210
- ★ IN OPERATION: since November, 1976
- ★ RESERVATIONS: direct or Sheraton Corporation
- ★ ROOMS: 200
- ★ SUITES: 2
- ★ RESTAURANTS: Nauratna, Tajbano, Bagh-e-Bahar (night club) and Samovar
- ★ BARS: 1
- ★ DISCOTHEQUE: no
- ★ SHOPS: 7
- ★ CONFERENCE ROOMS: 3 (20 to 200)
- ★ BANQUETING ROOMS: 3 (25 to 175)
- ★ STANDARD BEDROOM SIZE: 29 m^2
- ★ PRIVATE BALCONIES: no
- ★ SWIMMING POOL: yes – fresh water, 218 m^2
- ★ RECREATIONAL ACTIVITIES: croquet, mini golf, tennis, archery, horse carriage, camel and elephant rides, health club and beauty parlour; sightseeing tours to sites of historical interest can be arranged
- ★ GARDENS: yes
- ★ NO. OF STAFF: 400
- ★ ROOM SERVICE: around the clock
- ★ ORIENTATION: all rooms have a view either of the gardens, swimming pool or the Taj Mahal
- ★ CREDIT CARDS: Diners Club, Bank of America and American Express
- ★ OWNING COMPANY: I.T.C. Ltd
- ★ GENERAL MANAGER: Mr. Nripjit Singh Chawla
- ★ DISTANCE TO SHOPS: 3 km
- ★ DISTANCE FROM AIRPORT: 9 km

If Shah Jahan came back to life and wanted to build another Taj Mahal, he could not because all the marble has been used inside this hotel. This haven of coolness and good taste is one of the most remarkable hotels in India – conceived on an unusually clever architectural theme, with gardens and pool in the middle and long corridor fingers going off in all directions. The lobby is a revelation: amid all this marbled magnificence, the fatigue, the heat and the sometimes overwhelming feel of India all fall off you like scales. If you are lucky enough to have a suite – say the Raja Man Singh for instance – prepare yourself for more: this is presumably how the Moguls lived, with cushions everywhere, great canopied bed and swing seats hanging from the ceiling. The great pity of it is that people only stay a day or two – to see the Taj. This hotel deserves much more – it is friendly, tremendously hospitable, unflappable even when faced with multi-tongued tourists. Service glides about and the food, both Indian and international, is above average.

Bombay

THE TAJ MAHAL INTER-CONTINENTAL HOTEL, Apollo Bunder, Bombay 400 039

- ★ TELEPHONE: 243366
- ★ CABLES: Palace, Bombay
- ★ TELEX: 11-2442 TAJB IN and 11-6175 TAJB IN
- ★ IN OPERATION: 78 years
- ★ RESERVATIONS: Inter-Continental Hotels Corp, New York/Utell International, worldwide/Horis Hotel Reservation and Information System (Swissair)
- ★ ROOMS: 558 doubles 25 singles
- ★ SUITES: 43
- ★ RESTAURANTS: 6 – Tanjore, Golden Dragon, Rendezvous, Shamiana, Sea Lounge and Ballroom
- ★ BARS: Harbour Bar and Apollo Bar
- ★ DISCOTHEQUE: yes – also a dance band in the Rendezvous Restaurant and Indian classical dances and music every night in the Tanjore Restaurant
- ★ SHOPS: 24 – shopping arcade on the ground floor selling books, records, boutiques, carpets, handicrafts, jewellery, shoes, leathergoods, textiles, tobacconists etc
- ★ CONFERENCE ROOMS: 9 (20 to 800)
- ★ BANQUETING ROOMS: 11
- ★ STANDARD BEDROOM SIZE: 26 m^2 (new wing) and 31 m^2 (old wing)

★ PRIVATE BALCONIES: yes – most rooms
★ SWIMMING POOL: yes – fresh water
★ RECREATIONAL ACTIVITIES: health club with sauna, also tennis and golf arranged on request
★ GARDENS: yes
★ NO. OF STAFF: 1,640
★ ROOM SERVICE: around the clock
★ ORIENTATION: rooms face the sea or swimming pool area

★ CREDIT CARDS: American Express, Diners Club, Master Charge and Carte Blanche
★ OWNING COMPANY: Indian Hotels Co Ltd
★ GENERAL MANAGER: Mr. J. D. F. Lam
★ DISTANCE TO BEACH: 18 km
★ DISTANCE TO SHOPS: walking distance
★ DISTANCE FROM AIRPORT: 20 km

Until its sister hotel in Delhi matures a little, this is still India's finest hotel. It has age and tradition, modernity, fantastic good taste and super-efficient service. It has been a landmark of the sub-continent for a long time – at least its fanciful Indo-Saracenic half has, and now that it also possesses a really elegant tower block, most world travellers passing through the portals of the Taj and trying out its delights are full of praise. The Taj is the Taj and I do not think it can ever really be imitated. You have a choice of a room in the old galleried wing or one, equally good in a different way, in the new wing. I would choose the old wing with its grand staircases, its Indian curlicues, its magnificent ceilings and the windows looking on to the Gateway to India. I once had a suite there that had 42 pieces of furniture in it. Service is impeccable and the Taj has the highest staff-to-guest ratio in Asia, possibly the world. It's a world of its own, moving fast if you so wish or at the sedate pace of the Orient if that's what you like best. With six restaurants, one never goes hungry or looking for a change elsewhere – I adore those Sunday buffets in the Grand Ballroom, also the Chinese food and the decor in the Indian restaurant. The Taj is a hotel for real connoisseurs.

Goa

FORT AGUADA BEACH RESORT, Sinquerim, Bardez, Goa 403515

★ TELEPHONE: 3401/2186
★ CABLES: Fortaguada-Goa
★ TELEX: 0194-206 Taj In
★ IN OPERATION: since December, 1974
★ RESERVATIONS: The Taj Group of Hotels, c/o Inter-Continental Hotels Corporation/Utell International, worldwide
★ ROOMS: 120
★ SUITES: none but 24 terrace rooms
★ RESTAURANTS: 2
★ BARS: 3
★ DISCOTHEQUE: yes – and live music
★ SHOPS: 5
★ CONFERENCE ROOMS: 2 (60 to 250)
★ BANQUETING ROOMS: no
★ STANDARD BEDROOM SIZE: 26 m²
★ PRIVATE BALCONIES: yes – most rooms, 32 cottages
★ SWIMMING POOL: yes – fresh water

★ GARDENS: yes
★ RECREATIONAL ACTIVITIES: tennis, cycling, target practice with airguns, basketball, volleyball, sailing, fishing, rowing and various indoor games
★ NO. OF STAFF: 270
★ ROOM SERVICE: 07.00–23.00
★ ORIENTATION: all rooms face the sea
★ CREDIT CARDS: Diners Club, American Express and Bankamericard
★ FURTHER DEVELOPMENTS: an additional one hundred cottages in a coconut grove with its own restaurant, bar and swimming pool
★ OWNING COMPANY: Indian Resort Hotels Ltd
★ GENERAL MANAGER: Ms Asha Rishi
★ DISTANCE TO BEACH: 100 m
★ DISTANCE TO SHOPS: 20 km
★ DISTANCE FROM AIRPORT: 46 km

Only a decade or so ago if one had suggested that you should go to India for a beach holiday you would have no doubt called the padded wagon. But the hippy trail led to Goa and tourists followed after when people began building small beach hotels, mostly around Madras and finally, seven years ago, the prestigious Taj Group took the plunge and built Fort Aguada. Expensively built on this rather remote but matchless beach, very well conceived and expertly managed, at Fort Aguada you can watch the hippies at the other end of the beach in comfort. For all those who love India, especially those relics of the former European presence, Goa is marvellous. It's Indian and it is also charmingly Portuguese (they still sing fado and make wine . . .). As for the hotel, it is more than acceptable. Rooms are fairly large, airy and cool and the furnishings have been chosen with care though obviously one does not spend much time inside – with all that beach and magnificent coconut grove close by. If you like the local food, with or without the Portuguese overtones, you'll be very happy here. All in all, Goans are the best cooks in India.

Jaipur

THE RAMBAGH PALACE, Jaipur 302 005

★ TELEPHONE: 75141
★ CABLES: Rambagh
★ TELEX: 36 254-RBAG IN
★ RESERVATIONS: Taj Mahal Hotel, Bombay/ The Taj Group of Hotels, c/o Inter-Continental Hotels Corporation/ Utell International, worldwide
★ ROOMS: 105
★ SUITES: 12
★ RESTAURANTS: 2
★ BARS: 1
★ DISCOTHEQUE: yes
★ SHOPS: 15
★ CONFERENCE ROOMS: 4 (30 to 300)
★ BANQUETING ROOMS: 2 (150 to 300)
★ STANDARD BEDROOM SIZE: variable
★ PRIVATE BALCONIES: yes
★ SWIMMING POOL: yes – fresh water, 75 × 45 m

★ RECREATIONAL ACTIVITIES: squash and golf, with horse riding on request, beauty parlour
★ GARDENS: yes
★ NO. OF STAFF: 250
★ ROOM SERVICE: around the clock
★ ORIENTATION: most of the rooms overlook beautiful gardens
★ FURTHER DEVELOPMENTS: additional rooms and coffee shop
★ CREDIT CARDS: Diners Club, American Express and Bankamericard
★ OPERATING COMPANY: Indian Hotels Co Ltd
★ GENERAL MANAGER: Vikram Singh
★ DISTANCE TO SHOPS: 3 km
★ DISTANCE FROM AIRPORT: 11 km

Psychiatrists everywhere should send their patients being treated for identity crises to this hotel. At Rambagh on special days, they send a ceremonial elephant to meet you at the gate. At the majestic pace which only an elephant can offer, you reach the splendid terrace where the gorgeous liveried staff await you with garlands of flowers and a cool 'nimbu-pani' (lime juice and water). The welcome at this immense and stately pile, all turrets and cupolas and galleries and gardens with peacocks strutting about, will turn the sickest nonentity into an instant maharajah. Rambagh was the home of Jaipur's own ruling prince, of course – no imitations. Rooms here vary a lot – some are somewhat spartan so do ask to see yours first.

The best are awe-inspiring with pre-1930 London bathrooms, with Oriental touches everywhere that have an unmistakable Bombay/Maple's touch so typical of princely India. The dining room with its painted ceiling is magnificent and so is the Chinese Room. The numberless staff are everywhere, smiling and cheerful, padding along miles of corridors. Rambagh's panache is the stuff of romance but the storybook never tells you what the prince and princess had for dinner – which perhaps is just as well since food is not Rambagh's great point and the man who comes here for gastronomy should stay home. Who cares? All around you lies the fabled Pink City and that is surely worth travelling for.

Madras

TAJ COROMANDEL HOTEL, Nungambakkam High Road, Madras 600 034

- ★ TELEPHONE: 848888
- ★ CABLES: Hotelorent
- ★ TELEX: 041-7194
- ★ IN OPERATION: since 1975
- ★ RESERVATIONS: Taj Group of Hotels, New York/Utell International, worldwide
- ★ ROOMS: 225
- ★ SUITES: 27
- ★ RESTAURANTS: 3 – the Mysore, the Golden Dragon and the Pavilion (coffee shop)
- ★ BARS: 1
- ★ DISCOTHEQUE: no – but live music in Coffee Shop every night except Mondays
- ★ SHOPS: 18
- ★ CONFERENCE ROOMS: 2 (75 and 110)
- ★ BANQUETING ROOMS: 2 (75 to 1,500)
- ★ STANDARD BEDROOM SIZE: 42 m^2

- ★ PRIVATE BALCONIES: only three suites have private terraces
- ★ SWIMMING POOL: yes – fresh water, 18 × 9 m
- ★ GARDENS: no
- ★ NO. OF STAFF: 520
- ★ ROOM SERVICE: around the clock
- ★ ORIENTATION: all rooms overlook the city
- ★ FUTURE DEVELOPMENTS: plans for a health club, sauna and a discotheque
- ★ CREDIT CARDS: Diners Club, American Express, Visa, Bankamericard and Master Charge
- ★ OWNING COMPANY: Oriental Hotels Ltd
- ★ GENERAL MANAGER: Mr. Maneck B. Patel
- ★ DISTANCE TO BEACH: 6 km
- ★ DISTANCE TO SHOPS: 1½ km
- ★ DISTANCE FROM AIRPORT: 13 km

In the imposing pace of competition from princely palaces one might be forgiven the thought that it is hardly worth much effort when it comes to erecting a large modern hotel. But at the Taj Coromandel – by now the finest modern hotel in southern India – so successful were the architects and designers, it is now a famous feature of that so little known part of the sub-continent. Superbly elegant, with very fine and colourful decor, the public rooms like the Indian restaurant or its Chinese counterpart shine with that glittering Eastern appeal which is really overwhelming when it is done in such good taste. Colour schemes are very clever – running into the reds and golds in the public rooms and to the pale blue and cool greens in the bedrooms which are vast and sumptuously furnished. The suites are maharajah-sized. Service, as always in India, is ready and smiling while the variety and quality of the very hot food native to the region are the opposite of boring. Mahabalipuram and Kanchipuram are not far away: a visit to both is obligatory.

Mysore

LALITHA MAHAL PALACE HOTEL, Mysore 570011

- ★ TELEPHONE: 23650
- ★ CABLES: Tourism Mysore
- ★ TELEX: 0846 217
- ★ IN OPERATION: 8 years
- ★ RESERVATIONS: Ashok Reservations Service, New Delhi/John Miller, Australia/Air India Offices, worldwide/Government of India Tourist Information Offices
- ★ ROOMS: 48
- ★ SUITES: 6
- ★ RESTAURANTS: 1
- ★ BARS: 1

- ★ DISCOTHEQUE: no
- ★ SHOPS: 3
- ★ CONFERENCE ROOMS: 1 (140 m^2)
- ★ BANQUETING ROOMS: 1 (50 to 150)
- ★ STANDARD BEDROOM SIZE: 20 m^2–55 m^2
- ★ PRIVATE BALCONIES: yes – terraces
- ★ SWIMMING POOL: 1 – fresh water
- ★ RECREATIONAL ACTIVITIES: tennis, billiards, card room
- ★ GARDENS: yes – including tropical garden
- ★ NO. OF STAFF: 100
- ★ ROOM SERVICE: 07.00–23.00

★ ORIENTATION: east and west
★ CREDIT CARDS: American Express, Diners Club and ITDC
★ OWNING COMPANY: India Tourism
Development Corporation Ltd
★ GENERAL MANAGER: V. M. Rao
★ DISTANCE TO SHOPS: 5 km
★ DISTANCE FROM AIRPORT: 500 km

In olden days, when they had too much money and not much to spend it on, India's erstwhile maharajahs built themselves palaces, preferably along the lines of those they believed Western monarchs had. This one is a mad and delicious hybrid, with touches of Buckingham Palace, King's Cross Station and some North of England county hall. The result is, to say the least, an eyeful and it's fun just being there – in a room the size of which will make you blink, a restaurant that looks faintly Ritz-ish and a staircase just like Francis Josef used to have. Located here, in this marvellous city of Mysore, it should not be missed by all those who enjoy the incongruities of the sub-continent. What's more you are also treated like a maharajah. There is a man in full, vaguely military uniform who greets you at the front steps of this immense spun-sugar place, regiments of staff running up and down the corridors and vast grounds full of tropicana. A good swimming pool too. The whole place is clean, resplendent and a very good effort in sailing on a new tack. The food, as long as it is Indian, is excellent. When it pretends to be what Indians term 'Continental', it requires a sense of humour to be appreciated. But if this is the way maharajahs used to live, I think I can stand it for a few days.

New Delhi

HOTEL OBEROI INTER-CONTINENTAL, Dr Zakir Hussain Marg, New Delhi

★ TELEPHONE: 699571
★ CABLES: INHOTELCOR/OBHOTEL
★ TELEX: 2372, 3829
★ IN OPERATION: since 1965
★ RESERVATIONS: Oberoi Hotels (I) Pvt Ltd, New York/Loews Representatives, New York, Los Angeles and London
★ ROOMS: 270 doubles 43 singles
★ SUITES: 17
★ RESTAURANTS: 5 – The Taj, Coffee Shop, Cafe Chinoise, Moghul Room and Cafe Expresso
★ BARS: 2
★ DISCOTHEQUE: yes
★ SHOPS: yes
★ CONFERENCE ROOMS: 1 (up to 1,000)
★ BANQUETING ROOMS: 1 (800 to 1,000)
★ PRIVATE BALCONIES: some
★ SWIMMING POOL: yes
★ RECREATIONAL ACTIVITIES: Health Club facilities
★ GARDENS: yes
★ NO. OF STAFF: 1,043
★ ROOM SERVICE: around the clock
★ ORIENTATION: east and west
★ CREDIT CARDS: American Express, Bankamericard, Diners Club, Carte Blanche
★ OWNING COMPANY: East India Hotels Ltd
★ GENERAL MANAGER: J. S. Parmar
★ DISTANCE TO CITY: 9 km
★ DISTANCE FROM AIRPORT: 16 km

Basically the first modern hotel to be built in Delhi, the Oberoi Inter-Continental suffered for some years from the fact that it had no competition. Now it has and, at the same time since it is now operated by one of India's great hotel companies, it is now smoother, less institutional and far, far better. It would be a mistake to ignore it because here Indian gentleness has combined with Western efficiency in the small things to produce a hotel which is now mature and without a doubt one of the three or four best in the sub-continent. Happily, there is relatively little 'showbiz' feel about the place: it is well designed, beautifully furnished in a style that nobody could object to and its services work like a dream – even the room service people know you by name when you telephone. As for the staff, roughly two for every guest, it works like a dream with nothing being too much trouble and everything being done without the guest ever being disturbed. Lately, the food has greatly improved and can now compete on a big-city basis with any other hotel and satisfy the most demanding international traveller. Although competition in this city is now very tough indeed, the Oberoi Inter-Continental can certainly hold its own.

THE TAJ MAHAL HOTEL, Number One Mansingh Road, New Delhi 110011

★ TELEPHONE; 38 61 62
★ CABLES: Tajdel
★ TELEX: 31 3604 Tajd IN
★ IN OPERATION: since December, 1978
★ RESERVATIONS: The Taj Group of Hotels, New York/Utell International, worldwide
★ ROOMS: 70 doubles   200 singles
★ SUITES: 29
★ RESTAURANTS: 4 – House of Ming, Haveli, Machan and Casa Medici
★ BARS: 1
★ DISCOTHEQUE: no – only live music
★ SHOPS: Khazana Shopping Centre run by the hotel
★ CONFERENCE ROOMS: 5 (85 to 550)

★ BANQUETING ROOMS: 5 (85 to 550)
★ STANDARD BEDROOM SIZE: 30 m^2
★ PRIVATE BALCONIES: yes
★ SWIMMING POOL: yes – fresh water
★ GARDENS: yes
★ NO. OF STAFF: 860
★ ROOM SERVICE: around the clock
★ ORIENTATION: east and west
★ CREDIT CARDS: American Express, Diners Club and Bankamericard
★ OWNING COMPANY: The Indian Hotels Co Ltd
★ GENERAL MANAGER: Mr. Ravi Dubey
★ DISTANCE TO SHOPS: walking distance
★ DISTANCE FROM AIRPORT: 10 km

The illustrious company which built this hotel has a ceaseless urge to find the best so it is no wonder that the Delhi Taj is a talking point among habitual travellers. It is the most magnificent, the most costly, the most soigné new hotel in the whole of India and when you know that they even grow their own basil to get the pizzas exactly right, you will gather that no effort has been spared. It has been built of pink sandstone outside and it seems to be 100 per cent marble inside – cool, supremely beautiful and so elegant that one feels like a latter-day Moghul emperor. Public rooms, as usual in this chain, are superbly designed and here and there are works of art such as only India can produce. Bedrooms and studios are stunningly lovely, with pale, fresh colours, lots of storage space and shining bathrooms. The restaurants, especially the Chinese one, are quite superb and the so-called coffee shop is a work of art. Obviously, as a new hotel, it needs 'wearing in' but with superb management and a willing staff, this won't take long and the Delhi Taj will take its place among the great hotels of the world.

Srinagar

HOTEL OBEROI PALACE, Gupkar Road, Srinagar, Jammu & Kashmir

★ TELEPHONE: 75641-43
★ CABLES: Obhotel
★ TELEX: 375-201-LXSR
★ IN OPERATION: since 1955
★ RESERVATIONS: LRI, worldwide/PRI, Frankfurt
★ ROOMS: 55 doubles   30 singles
★ SUITES: 19
★ RESTAURANTS: 2
★ BARS: 2
★ DISCOTHEQUE: yes
★ SHOPS: 8
★ CONFERENCE ROOMS: 3 (up to 50)
★ BANQUETING ROOMS: 4 (50 to 120)
★ STANDARD BEDROOM SIZE: 30 m^2
★ PRIVATE BALCONIES: no
★ SWIMMING POOL: no – one can swim in the Dal Lake facing the hotel

★ RECREATIONAL ACTIVITIES: golf, badminton, table tennis and horse riding
★ GARDENS: yes
★ NO. OF STAFF: 250
★ ROOM SERVICE: around the clock
★ ORIENTATION: rooms face gardens and lake
★ FURTHER DEVELOPMENTS: a swimming pool and restaurant
★ CREDIT CARDS: American Express, Bankamericard and Diners Club
★ OWNING COMPANY: The East India Hotels Ltd
★ GENERAL MANAGER: Mr. Rakesh Mathur
★ DISTANCE TO SHOPS: 5 km
★ DISTANCE FROM AIRPORT: 16 km

The Hindu maharajah of Muslim Kashmir used to live here. It could not be said that he denied himself anything. One drives along Dal Lake, the Pearl of Kashmir, and there in a setting fit for mountain gods is this great pile of a place set among exotic gardens, with fountains playing and staff in glittering livery who consider it a favour to carry your bags. One hesitates to walk in over those fine silk Bokhara carpets dating from the eighteenth century but apparently they are much more hard wearing than the nylon variety. Rooms and suites vary in size but most of them are princely in size and furnishings, with lots of those little Oriental whatnots which obviously have their use – if only one knew what it is. The staff are everywhere at attention – like a multicoloured battalion of willing soldiers. Down the garden path on the lake, brilliantly hued shikaras wait to glide you along to the world-famous Shalimar Gardens and those Utopian valleys of Gulmarg and Pahalgam are a short drive away. Like everywhere in India, food is somewhat 'fantaisiste' – running from the very good to the odd. Whatever you do, insist on a room in the palace itself. The new wing is for travel agents.

Udaipur

LAKE PALACE HOTEL, Pichola Lake, Udaipur

- ★ TELEPHONE: 3241/2/3/4/5
- ★ CABLES: Lakepalace
- ★ TELEX: 33-203 LPAL IN
- ★ IN OPERATION: since 1961
- ★ RESERVATIONS: via Taj Mahal Hotel, Bombay/Utell International, worldwide/The Taj Group of Hotels, c/o Inter-Continental Hotels Corporation
- ★ ROOMS: 85
- ★ SUITES: 7
- ★ RESTAURANTS: 1
- ★ BARS: 1
- ★ DISCOTHEQUE: no
- ★ SHOPS: 6
- ★ CONFERENCE ROOMS: 2 (60 and 300)
- ★ BANQUETING ROOMS: 2 (60 and 300)
- ★ STANDARD BEDROOM SIZE: 28 m²
- ★ PRIVATE BALCONIES: yes – some rooms
- ★ SWIMMING POOL: yes – fresh water
- ★ GARDENS: yes

★ NO. OF STAFF: 140
★ ROOM SERVICE: around the clock
★ ORIENTATION: all rooms face the lake
★ CREDIT CARDS: American Express and Diners Club

★ OWNING COMPANY: Indian Hotels Co Ltd
★ GENERAL MANAGER: Mr. Param Gurung
★ DISTANCE TO SHOPS: 1 km
★ DISTANCE FROM AIRPORT: 20 km

Many people, myself included, believe that the Lake Palace is the most beautiful hotel building in the world. A former maharajah's palace, it occupies every inch of a tiny island in the middle of Udaipur's sacred lake and at times, specially at dawn, it looks like some Oriental dream floating on a silvery mirror. It has towers, cupolas, tiny miradors, fountains playing and a decor of such astonishing beauty and authenticity that it grips your heart. Very, very romantic, especially if you can have one of the corner rooms. Everywhere are frescoed walls and delicate marble screens and there is even a swimming pool under the mango trees. One has to go ashore by boat to visit that marvellously colourful city of Udaipur which has enormous appeal. In the hotel alas, whoever designed the new dining room dropped a stitch or two – it isn't what it should be. Neither is the food but who needs to eat when there is so much to feast the eye?

INDONESIA
Bali

HOTEL BALI OBEROI, Kuta Beach, P.O. Box 351, Denpasar, Bali

★ TELEPHONE: 5581
★ CABLES: Balioberoi
★ TELEX: 35125 OBHOTELDPR
★ IN OPERATION: since 1978
★ RESERVATIONS: Loews Representation International/Utell/Oberoi Hotels (India)/S.T.R. Frankfurt/Odner Hotel Representatives
★ ROOMS: 60 lanai cottages
★ SUITES: 13 villas, 1 presidential villa with private swimming pool and 1 club house with personal valets
★ RESTAURANTS: 2
★ BARS: 1
★ DISCOTHEQUE: no
★ SHOPS: 4
★ CONFERENCE ROOMS: 1 (60)
★ BANQUETING ROOMS: none
★ STANDARD BEDROOM SIZE: 5 m × 4 m
★ PRIVATE BALCONIES: yes
★ SWIMMING POOL: yes – fresh water 25 × 12 m

★ RECREATIONAL ACTIVITIES: table tennis, billiards, indoor games, surfing, floodlit tennis court, sauna, massage, daily video films and frequent Balinese dances at hotel's open-air amphitheatre
★ GARDENS: 30 acres; additionally each villa has its own private garden courtyard
★ NO. OF STAFF: 200
★ ROOM SERVICE: around the clock
★ ORIENTATION: all directions
★ CREDIT CARDS: American Express, Diners Club, Visa, Mastercharge
★ OWNING COMPANY: P. T. Widja Putra Karya
★ GENERAL MANAGER: Mr. Kamal Kant Kaul
★ DISTANCE TO BEACH: on the beach
★ DISTANCE TO SHOPS: 4 km
★ DISTANCE FROM AIRPORT: 9 km

Bali, say the connoisseurs, isn't what Bali used to be. I too knew this fantastically beautiful and unique island when it was paradise but if you insist on following your travel agent you will end up in a tourist packing plant; a here today, gone tomorrow kind of place and, frankly, it will serve you right – rather like ordering Californian wine in Burgundy. The difference is to be seen at the Bali Oberoi, a small, charming and cleverly conceived hotel on Kuta Beach, well away from the obvious spots. Here you have your own private villa or lanai suite and splendiferous gardens. Even your bathroom has a garden and if you want service, just hit the gong out front and a smiling Balinese room-boy will appear as if by magic. The beach is a mile long and immaculate. The decor is Balinese but modern, genuine and in excellent taste. There is an outdoor theatre where Balinese girls perform for you those extraordinarily intricate dances. The food is both international – acceptable – and Indonesian, perfect once you get used to it. Then you get away, far away and the real Bali greets you – intensely green paddies, haughty mountains, smiling villagers and a rhythm of life which has not changed in four thousand years. That's what you have come for – that and the Bali Oberoi.

Jakarta

THE JAKARTA MANDARIN, P.O. Box 3392, Jakarta

★ TELEPHONE: 321307
★ CABLES: Mandahotel Jkt
★ TELEX: 45755 Manda Jkt
★ IN OPERATION: since 1979
★ RESERVATIONS: Hotel Representative Inc
★ ROOMS: 450 doubles/twin
★ SUITES: 19
★ RESTAURANTS: 5 – The Spice Garden, The Club Room, The Marquee Coffee Shop, The Clipper Lounge and Pelangi Terrace
★ BARS: 3
★ DISCOTHEQUE: live music in bar
★ SHOPS: 8
★ CONFERENCE ROOMS: 2 (65 to 480)
★ BANQUETING ROOMS: 2 (100 to 500)
★ STANDARD BEDROOM SIZE: 36.5 m²
★ PRIVATE BALCONIES: no
★ SWIMMING POOL: yes – fresh water, 150 m²
★ RECREATIONAL ACTIVITIES: physical fitness centre and sauna, jogging track, air conditioned squash courts

★ GARDENS: none
★ NO. OF STAFF: 825
★ ROOM SERVICE: around the clock
★ ORIENTATION: facing the Welcome Monument and the main avenue of Jakarta
★ CREDIT CARDS: Carte Blanche, American Express, Eurocard, Diners Club, Visa and Mandarin
★ OWNING COMPANY: Mandarin International Hotels Ltd
★ GENERAL MANAGER: Daniel P. McCafferty
★ DISTANCE TO BEACH: approximately 3 hours' drive
★ DISTANCE TO SHOPS: 10 minutes to main department store
★ DISTANCE FROM AIRPORT: 10 km (Kemayoran Domestic Airport) and 17 km (Halim International Airport)

If there is one thing all hotel men fear it is the arrival on the scene of a new Mandarin. Like Rolls Royce bringing out a new model, it is a long time coming but unbeatable because the prestige, investment courage and expertise of this company are very rare in the world today. The Jakarta Mandarin has two authentic stone Sumatra statues topped by golden canopies in the lobby. Their stiff remote gaze in formalised attitude is the reverse of the impression made by this hotel whose welcome is unrivalled. It's the kind of hotel where even the lowly chairs in the coffee shop have been custom-made to the right design. Rooms and suites are palatial – gorgeously upholstered furniture, teak-fronted wardrobes, superb lighting, a proper writing desk as well as a three-mirror dressing table and everywhere splendid Indonesian materials. The Royal Orchid Restaurant, one of five, is magnificently decorated in rich browns, greens and gold and the cooking is commensurate with well cared for French cheeses. What really counts in the end is Mandarin service, probably the best in the world today – trained, intelligent, attentive, but above all trained. Nothing succeeds like success of course and the Mandarin Group is expanding very fast in the Far East. Can they keep it up? My own bet is on them.

IRAQ
Baghdad

HOTEL BABYLON OBEROI, P.O. Box 5273, Baghdad

- ★ TELEPHONE: not available at time of going to press
- ★ CABLES: no
- ★ TELEX: no
- ★ IN OPERATION: July, 1982
- ★ RESERVATIONS: Loews Representative, worldwide
- ★ ROOMS: 285
- ★ SUITES: 5
- ★ RESTAURANTS: 6 – French Restaurant, Coffee Shop, National Restaurant, Open Air Nightclub (summer), Indoor Nightclub (winter), Indian Restaurant (roof top)
- ★ BARS: 6
- ★ DISCOTHEQUE: live music in nightclub
- ★ SHOPS: 6 – drugstore, boutique, jeweller, handicrafts, bank, beauty/barber shop
- ★ CONFERENCE ROOMS: 5 (up to 25)
- ★ BANQUETING ROOMS: 1 (up to 450)
- ★ STANDARD BEDROOM SIZE: 25 m²
- ★ PRIVATE BALCONIES: most rooms have terraces
- ★ SWIMMING POOL: 2 – heated indoor fresh water pool and outdoor fresh water pool
- ★ RECREATIONAL ACTIVITIES: health club with sauna and gymnasium, bowling alley, tennis courts and casino
- ★ GARDENS: yes
- ★ NO. OF STAFF: 516
- ★ ROOM SERVICE: around the clock
- ★ ORIENTATION: rooms overlook palm groves or River Tigris
- ★ CREDIT CARDS: none
- ★ OWNING COMPANY: Oberoi Hotels (I) Pvt Ltd
- ★ GENERAL MANAGER: Madan Misra
- ★ DISTANCE TO CITY: 5 km
- ★ DISTANCE FROM AIRPORT: 20 km

There is a great temptation to say that Haroun-el-Rashid never had it so good but obviously this would be both mischievous and misleading. All the same, Baghdad being Baghdad, anyone who has been there will tell you that the Iraqi capital badly needed an international hotel and now it has one. Though Babylon is a long ways off, the name obviously looks better on notepaper and the hotel is in fact built – with much concrete – to look like a facsimile of the Tower of Babel though, in this case, the staff do understand what you are saying and you do get the right breakfast. In fact, sometimes you get two – though this did not happen to me.

One can pass any comment one likes about new hotels looking like this one or that but one fact remains: what did one do in Baghdad before the Babylon Oberoi opened its door – and I leave the answer to you. Here the laundry works, so does the plumbing and with six restaurants and six bars one is tempted to forget the extravagances of Indo-Babylonian twentieth century decor. If it's got to be Baghdad, it's got to be this one.

ISRAEL
Caesarea

DAN CAESAREA GOLF HOTEL, Caesarea

- ★ TELEPHONE: 063-62266
- ★ CABLES: Cedan
- ★ TELEX: 04-46216
- ★ IN OPERATION: 11 years
- ★ RESERVATIONS: Dan Hotels Group, London/Israel Hotel Representatives, New York
- ★ ROOMS: 105
- ★ SUITES: 6
- ★ RESTAURANTS: 3 – Dining Room, Coffee Shop and Swimming Pool Bar
- ★ BARS: 2
- ★ DISCOTHEQUE: yes
- ★ SHOPS: 2 – boutique and newspapers and gifts
- ★ CONFERENCE ROOMS: 1 (100 to 150)
- ★ BANQUETING ROOMS: 1 (350)
- ★ STANDARD BEDROOM SIZE: 22 m²

- ★ PRIVATE BALCONIES: yes
- ★ SWIMMING POOL: yes – fresh water, L-shaped, 800 m²
- ★ GARDENS: yes
- ★ NO. OF STAFF: 150
- ★ ROOM SERVICE: 07.00–24.00
- ★ RECREATIONAL ACTIVITIES: tennis, gymnasium, sauna and turkish bath, volley ball and cycling. Also golf, horse riding and skin diving nearby
- ★ ORIENTATION: Half the rooms face the sea, the other half the swimming pool and gardens
- ★ GENERAL MANAGER: David Ellenbogen
- ★ CREDIT CARDS: Diners Club, American Express, Eurocard and Bankamericard
- ★ OWNING COMPANY: Dan Hotels Corporation Ltd
- ★ DISTANCE TO BEACH: 1½ km
- ★ DISTANCE TO SHOPS: 2 km
- ★ DISTANCE FROM AIRPORT: 80 km

Having heard some so-so reports about this hotel, I was glad to have a chance to return there when I was in Israel a while back and all I can say is that my correspondents must have been unlucky in some respect. I found the Dan Caesarea extremely good, as it was when I first saw it – cool and practical, with pleasant balconies and very good room service and a host of services which one does not always find in Israel. There is a very good swimming pool, a magnificent 18-hole golf course and the gardens are very 'soigné'. The food is really quite good (bearing in mind that most Israelis are not gastronomes). The Romans, whose capital this was, knew all about the right places and Caesarea is well worth visiting for its antiquities and especially the superb aquaduct and the theatre. One is never very far from other sights and come to think of it, this is about the only country hotel in Israel where I would feel happy.

Jerusalem

KING DAVID HOTEL, King David Street, Jerusalem

- ★ TELEPHONE: 02-221111
- ★ CABLES: Kindotel
- ★ TELEX: 25228
- ★ IN OPERATION: since 1931
- ★ RESERVATIONS: Israel Hotel Representatives, New York/Dan Hotels Group, London and Zurich/Hotel Representative Inc
- ★ ROOMS: 258
- ★ SUITES: 29
- ★ RESTAURANTS: 3
- ★ BARS: 1
- ★ DISCOTHEQUE: no
- ★ SHOPS: 8 – jewellery, gifts, drugstore, travel agent, fashion boutique and art gallery
- ★ CONFERENCE ROOMS: 7 (20 to 230)
- ★ BANQUETING ROOMS: 7 (12 to 250)
- ★ STANDARD BEDROOM SIZE: 25 m²
- ★ PRIVATE BALCONIES: yes
- ★ SWIMMING POOL: yes – fresh water, 25 × 13 m
- ★ RECREATIONAL ACTIVITIES: tennis and sauna
- ★ GARDENS: yes
- ★ NO. OF STAFF: 300
- ★ ROOM SERVICE: around the clock
- ★ ORIENTATION: facing gardens, pool and Old City
- ★ FURTHER DEVELOPMENTS: plans to add an extra 100 rooms and a banqueting hall to accommodate 600 persons

★ CREDIT CARDS: Amexco, Diners Club, Visa and Master Charge

★ OWNING COMPANY: Dan Hotels Corporation

★ GENERAL MANAGER: Mr. Ilan Fink

★ DISTANCE TO SHOPS: 1 km

★ DISTANCE FROM AIRPORT: 50 km

There are hotels in this world (Raffles in Singapore, Shepherds in Cairo among many) whose names are legendary. This list includes the King David though it achieved fame once too often by being blown up during Israel's birthpangs. Then it was rebuilt, in a somewhat less extroverted, antiquarian mood, but managed to find its persona again through hard work, good management and the fact that it is in this unique city. It is palatially vast, cool and distinguished and its political importance has given way to top flight tourism and state visitors. Rooms are very well laid out and the public rooms could hold any international conference with ease. The food is international, perhaps a little plain as befits a nation with curiously Spartan habits. What I like most about it, however, is the sense of tradition and the quality of the service – people are happy to see you, happy to help and so glad you came.

KING SOLOMON SHERATON, 32 King David Street, Jerusalem 94101

★ TELEPHONE: (02) 241433

★ CABLES: no

★ TELEX: 26434

★ IN OPERATION: since May, 1981

★ RESERVATIONS: International reservations system operating at Sheraton Hotels, worldwide

★ ROOMS: 111

★ SUITES: 14 junior 16 de luxe 2 diplomatic 1 presidential

★ RESTAURANTS: 4 – The Cafe, The Carvery, Lobbylounge and The Teppanyaki. All restaurants kosher. Japanese Restaurant opening shortly

★ BARS: 1

★ DISCOTHEQUE: piano in Lobbylounge

★ SHOPS: 8 including duty free shop, jewellery, Judaic art, King Solomon boutique, gift shop, news stand, florist and bank

★ CONFERENCE ROOMS: none

★ BANQUETING ROOMS: 1 (up to 12)

★ STANDARD BEDROOM SIZE: 25 m²

★ PRIVATE BALCONIES: 27 private balconies or terraces, including all suites

★ SWIMMING POOL: yes – fresh water, 14 × 6.5 m

★ GARDENS: no

★ NO. OF STAFF: 150

★ ROOM SERVICE: around the clock

★ ORIENTATION: all suites and many rooms face Jerusalem's Old City. Others face New City

★ CREDIT CARDS: American Express, Diners Club, Mastercharge, Eurocard and Visa

★ OWNING COMPANY: Sheraton Hotels (management)

★ GENERAL MANAGER: Phil Navon

★ DISTANCE TO SHOPS: walking distance

★ DISTANCE FROM AIRPORT: 40 km

Jerusalem, a city which no one who is a real traveller can afford to miss, has never been very lucky with its hotels – I always had the feeling that had it not been for Jerusalem itself I could well have stayed away. Now things are improving and one of the reasons is the King Solomon Sheraton. Though it is not quite as grand and as sophisticated as its Tel Aviv sister, this hotel is going to be a winner. For one thing, its terrace overlooks the Old City – surely one of the greatest sights in the world. For another, the hotel works, silently and without fuss, i.e. you don't have to call the plumber all the time and the staff are finding their feet without too much trouble. The architecture takes a bit of getting used to until one realises that in this climate there is a very good reason for it. Inside, the decor is better than one would expect from the outside – reasonably subdued, in quite good taste and without too many frills. The lobby is cool and elegant and the rooms are amazingly quiet and very well furnished in an international style. The food – always a tricky subject when a hotel first opens – is getting better all the time. My guess is that the King Solomon Sheraton is going to turn out to be a godsend in what is essentially a hotel desert.

Tel Aviv

TEL AVIV SHERATON, 115 Hayarkon Street, Tel Aviv 63573

★ TELEPHONE: (03) 286222
★ CABLES: Sheraco Tel Aviv
★ TELEX: 342269
★ IN OPERATION: 5 years
★ RESERVATIONS: Sheraton International Reservations Offices
★ ROOMS: 365
★ SUITES: 21
★ RESTAURANTS: 4 – Kum Kum Restaurant, Twelve Tribes Grill Room, Genesis (vegetarian), Lobbylounge (snacks). All restaurants kosher
★ BARS: 2
★ DISCOTHEQUE: yes – and pianist in Lobbylounge
★ SHOPS: 6 – ladies fashions, jewellery, gift shop, art gallery, duty free shop, beauty parlour
★ CONFERENCE ROOMS: 3 (12 to 180)
★ BANQUETING ROOMS: 3 (100 to 200)
★ STANDARD BEDROOM SIZE: 24 m²

★ PRIVATE BALCONIES: all rooms
★ SWIMMING POOL: outdoor pool, fresh water. New pool planned for winter 1982
★ RECREATIONAL ACTIVITIES: swimming, boating at Tel Aviv Marina
★ GARDENS: no
★ NO. OF STAFF: 420
★ ROOM SERVICE: around the clock
★ ORIENTATION: sea and Jaffa, sea and marina, sea and city from all double rooms
★ CREDIT CARDS: all major credit cards
★ OWNING COMPANY: Hotel Cosmopolitan (1974) Ltd (owning company), Sheraton management
★ GENERAL MANAGER: Harold Richman
★ DISTANCE TO BEACH: on beach front'
★ DISTANCE TO SHOPS: walking distance
★ DISTANCE FROM AIRPORT: 25 km

Without any doubt this is one of the best two or three hotels in the whole of the Middle East. In that strip between the blue Mediterranean and the more mundane delights of Dizengoff, the Tel Aviv Sheraton is the only hotel worth living in – a well-conceived, well-run place where functionalism and good taste marry to live happily ever after. Of course, it's modern but in the best sense of the word. A great lobby, spacious rooms all beautifully furnished with a care for small details which is a delight to see. Decor is beautifully muted – nothing jars here because the usual Israeli concrete exhuberance has been kept at bay. Service is efficient and discreet and the food so far above what it is in the rest of the country that it is remembered with pleasure. In the Twelve Tribes Grill, it is international, stately and served with a good sense of showmanship. What is most surprising, however, is that the usually humble coffee shop, here called Kum Kum, is a very acceptable restaurant in its own right. That's rare. The staff are charming – most of them are students working their way through college (a great idea) and they are all intelligent, multi-lingual and good company. One of the two or three best hotels in the Middle East? It's certainly the best in Israel.

ITALY

Asolo

HOTEL VILLA CIPRIANI, Via Canova, 298, Asolo (Treviso)

★ TELEPHONE: 0423-52166
★ CABLES: Villacipriani, Asolo
★ TELEX: 411060 CIPRAS I
★ IN OPERATION: since 1962
★ RESERVATIONS: Ciga Hotels, Inc, worldwide/Relais et Chateaux, Europe
★ ROOMS: 31 doubles 1 single
★ SUITES: 4

★ RESTAURANTS: 2 – Verandah Restaurant with interconnecting dining room
★ BARS: 1
★ DISCOTHEQUE: no
★ SHOPS: none – but some small showcases
★ CONFERENCE ROOMS: 1 (15 to 20)
★ BANQUETING ROOMS: 1 (100)

★ STANDARD BEDROOM SIZE: 17–18 m²
★ PRIVATE BALCONIES: yes – 2 rooms with private terraces and other rooms with direct access to the garden
★ SWIMMING POOL: no
★ RECREATIONAL ACTIVITIES: tennis and an 18-hole golf course 30 km away
★ GARDENS: yes
★ NO. OF STAFF: 38
★ ROOM SERVICE: around the clock
★ ORIENTATION: the entrance facade faces north-east, the garden facade faces south-east and the rest of the building faces hills and mountains

★ FURTHER DEVELOPMENTS: enlargement of present garage and parking space, new conference room for 60/80 persons, 6/8 additional rooms and it is hoped a swimming pool in the valley
★ CREDIT CARDS: American Express, Diners Club, Bankamericard, Visa, Eurocard and Master Charge
★ OWNING COMPANY: Cigahotels – Italian Grand Hotel Co
★ GENERAL MANAGER: Sandro Matassini
★ DISTANCE TO SHOPS: walking distance
★ DISTANCE FROM AIRPORT: 60 km (Venice)

The canal-bound Venetians always had an eye on 'les plaisirs champêtres' – escaping from time to time to some improbably beautiful Renaissance villa on the Brenta. This hotel is one such and who could wish for better? In this little town, once the home of Eleonora Duse and Robert Browning, is the charming, sixteenth-century villa looking over the green hills. It is a rather difficult place to describe because one really has to be there to absorb the atmosphere of gentle timelessness. One eats al fresco most of the time – the Cipriani cuisine is excellent. The rooms are smallish but beautifully furnished and very comfortable, with flowered balconies everywhere. Public rooms are aristocratically well proportioned and the staff are quite charming and helpful. It is the next best thing to having your own villa within hailing distance of both Venice and glorious Vicenza.

Bellagio

GRAND HOTEL VILLA SERBELLONI, Via Roma 1, I-22021 Bellagio

★ TELEPHONE: (031) 950216
★ CABLES: Serbotel
★ TELEX: 380330 Sernot I
★ IN OPERATION: since 1873
★ RESERVATIONS: direct
★ ROOMS: 98 doubles   12 singles
★ SUITES: 7
★ RESTAURANTS: 1, plus breakfast room and lakeside terrace
★ BARS: 2
★ DISCOTHEQUE: dancing and orchestra every night in the main hall
★ SHOPS: 2 – ladies' hairdresser and boutique
★ CONFERENCE ROOMS: 4 (30 to 300)
★ BANQUETING ROOMS: 4 (25 to 300)
★ STANDARD BEDROOM SIZE: 25 m²

★ PRIVATE BALCONIES: yes – some rooms
★ SWIMMING POOL: yes – fresh water, heated, 10 × 20 m
★ RECREATIONAL ACTIVITIES: tennis and golf at Grandola, 20 minutes away by car
★ GARDENS: yes – park directly on lakeside
★ NO. OF STAFF: 100
★ ROOM SERVICE: around the clock
★ ORIENTATION: west
★ CREDIT CARDS: Visa
★ OWNING COMPANY: R. Bucher
★ GENERAL MANAGER: R. Bucher
★ DISTANCE TO BEACH: directly
★ DISTANCE TO SHOPS: directly
★ DISTANCE FROM AIRPORT: 70 km (Linate-Milano)

Anyone who has read previous editions of this guide knows that the editorial presence has a weakness for great staircases. Frescoed ceilings have much the same power and those are the two reasons why I would go back to the Villa Serbelloni as often as I can. It has style, beauty, urbanity and that grand hotel feeling which cannot be easily manufactured. There, below, is Lake Como too, spreading like a cerulean tablecloth amid entirely formal hills.

Villa Serbelloni has been here a long time – sixteenth-century with here and there some eighteenth-century extravaganzas. I don't care for the bar very much – rather precious – but that is about the only objection. Rooms are large, airy and high-ceilinged, with gilt, marble and curlicued Italian furniture of the period. Linen is fresh and sweet smelling and bathrooms are convention-sized for the most part. The management is cautious, careful, a little distant perhaps but immensely professional and runs its staff with silent ease. The food can often be great, mostly good and only occasionally a little indifferent but it is always served by the most proficient Italian waiters. If it is Como you wish to see, Villa Serbelloni is undoubtedly the place to be.

Candeli

HOTEL VILLA LA MASSA, 50010 Candeli-Firenze

★ TELEPHONE: 055-630051
★ CABLES: Villamassa
★ TELEX: 573555
★ IN OPERATION: 32 years
★ RESERVATIONS: direct
★ ROOMS: 33 doubles 4 singles
★ SUITES: 6
★ RESTAURANTS: 3 – including La Cave Restaurant (not operating in July and August)
★ BARS: 2
★ DISCOTHEQUE: yes – also piano in the restaurant and piano bar from 22.00 to 02.00
★ SHOPS: none
★ CONFERENCE ROOMS: 3 (20 to 60)
★ BANQUETING ROOMS: 2 (up to 80)
★ STANDARD BEDROOM SIZE: 16 m²
★ PRIVATE BALCONIES: only a few
★ SWIMMING POOL: yes – fresh water, 60 m²
★ RECREATIONAL ACTIVITIES: golf and tennis nearby
★ GARDENS: yes
★ NO. OF STAFF: 40
★ ROOM SERVICE: 07.00–02.00
★ ORIENTATION: south
★ FURTHER DEVELOPMENTS: a tennis club
★ CREDIT CARDS: American Express, Visa and Diners Club
★ OWNING COMPANY: I.R.A. S.p.A.
★ GENERAL MANAGER: P. Nocentini
★ DISTANCE TO SHOPS: 5 km
★ DISTANCE FROM AIRPORT: 100 km

A divinely beautiful and tranquil Tuscan villa a short walk from the centre of noisy Florence, La Massa is a place in a thousand – mellow, faded yellow walls and greeny blue shutters facing a well-treed garden of sylvan repose. On the other side of the house, the dining terrace lines the bank of the Arno – a view that makes most meals into seven-hour marathons of sensual delight. Inside, the rather stark white of the walls is relieved by magnificent splashes of colour in furnishings and furniture and lovely carpets reign over red tiled floors. The rooms, admittedly rather on the small side, are perfection itself – very, very pretty indeed in a chintzy way and lovingly tended and everything shines with cleanliness and care. Even in the rooms, flowers are changed every morning and in the utter peace of this splendid place one can really reflect on the splendours of the nearby city without having one's eardrums assaulted by the Lambrettas. A real oasis of peace. Food, which used to be La Massa's weak point, is now very much better thanks to the addition of an extra kitchen. Highly recommended.

Capri

GRAND HOTEL QUISISANA, Via Camerelle No. 2, 80073 Capri

★ TELEPHONE: 081-8370788
★ CABLES: Quisisana Capri
★ TELEX: 710520
★ IN OPERATION: since 1900
★ RESERVATIONS: Robert F. Warner, Inc, London and New York
★ ROOMS: 100 doubles 15 singles
★ SUITES: 27
★ RESTAURANTS: 2 – Colombaia Restaurant and Quisi Restaurant
★ BARS: 2
★ DISCOTHEQUE: piano bar
★ SHOPS: none
★ CONFERENCE ROOMS: 5 (10 to 600)
★ BANQUETING ROOMS: 3 (15 to 400)
★ STANDARD BEDROOM SIZE: 30 m²
★ PRIVATE BALCONIES: yes – all rooms that face the sea
★ SWIMMING POOL: yes – fresh water, 150 m²

★ RECREATIONAL ACTIVITIES: 3 tennis
courts, sauna and massage
★ GARDENS: yes – large park
★ NO. OF STAFF: 150
★ ROOM SERVICE: 07.00–24.00
★ ORIENTATION: most rooms face south to
gardens and the sea
★ FURTHER DEVELOPMENTS: proposals to
build a new swimming pool and extend
the Colombaia Restaurant

★ CREDIT CARDS: Diners Club, Amexco
and Eurocard
★ OWNING COMPANY: Hotelverwaltung
M.G.S.
★ GENERAL MANAGER: Dante Cattaruzza
★ DISTANCE TO BEACH: 1 km
★ DISTANCE TO SHOPS: walking distance
★ DISTANCE FROM AIRPORT: Naples airport
40 minutes by hydrofoil

Capri in the high summer is a curious, polyglot mixture of heaven and hell. In the so-called off season (which is most of the year) it goes back to being one of the most sensationally beautiful small islands in the world. But, winter or summer, the Quisisana reigns supreme as it has done since the first year of the century – a great lady of a hotel, distinguished and beautifully cared for. It sees little passing flotsam (too expensive for that) and for those who care for hotel excellence, and Capri too, it is a reward indeed. Cool marble halls, splendid carpets and hangings, furniture that has stood the test of time and the bedrooms, quite large for the most part, are supremely comfortable. Many have their own balconies and breakfast on one's terrace with Capri all around is an overwhelming experience. The food is *con amore* and the service is enchantingly discreet. Improvements by the intelligent management in recent years have much enhanced this lovely grand hotel.

Cernobbio

GRAND HOTEL VILLA D'ESTE, Via Regina 40, 22010 Cernobbio, Lake Como

★ TELEPHONE: 511471-512471
★ CABLES: Villaeste Cernobbio
★ TELEX: 380025 Vilest I
★ RESERVATIONS: Hotel Representative Inc
★ ROOMS: 114 doubles   39 singles
★ SUITES: 27
★ RESTAURANTS: 2
★ BARS: 4
★ DISCOTHEQUE: yes – and nightclub
★ SHOPS: 4 – jewellery, boutique,
hairdresser and silk textiles
★ CONFERENCE ROOMS: 8 (10 to 250)
★ BANQUETING ROOMS: 4 (45 to 280)
★ STANDARD BEDROOM SIZE: 25 m²
★ PRIVATE BALCONIES: yes – most rooms
★ SWIMMING POOL: yes – freshwater (two
outdoor and one indoor)

★ RECREATIONAL ACTIVITIES: 8 tennis
courts, 1 squash court, sauna, gym,
18-hole golf course 20 minutes away
and waterskiing, sailing and boating
★ GARDENS: yes
★ NO. OF STAFF: 200
★ ROOM SERVICE: 07.00–23.00
★ ORIENTATION: main facade and annexe
on lake, other sides face the gardens
★ CREDIT CARDS: American Express and
Visa
★ OWNING COMPANY: Villa D'Este S.p.A.
★ GENERAL MANAGER: Mario Arrigo
★ DISTANCE TO SHOPS: 5 km (Como)
★ DISTANCE FROM AIRPORT: 45 km

A sixteenth-century cardinal built the place since he liked to have his heaven here on earth. It is not known whether he made it to the ultimate address but the palazzo he left behind on the shore of Italy's most beautiful lake became home to emperors, kings and princes until a century ago when it opened its doors to us mere mortals. All one needs is money – and taste – because that is something the world-famous Villa d'Este has and requires from visitors. It is superbly palatial, colonnaded and porticoed, tapestried and marbled with a mellowness which only time can bring. It's the same with the ten-acre gardens – they were laid out in the eighteenth century, with a few monumental follies here and there and they have been growing more beautiful ever since. Villa d'Este is a way of life I wish I had the opportunity to get used to. Rooms, especially in the main building, are baronially handsome and service goes with it – quiet, unobtrusive and efficient. In the summer one dines out in the gardens and whether in or out the food is delicious. When you stay at Villa d'Este and the day trippers' boats come gliding on the lake, you just turn your eyes the other way.

Fiesole

VILLA SAN MICHELE, Via Doccia, 50014 Fiesole, Florence

- ★ TELEPHONE: 59451/2
- ★ CABLES: San Michele Fiesole
- ★ TELEX: no
- ★ IN OPERATION: 30 years
- ★ RESERVATIONS: direct
- ★ ROOMS: 28 doubles 2 singles
- ★ SUITES: 2
- ★ RESTAURANTS: 2
- ★ BARS: 2
- ★ DISCOTHEQUE: no
- ★ SHOPS: none
- ★ CONFERENCE ROOMS: 1 (40)
- ★ BANQUETING ROOMS: 1 (60)
- ★ STANDARD BEDROOM SIZE: 24 m^2
- ★ PRIVATE BALCONIES: no – but general terrace

- ★ SWIMMING POOL: no
- ★ GARDENS: yes – private park overlooking the whole of Florence
- ★ NO. OF STAFF: 35
- ★ ROOM SERVICE: 07.00–24.00
- ★ ORIENTATION: south
- ★ FURTHER DEVELOPMENTS: a swimming pool
- ★ CREDIT CARDS: American Express, Eurocard and Bankamericard
- ★ OWNING COMPANY: Cipriani S.p.A.
- ★ GENERAL MANAGER: vacant
- ★ DISTANCE TO SHOPS: minutes by car
- ★ DISTANCE FROM AIRPORT: 7 km

A hotel whose facade (and possibly more) was designed by Michelangelo gives me the cultural sensation equal to a bedroom in the Winter Palace. If this were the only reason to stay at the Villa San Michele, it would be reason enough – but it is not. Here is a gracious and perfectly beautiful country hotel overlooking Florence and well away from the noise, looking over terraced gardens and managing to produce a feeling of wellbeing which is beyond compare. A former Franciscan monastery, it still has its own chapel and the cells transformed into magnificent bedrooms. Now the hotel has been acquired by one of the most distinguished hotel companies in Italy, no doubt San Michele will be even better than it was which, frankly, would be difficult. The place is done up with impeccable taste and every piece of furniture is just right for that spot. Out there, on the long arched terrace, Italian light-fantastic cuisine blends wonderfully with the panorama. It's Florence at its best – without the hellish and raucous Vespas.

Florence

HOTEL EXCELSIOR, Piazza Ognissanti, 3, Florence

- ★ TELEPHONE: 294301
- ★ CABLES: Italexotel
- ★ TELEX: 570022 Excefi I
- ★ IN OPERATION: since 1958
- ★ RESERVATIONS: Italian Grand Hotels Ltd, (CIGA) worldwide/Landia International Services Ltd, worldwide
- ★ ROOMS: 148 doubles 59 singles
- ★ SUITES: 10
- ★ RESTAURANTS: 1 – 'U Cestello'
- ★ BARS: 2 – 'Donatello' bar and cocktail lounge
- ★ DISCOTHEQUE: no – but piano music in the bar
- ★ SHOPS: none – only show windows
- ★ CONFERENCE ROOMS: 5 (up to 510)
- ★ BANQUETING ROOMS: 5 (up to 510)

- ★ STANDARD BEDROOM SIZE: 15/16 m^2
- ★ PRIVATE BALCONIES: yes
- ★ SWIMMING POOL: no
- ★ RECREATIONAL ACTIVITIES: golf nearby
- ★ GARDENS: no
- ★ NO. OF STAFF: 210
- ★ ROOM SERVICE: around the clock
- ★ ORIENTATION: rooms overlook the river, Piazza Ognissanti and Borgognissanti
- ★ CREDIT CARDS: all main credit cards
- ★ OWNING COMPANY: Cigahotels Centro Nord, S.p.A.
- ★ GENERAL MANAGER: Paolo Biscioni
- ★ DISTANCE FROM SHOPS: within shopping centre
- ★ DISTANCE FROM AIRPORT: 80 km (Pisa) and 6 km (Peretola)

Following the last edition, many readers wrote to ask why, among several hotels in Tuscany, there was not a single one in Florence itself. Uttering polite noises I explained that it is very difficult to sleep in this fantastically beautiful city simply because of the noise of traffic and people. However, on a more recent visit to the grand old Excelsior, always a very good hotel, I discovered that it had been completely refurbished, including insulation and air conditioning, which means that now we can sleep happily right on the bank of the Arno. This grand city hotel, with more than a little 'bella figura', has now been restored to its former glories – a magnificent lobby, beautifully furnished with period furniture and a better than average Italian welcome. I particularly liked the Donatello Bar, not one of those gaudy affairs with shiny mosaic but a place where you can sit in comfort and enjoy your drink while looking around. The newly decorated rooms are handsomely done up, with very comfortable beds and enough wardrobe space for a duchess. Service is much better than it was a few years ago and the food has also improved. A walk away are the Ponte Vecchio and the Piazza della Signoria.

Milan

HOTEL PRINCIPE & SAVOIA, Piazza della Repubblica, 17, Milano

- ★ TELEPHONE: 02/6230
- ★ CABLES: Principal
- ★ TELEX: 310052
- ★ IN OPERATION: since 1927
- ★ RESERVATIONS: Cigahotels
- ★ ROOMS: 199 doubles 75 singles
- ★ SUITES: 20
- ★ RESTAURANTS: 1
- ★ BARS: 1
- ★ DISCOTHEQUE: piano bar
- ★ SHOPS: 1
- ★ CONFERENCE ROOMS: 4 (140 to 350)
- ★ BANQUETING ROOMS: 5 (140 to 300)
- ★ STANDARD BEDROOM SIZE: 35 m²
- ★ PRIVATE BALCONIES: yes
- ★ SWIMMING POOL: no
- ★ GARDENS: yes
- ★ NO. OF STAFF: 300
- ★ ROOM SERVICE: around the clock
- ★ ORIENTATION: south
- ★ CREDIT CARDS: Amexco, Diners Club, Eurocard, Bankamericard
- ★ OWNING COMPANY: Cigahotels
- ★ GENERAL MANAGER: Roberto Bucciarelli
- ★ DISTANCE TO SHOPS: 10 minutes
- ★ DISTANCE FROM AIRPORT: 10 km

If you have to go to Milan, and I would much rather not, there is only one place to stay – the Principe e Savoia, one of those oldish city hotels that seems to march with the times without too many hiccups. There is almost as much marble in the bathrooms as in the lobby, some beautiful ceilings and a fair sprinkling of very valuable antiques which help to give it a good deal of elegant character. Some people prefer the new and very smart rooms in the annex but I tend to go for those in the central building which are more traditional and extremely comfortable, with good period-less furniture and excellent beds. Telephones answer 'pronto' in a split second and in another split second switch to your language with ease and urbanity. A good deal of attention is obviously paid to cleanliness and freshness and the food, served in a restaurant which is rather undistinguished-looking is far better than the decor.

Montecatini Terme

GRAND HOTEL & LA PACE, Corso Roma 12, 51016 Montecatini Terme

- ★ TELEPHONE: (0572) 75801
- ★ CABLES: Paceotel
- ★ TELEX: 570004 Paceot
- ★ IN OPERATION: since 1870
- ★ RESERVATIONS: Hotel Representative Inc
- ★ ROOMS: 96 doubles 60 singles
- ★ SUITES: 14
- ★ RESTAURANTS: 3
- ★ BARS: 2
- ★ DISCOTHEQUE: no – piano bar
- ★ SHOPS: none
- ★ CONFERENCE ROOMS: 5 (10 to 220)

★ BANQUETING ROOMS: 2 (150 and 500)
★ STANDARD BEDROOM SIZE: 20 m²
★ PRIVATE BALCONIES: yes
★ SWIMMING POOL: yes – fresh water, 30 m
★ RECREATIONAL ACTIVITIES: Health Spa with sauna, solarium, massage, underwater massage, tennis, also horse riding and golf nearby
★ GARDENS: yes

★ NO. OF STAFF: 96
★ ROOM SERVICE: 07.00–22.00
★ ORIENTATION: south
★ CREDIT CARDS: American Express
★ OWNING COMPANY: privately owned
★ GENERAL MANAGER: Gino Degli Innocenti
★ DISTANCE TO BEACH: 60 km
★ DISTANCE TO SHOPS: walking distance
★ DISTANCE FROM AIRPORT: 50 km (Pisa)

One of the oddities about writing this book is that unless readers send in comments, one never quite knows who goes where. One German lady from Stuttgart left me in no doubt. She went to the celebrated 'La Pace' and wrote me four pages about it: 'Splendid . . . an amazing place . . . one of the most beautiful hotels I have ever visited . . . one feels like royalty in disguise'. Naturally I am glad she liked this grand old lady of all Italian spa hotels since I have always had a special reverence for it.

The vast public rooms are palatial and so are the furnishings. Everywhere one finds vistas of marble columns, great sweeps of delightfully natural grassland, mysterious nymphs beckoning into the glades – but there is nothing mysterious about the service which seems to glide along on marbled floors, loaded with silverware and tempting morsels. The food in the Versailles-sized restaurant could even tempt me to go to 'La Pace' to take the waters – it would almost be worth it. Rooms are good though some tend to be smaller than one would hope in such a huge building but on the whole they are extremely comfortable and practical.

Though the hotel can be very convivial in the international sense, I have always felt that this was the kind of place I would like to go for a personal 'retreat' like the anchorites of old. One could enjoy solitude and not suffer too much.

Positano

HOTEL LE SIRENUSE, Via C. Colombo, 30, Positano (Salerno)

★ TELEPHONE: 089-875066
★ CABLES: Sirenuse Positano
★ TELEX: 770066 Sirhtl I
★ IN OPERATION: since 1951
★ RESERVATIONS: Utell International, New York, London/American International, New York
★ ROOMS: 58 doubles 2 singles some with jacuzzi
★ SUITES: 8
★ RESTAURANTS: 1
★ BARS: 2
★ DISCOTHEQUE: no
★ SHOPS: none
★ CONFERENCE ROOMS: 1 (up to 50)
★ BANQUETING ROOMS: 1 (up to 150)
★ STANDARD BEDROOM SIZE: 25 m²

★ PRIVATE BALCONIES: yes
★ SWIMMING POOL: yes – heated, fresh water, 20 × 6 m
★ GARDENS: no
★ NO. OF STAFF: 55
★ ROOM SERVICE: 07.00–23.00
★ ORIENTATION: rooms facing the sea
★ CREDIT CARDS: Amexco, Diners Club and Visa
★ OWNING COMPANY: Marchese Aldo Sersale
★ GENERAL MANAGER: L. Bozza
★ DISTANCE TO BEACH: 100 m
★ DISTANCE TO SHOPS: 100 m
★ DISTANCE FROM AIRPORT: 65 km (Napoli Capodichino)

The president of a multi-national corporation sent this cable from Le Sirenuse: 'Thank you for simply making my holiday and restoring my faith in the Italian way of life.' It's good to get it right sometimes and he was most welcome. Right in the middle of the Positano hillside, constructed from several of the colour-washed cubist houses that perch like the audience in an amphitheatre, Le Sirenuse is the creation of a very intelligent, very aristocratic lady who, in the course of time, acquired five houses with floors on seven different levels, added labyrinthine marble passages, furnished bedrooms the way she would have liked for herself, added a gaggle of terraces, a truly panoramic swimming pool and filled every corner with just the right bibelots. The result is that you get all the best of Positano without any of the aggro and only people like you share the place – it attracts a very good class of customer. Like most hotels in Italy, Le Sirenuse has had its problems with staff but all is now well, including the deliciously simple Italian fare, and if you want to see the overwhelming beauty of the Amalfi coast, this is the place to go, but not in July or August – October is the month I prefer here.

Rome

HOTEL EXCELSIOR, Via Vittorio Veneto 125, 00187 Rome

- ★ TELEPHONE: 4708
- ★ CABLES: Excelsior Roma
- ★ TELEX: Excelsior 610232
- ★ RESERVATIONS: Cigahotels
- ★ ROOMS: 415
- ★ SUITES: 37
- ★ RESTAURANTS: 2
- ★ BARS: 2
- ★ DISCOTHEQUE: no
- ★ SHOPS: 5
- ★ CONFERENCE ROOMS: 5 (40 to 600)
- ★ BANQUETING ROOMS: 6 (20 to 400)
- ★ STANDARD BEDROOM SIZE: 32 m²
- ★ PRIVATE BALCONIES: yes

- ★ SWIMMING POOL: no
- ★ GARDENS: no
- ★ NO. OF STAFF: 350
- ★ ROOM SERVICE: around the clock
- ★ ORIENTATION: main facade faces Via Veneto
- ★ CREDIT CARD: American Express, Diners Club, Bankamericard, Carte Blanche and Eurocard
- ★ OWNING COMPANY: Cigahotels
- ★ GENERAL MANAGER: Francesco Chiais
- ★ DISTANCE TO SHOPS: walking distance
- ★ DISTANCE FROM AIRPORT: 30 km

I have always felt that if one wants to see 'La vita all'Italiana', the best place to do so in comfort is the lobby of the Excelsior. All the chivalry and gallantry of the larger-than-life monde and demi-monde are here – film starlets, movie moghuls, richer than rich industrialists, hungry writers and those legions of beautiful but penniless people who are sure that something is going to turn up today – extras in a permanent Orson Welles–Humphrey Bogart film. Yet the fact is that the Excelsior is also one of the great hotels of the world, one which knows everything, has seen everything and is no longer capable of being in the least surprised. It has a kind of worldly-wise ambience which is quite remarkable with all the expected grandness of a grand hotel-size in public rooms, lovely period furniture, vast bathrooms and service omnipresent. The food is unexpectedly good in such circumstances and one is always surprised at how good the Excelsior remains under pressure that could easily make it very bad.

HASSLER VILLA MEDICI, Trinita dei Monti 66, 00187 Rome

- ★ TELEPHONE: 678.2651/679.2651
- ★ CABLES: Haslerhotel
- ★ TELEX: 610208
- ★ IN OPERATION: since 1944
- ★ RESERVATIONS: Hotel Representative Inc
- ★ ROOMS: 98
- ★ SUITES: 10
- ★ RESTAURANTS: 2 – roof restaurant and garden open air restaurant during the summer
- ★ BARS: 1
- ★ DISCOTHEQUE: no – but pianist in the bar
- ★ SHOPS: none
- ★ CONFERENCE ROOMS: 2 (25 to 60)

- ★ BANQUETING ROOMS: 2 (25 to 60)
- ★ STANDARD BEDROOM SIZE: variable
- ★ PRIVATE BALCONIES: yes – some rooms
- ★ SWIMMING POOL: no
- ★ GARDENS: yes
- ★ NO. OF STAFF: 150
- ★ ROOM SERVICE: 06.00–23.30
- ★ ORIENTATION: front faces Spanish Steps, near the Pincio Gardens
- ★ CREDIT CARDS: no
- ★ OWNING COMPANY: Alberghi Eden E Hassler S.p.A.
- ★ GENERAL MANAGER: Mr. Nadio Benedetti
- ★ DISTANCE TO SHOPS: immediate
- ★ DISTANCE FROM AIRPORT: 35 km

Down below are the Spanish Steps. Next door is Trinita dei Monti and within a credit card's throw are all those tempting shops of the Via Sistina and the Via Condotti. If this makes the Hassler sound like a vulgar tourist's one-night-stand, go in and think again. This is one of the most elegant, most private, most refined of all the smaller hotels in European capitals – a place of exquisite taste, smooth, silent service and quality in every single detail. The word plastic is never mentioned at the Hassler. Neither is the word 'group' since this is a hotel for individuals lucky enough to be able to afford it and even luckier in being able to get in at all. The colour schemes are particularly good and here and there are antiques that must be worth a few million, million lira. The rooms are so discreet, so quiet (and in Rome too) and so beautifully organised that you immediately feel at home – if this is the kind of home you have. At the top is a sensationally beautiful restaurant where one spends as much time looking at the view as one does inspecting one's food. The Hassler is for People with an upper-case P.

LE GRAND HOTEL, Via V. E. Orlando, 3, 00185 Rome

★ TELEPHONE: 06/4709
★ CABLES: Granotel Roma
★ TELEX: 610210 Granro I
★ IN OPERATION: since 1894
★ RESERVATIONS: Cigahotels
★ ROOMS: 117 doubles 22 singles
★ SUITES: 36
★ RESTAURANTS: 3 – 'Le Maschere', 'Le Rallye' and 'Le Pavilion'
★ BARS: 2
★ DISCOTHEQUE: no
★ SHOPS: none
★ CONFERENCE ROOMS: 12 (10 to 600)
★ BANQUETING ROOMS: 12 (10 to 300)
★ STANDARD BEDROOM SIZE: 20 m²

★ PRIVATE BALCONIES: yes – some rooms
★ SWIMMING POOL: no
★ RECREATIONAL ACTIVITIES: sauna and massage
★ GARDENS: no
★ NO. OF STAFF: 218
★ ROOM SERVICE: around the clock
★ ORIENTATION: south
★ CREDIT CARDS: Amexco, Bankamericard, Eurocard, Carte Blanche and Visa
★ OWNING COMPANY: Cigahotels
★ GENERAL MANAGER: Mario Miconi
★ DISTANCE TO SHOPS: walking distance
★ DISTANCE FROM AIRPORT: 30 km

If you already have an apartment in Manhattan, a studio on the Ile St. Louis and your own Greek island, there is only one thing missing from your life – a suite at the Grand in Rome, one of the world's truly grand, grand hotels. Its fin de siècle magnificence had the right parentage – Ritz and Escoffier opened it together and it has certainly not deteriorated since. Let others have the movie starlets-à-gogo. The Grand has itself, the greatest possible attraction. It is a sumptuous place – all marble and tapestries and gilt, magnificent mirrors and flattering chandeliers. The decor of Le Maschere Restaurant (scenes from the Comedia dell'Arte) is one of the two or three finest in any hotel eating place known to me. What is more, the food goes with it – splendidly delicate and even Romans agree that its pasta dishes are faultless. The staff – most of them seem to have matured with the hotel – are the last word in jovial courtesy – Italian style – they know everything, including how to get an audience with the Pope.
Not all rooms are alike – they just share a high standard. The best ones and the suites, of course, will ensure that you never want to leave – so much solid, good-taste comfort is hard to come by these days. The beds are superb, the wardrobes huge and in my bathroom there were three kinds of soap and a little note to say that if I did not like any of them I should ask for others. Perhaps what matters most at the Grand is that if you stay there, even the most superior Roman will recognise your existence.

Sardinia
HOTEL CALA DI VOLPE, 1-07020 Porto Cervo, Costa Smeralda

★ TELEPHONE: 0789 96083
★ CABLES: Calavolpe Portocervo
★ TELEX: 790274

★ IN OPERATION: 18 years
★ RESERVATIONS: Hotel Representative Inc
★ ROOMS: 125

★ RESTAURANTS: 1 – plus a poolside barbecue
★ BARS: 3
★ DISCOTHEQUE: yes
★ SHOPS: 5 – boutiques, drugstore and hairdressers
★ CONFERENCE ROOMS: none
★ BANQUETING ROOMS: none
★ STANDARD BEDROOMS SIZE: 20/30 m²
★ PRIVATE BALCONIES: yes
★ SWIMMING POOL: yes – salt water
★ RECREATIONAL ACTIVITIES: boating, water skiing, underwater fishing, tennis and golf close by. Private harbour for pleasure boats
★ GARDENS: yes
★ NO. OF STAFF: 185
★ ROOM SERVICE: around the clock
★ ORIENTATION: mainly south
★ CREDIT CARDS: American Express, Diners Club and Master Charge
★ OWNING COMPANY: Costa Smeralda Corporation
★ GENERAL MANAGER: G. Daina
★ DISTANCE TO BEACH: walking distance
★ DISTANCE TO SHOPS: walking distance
★ DISTANCE FROM AIRPORT: 30 km (Olbia)

Architect Jacques Couelle is celebrated the world over as the master of 'the perfect imperfect' and he spent years designing Cala di Volpe for his then client, the Aga Khan and, although I personally dislike the present being made to look like the past, I must admit that this hotel succeeds where others of the kind would fail miserably. The reason isn't only money – just good taste aplenty with not a single offending note, not a single overstatement in this serpentine cluster of buildings hugging a heavenly peninsula. Rooms are deceptively simple and highly luxurious when you look into the details and the apparent rusticity of the decor comes off with a gentle flourish. Service is impeccable and the food very distinguished indeed and all around you is the incredible Costa Smeralda. What makes Casa di Volpe in the long run is its guests – their lifestyle, their clothes, their personality adds to the hotel picture.

HOTEL PITRIZZA, Liscia di Vacca, 07020 Porto Cervo-Costa Smeralda

★ TELEPHONE: (0789) 9200/92161
★ CABLES: Hotel Pitrizza
★ TELEX: Cosme 790037
★ IN OPERATION: since 1964
★ RESERVATIONS: direct and travel agents
★ ROOMS: 22 doubles 6 singles
★ SUITES: 1 (1 double, 1 single, sitting room, bathroom)
★ RESTAURANTS: 1 – and barbecue
★ DISCOTHEQUE: none – but piano bar
★ SHOPS: none
★ CONFERENCE ROOMS: none
★ BANQUETING ROOMS: none
★ STANDARD BEDROOM SIZE: 26 m²
★ PRIVATE BALCONIES: yes – most of the rooms
★ SWIMMING POOL: yes – salt water, 150 m²
★ RECREATIONAL ACTIVITIES: tennis club
and golf club nearby; windsurfing, scuba diving, swimming, boat hire
★ GARDEN: yes – 4 acres
★ NO. OF STAFF: 53
★ ROOM SERVICE: round the clock
★ ORIENTATION: clubhouse faces north-east but each villa has a different orientation
★ CREDIT CARDS: American Express, Diners Club and Eurocard
★ OWNING COMPANY: Società Alberghiera Costa Smeralda
★ GENERAL MANAGER: Antonio Marson
★ DISTANCE TO BEACH: on the beach
★ DISTANCE TO SHOPS: 4 km to Porto Cervo Village
★ DISTANCE FROM AIRPORT: 30 km Olbia/Costa Smeralda. Private bus service to and from airport

Rusticity only becomes an art form when it is carried out with real respect for nature. Pitrizza is like that – one of the nicest, most informal and yet most elegant hotels I know in the Mediterranean. The Costa Smeralda has a lot of this, of course, but for me the small Pitrizza is the best – a place where one lives simply but gorgeously, comfortably and yet without any of the trappings which appear necessary elsewhere. Rooms are in small private villas, scattered over the rocks overlooking a divine beach. Any one of them will please you, with its own, ultra-private terrace, spacious rooms and décor that is deceptively simple. The Pitrizza is a club-like hotel whose members or habitués appear to know each other without in the least wishing for artificial conviviality. As a resort hotel this one must be one of the most superior for a very long way in all directions.

Siena

CERTOSA DI MAGGIANO, Strada di Certosa No. 82, Siena

★ TELEPHONE: 0577/288180 42083
★ CABLES: Certosotel
★ TELEX: 574221
★ IN OPERATION: since 1975
★ RESERVATIONS: direct/Relais et Chateaux, Paris
★ ROOMS: 5
★ SUITES: 9
★ RESTAURANTS: 1 – also buffet by the swimming pool in the high season
★ BARS: 1 – also one at the swimming pool from April to September
★ DISCOTHEQUE: no – but music in the library
★ SHOPS: none
★ CONFERENCE ROOMS: none
★ BANQUETING ROOMS: none
★ STANDARD BEDROOM SIZE: 28 m²
★ PRIVATE BALCONIES: yes
★ SWIMMING POOL: yes – fresh water, heated, 12 × 6 m

★ NO. OF STAFF: 20
★ RECREATIONAL ACTIVITIES: tennis and game of draughts in the garden on the ground
★ GARDENS: yes – a large park and promenades in an olive tree garden
★ ROOM SERVICE: 08.00–23.00
★ ORIENTATION: main facade overlooks the country
★ FURTHER DEVELOPMENTS: a further six rooms to be developed
★ CREDIT CARDS: American Express, Diners Club, Bankamericard and Visa
★ OWNING COMPANY: I.T.A.R. S.p.A.
★ GENERAL MANAGER: Anna Grossi Recordati
★ DISTANCE TO BEACH: 60 km
★ DISTANCE TO SHOPS: 1.5 km
★ DISTANCE FROM AIRPORT: 120 km (Pisa)

Whoever uses the word 'Siena' has uttered a noble word – one of two or three favourite Italian cities – I hardly need an excuse to go back and sit on that superlative Piazza del Campo and find the way back to those centuries when people had time to stop, think, create beauty and live with it. And, as is so often the case in Italy, I know just the right place to rest my head. Certosa di Maggiano is a delightful thirteenth-century Carthusian monastery, complete with arched cloister around a divinely proportioned square, ancient gardens with ancient olive trees and so few guests that one feels like being in a friend's house. Both bedrooms and public rooms are extremely tastefully furnished with very good pieces and floors shining with the patina of ages.

The flowers are always fresh and the books lining the library walls look as if they are occasionally read and there are splendid tapestries and paintings everywhere. The lady manager obviously loves the place and so do I because it is just right for Siena which is just a short walk away. The food, while not great, is very acceptable but what counts above all is the atmosphere of the place – calm, civilised and good-mannered.

Taormina

MAZZARO SEA PALACE, 98030 Taormina, Sicily

★ TELEPHONE: 0942/24004
★ CABLES: Palace

★ TELEX: 980041 Maseap
★ IN OPERATION: since 1972

★ RESERVATIONS: Hotel Representative Inc, New York and London/Italhotels, Torino/Steigenberger Reservation Service, Frankfurt
★ ROOMS: 63 doubles   14 singles
★ SUITES: 4
★ RESTAURANTS: 2 – Bougainvillea and Terrace Restaurant
★ BARS: 2 (Piano Bar)
★ DISCOTHEQUE: no – but live entertainment
★ SHOPS: 1
★ CONFERENCE ROOMS: 2 (30 to 300)
★ BANQUETING ROOMS: 1 (up to 300)
★ STANDARD BEDROOM SIZE: 30 m²
★ PRIVATE BALCONIES: yes
★ SWIMMING POOL: yes – salt water, heated, 120 m²
★ RECREATIONAL ACTIVITIES: water sports and tennis available at the Sporting Club in Taormina
★ GARDENS: yes
★ NO. OF STAFF: 75
★ ROOM SERVICE: 07.00–24.00
★ ORIENTATION: all rooms overlook the sea
★ CREDIT CARDS: American Express, Diners Club and Bankamericard
★ OWNING COMPANY: Tirrena Hotels
★ MANAGER: Giovanni Cacopardo
★ DISTANCE TO BEACH: on the beach
★ DISTANCE TO SHOPS: 2 km
★ DISTANCE FROM AIRPORT: 50 km

I have had one or two comments from people who don't like this hotel. Too modern, they say. I, on the contrary, feel that if a hotel is going to be modern, this is the way it should be – the best style, the best design. It is certainly no shy violet, hugging the sands of Taormina beach. You can't miss it, but for the rest it is to my mind an exceedingly good and thoughtfully planned beach hotel. Rooms are very large by continental standards; public rooms are vast and cool and one can glide in and out effortlessly and the private terraces – rare in this part of the world – are large enough to swing a tiger in yet one is never overlooked. What appeals to me most of all, after the cheap-and-nasty beach furniture one sees everywhere these days is that the Mazzaro variety is handsome, practical and always very clean. Food tends to be somewhat international but who cares in this case? Lovely, mellow Taormina is just up the road and its trattorie are legion. The Mazzaro could be the place for some sun-soaking. But don't go there in July or August.

SAN DOMENICO PALACE HOTEL, Piazza S. Domenico, 5, 98039 Taormina

- ★ TELEPHONE: 0942-23701
- ★ CABLES: Sandomenico
- ★ TELEX: 980013 DOMHOT
- ★ IN OPERATION: 100 years
- ★ RESERVATIONS: Utell International
- ★ ROOMS: 88 doubles 31 singles
- ★ SUITES: 10
- ★ RESTAURANTS: 2
- ★ BARS: 2
- ★ DISCOTHEQUE: no – but piano in the bar every night and a Sicilian mandolin orchestra on Fridays and Saturdays
- ★ SHOPS: none
- ★ CONFERENCE ROOMS: 3 (30, 100 and 450)
- ★ BANQUETING ROOMS: 1 (350)
- ★ STANDARD BEDROOM SIZE: 25 m²

- ★ PRIVATE BALCONIES: yes
- ★ SWIMMING POOL: yes – fresh water, 14 × 5 m
- ★ RECREATIONAL ACTIVITIES: tennis and water skiing
- ★ GARDENS: yes
- ★ NO. OF STAFF: 100
- ★ ROOM SERVICE: 07.00–23.00
- ★ ORIENTATION: south and facing Mount Etna
- ★ CREDIT CARDS: Bankamericard, American Express and Diners Club
- ★ OWNING COMPANY: Atahotels S.p.A.
- ★ GENERAL MANAGER: Francesco Forlano
- ★ DISTANCE TO BEACH: 4 km
- ★ DISTANCE TO SHOPS: 60 m
- ★ DISTANCE FROM AIRPORT: 50 km

Looking out to Taormina's Greek theatre and the distant profile of Mount Etna, the gardens of this hotel, overflowing with bloom and lovely trees dotted with formally rustic seats and ravishing pines of classical statuary, one looks down to a very large and handsome swimming pool. San Domenico started life as a Dominican monastery in the fourteenth century and the monastic austerity has been tempered with some of the later Renaissance exuberance which prosperity and a falling off of devotion brought in its train. The furnishings are quite beautiful, especially the antiques along the interior cloister. Sicily has always resisted conquerors, and even as rulers, this method has chiefly been the Mafia or its style. Here you will not be kidnapped or shot because you are too important to molest – they will only take you if they know your disposable assets to the last shilling. Sicily has ever been rough on its enemies and kind to its friends.

Venice

HOTEL CIPRIANI, Giudecca 10, 30123 Venice

★ TELEPHONE: 70-77-44
★ CABLES: Hotel Cipriani-Venezia
★ TELEX: 410162
★ IN OPERATION: since 1958
★ RESERVATIONS: Hotel Representative Inc, New York, London/Fairways & Swinford Travel Ltd, London
★ ROOMS: 90 doubles 4 singles
★ SUITES: 18
★ RESTAURANTS: 2 – Cipriani and Il Gabbiano
★ BARS: 2
★ DISCOTHEQUE: no – but piano bar
★ SHOPS: 2
★ CONFERENCE ROOMS: 4 (50 to 120)
★ BANQUETING ROOMS: 4 (50 to 250)
★ STANDARD BEDROOM SIZE: 40 m²
★ PRIVATE BALCONIES: yes
★ SWIMMING POOL: yes – salt water, 192 m²
★ RECREATIONAL ACTIVITIES: tennis and golf on the Lido. Own private yacht harbour – 10 berths
★ GARDENS: yes
★ NO. OF STAFF: 160
★ ROOM SERVICE: around the clock
★ ORIENTATION: rooms overlook water and gardens
★ FURTHER DEVELOPMENTS: completion of triennial plan by 1984, including a new bar and lobby and new de luxe junior suites wing
★ CREDIT CARDS: American Express
★ OWNING COMPANY: Hotel Cipriani S.p.A.
★ MANAGING DIRECTOR: N. Rusconi
★ DISTANCE TO BEACH: 10 minutes by boat
★ DISTANCE TO SHOPS: 4 minutes by boat
★ DISTANCE FROM AIRPORT: 10 km

For all those who love Venice but hate its crowds, there is only one address: Cipriani's. Here, on Giudecca, a mere few minutes from the heart of this immortal city, is a haven of peace and tranquillity run with omnipresent discretion by one of the great hoteliers of this world. Cipriani's is chic – perhaps the only word for it – but chic with a kind of easy-going grand manner: 'bella figura' if you like. The rooms and suites are all different, light and pleasant and some of them have their own terrace-garden right on the pool which, incidentally, is the only hotel pool in Venice. There is a gentleness about Cipriani which soon gets you. The famous gardens are so tenderly cared for that one would swear that's the way things grow, i.e. flowers blooming overnight. Dining out of doors in the soft, velvety Venetian night is one of the rarest pleasures of life. On re-examination, I still believe that the cuisine is the finest of any hotel in Venice and, happily, the world is full of ex-Cipriani chefs who made it here first. The perfect place in which to relax elegantly.

HOTEL GRITTI PALACE, Canal Grande 30100, Venice

★ TELEPHONE: 26044
★ CABLES: Palace Venice
★ TELEX: 410125 Gritti
★ IN OPERATION: since 1948
★ RESERVATIONS: Cigahotels
★ ROOMS: 74 doubles 17 singles
★ SUITES: 11
★ RESTAURANTS: 2
★ BARS: 1
★ DISCOTHEQUE: no
★ SHOPS: none
★ CONFERENCE ROOMS: 4 (15 to 150)
★ BANQUETING ROOMS: 4 (15 to 90)
★ STANDARD BEDROOM SIZE: 25 m²
★ PRIVATE BALCONIES: yes – some rooms
★ SWIMMING POOL: no
★ GARDENS: no
★ NO. OF STAFF: 110
★ ROOM SERVICE: around the clock
★ ORIENTATION: overlooks Grand Canal
★ CREDIT CARDS: American Express, Diners Club, Bankamericard and Eurocard
★ OWNING COMPANY: Cigahotels
★ GENERAL MANAGER: Nico Passante
★ DISTANCE TO BEACH: 2 km
★ DISTANCE TO SHOPS: 5 minutes
★ DISTANCE FROM AIRPORT: 10 km

What can one say about the Gritti that has not been said a thousand times before? The best loved hotel in the world? The most beautiful? The most original? The most intimate? All adjectival extravaganzas would be justified by this gem of a palace on the

Grand Canal and when you enter the world-famous Grill Room to look at the portrait of the old Doge whose home this was, you know that you have arrived, if not socially, then in a unique place. The Gritti is like a casket of jewels – perfection, artistry, great and never-failing good taste: the kind of place where one looks in vain for the almost inevitable faux pas. This is the kind of hotel hospitality which cannot be manufactured but only evolved over the years by a company, a management and a staff who really do care for beauty and quality. If you can have a canal-facing room, or better still, one of the corner ones you will surely feel as I do that nothing can match it. What is more, the Gritti is not just a beautiful antique. It works smoothly and with a kind of gallant cheerfulness that is remarkable. It seems that everybody instinctively knows what you want. I always end my Venice visit with dinner on the Grand Canal terrace – just to remind myself that heaven exists, here on earth, if you know the right address.

Venice Lido

EXCELSIOR HOTEL, Lungomare Marconi 40, Lido Venice

★ TELEPHONE: 760201
★ CABLES: Excelido
★ TELEX: 410023 Excelido
★ RESERVATIONS: Cigahotels
★ ROOMS: 252
★ SUITES: 18
★ RESTAURANTS: 3
★ BARS: 3
★ DISCOTHEQUE: yes – and open air night club
★ SHOPS: 9
★ CONFERENCE ROOMS: 9 (5 to 1,000)
★ BANQUETING ROOMS: 5 (500 to 2,500)
★ STANDARD BEDROOM SIZE: 40 m²

★ PRIVATE BALCONIES: yes
★ SWIMMING POOL: yes – fresh water
★ GARDENS: yes
★ NO. OF STAFF: 310
★ ROOM SERVICE: around the clock
★ ORIENTATION: rooms face Adriatic Sea and Lagoon
★ CREDIT CARDS: American Express, Diners Club, Eurocard, Bankamericard, Carte Blanche and Access
★ OWNING COMPANY: Cigahotels
★ GENERAL MANAGER: Alfredo Puricelli
★ DISTANCE TO BEACH: walking distance
★ DISTANCE FROM AIRPORT: 15 km

The finest grand hotel in all Italy, of the water-side hotels, the Excelsior lives the way it and its guests want and produces a feeling of well-being which is unique in such surroundings. The Excelsior has 'bella figura', that odd blend of showbiz, society and good taste that lifts it straight out of the ordinary. To be seen there is the most important thing of all to the Venetians and to be seen with the right companion is even more important because this is the cynosure of the up-market paparazzi. The new strand, with its well ordered army of cabanas, could only have been produced in Italy – you can be by the sea without spoiling your shoes. The Excelsior is chic, resplendent, very beautifully furnished and serviced by people who know what service is. I even like the modernised rooms where real designers have had a say. At night, dining on that divine terrace is one of the great moments of one's stay in Venice.

IVORY COAST
Abidjan

HOTEL IVOIRE INTER-CONTINENTAL, 08 B.P. 1 Abidjan 08

★ TELEPHONE: 44-10-45
★ CABLES: Inhotelcor Abidjan
★ TELEX: 3555 IHC HOT CI
★ IN OPERATION: since 1963
★ RESERVATIONS: Inter-Continental Hotels Corporation

★ ROOMS: 750
★ SUITES: 45
★ RESTAURANTS: 5
★ BARS: 3
★ DISCOTHEQUE: yes
★ SHOPS: 18

★ CONFERENCE ROOMS: 18 (30 to 2,000)
★ BANQUETING ROOMS: 9 (15 to 1,200)
★ STANDARD BEDROOM SIZE: 25 m²
★ PRIVATE BALCONIES: yes
★ SWIMMING POOL: yes – 2, fresh water, 312 m²
★ RECREATIONAL ACTIVITIES: tennis, 18-hole golf course, driving range, bowling alley, ice skating rink, health club with gymnasium, sauna and massage
★ GARDEN: yes
★ NO. OF STAFF: 850
★ ROOM SERVICE: around the clock

★ ORIENTATION: the back faces the residential Cocody area and the front faces the lagoon and the commercial area
★ CREDIT CARDS: Amexco, Diners Club, Carte Blanche, Master Charge, Visa, Bankamericard and Eurocard
★ OWNING COMPANY: Société du Palace de Cocody
★ GENERAL MANAGER: Tom J. Krooswijk
★ DISTANCE TO BEACH: 24 km
★ DISTANCE TO SHOPS: 10 minutes by car
★ DISTANCE FROM AIRPORT: 25 km

This is the best city hotel in black Africa. Having had the pleasure of revisiting the Ivoire, I am in no doubt at all about it. Though Abidjan – the Paris of West Africa – is not exactly the bush, running this kind of enterprise, very big and busy, cannot be easy but I have nothing but praise for management and staff. There is a huge, quite attractive tower block and a more sober, sideways one next door facing a gigantic pool and the famous lagoon. There, conference rooms, saunas, cinema, casino and, name it, the Ivoire has got it. Also some very attractive gardens, well laid out and well kept. American parentage and French influence have combined to produce a kind of hotel which is very rare in the African continent – everything works, laundry, service, messages, shopping, bars and restaurants. The choice of food is vast and attractive – I like the open-air Pavilion restaurant and also the spectacular Toit d'Abidjan. One is impressed by the expertise from the top-class general manager down to the room boy.

JAPAN
Hakone

FUJIYA HOTEL, 359 Miyanoshita, Hakone

★ TELEPHONE: (06460) 2-2211
★ CABLES: Fujiyahotel
★ TELEX: 2892-718
★ RESERVATIONS: direct
★ ROOMS: 158
★ SUITES: 13
★ RESTAURANTS: 3
★ BARS: 1
★ DISCOTHEQUE: no
★ SHOPS: 1
★ CONFERENCE ROOMS: 5 (8 to 260)
★ BANQUETING ROOMS: 3 (30 to 250)
★ STANDARD BEDROOM SIZE: 40 m²

★ PRIVATE BALCONIES: no
★ SWIMMING POOL: yes – 2, indoors and outdoors
★ GARDENS: yes
★ NO. OF STAFF: 200
★ ROOM SERVICE: 09.30–22.30
★ ORIENTATION: mainly east
★ CREDIT CARDS: American Express, Diners Club, Master Charge and Bankamericard
★ OWNING COMPANY: Fujiya Hotel Co
★ GENERAL MANAGER: Yuji A. Yamaguchi
★ DISTANCE FROM AIRPORT: 80 km (Tokyo)

If, apart from the big cities, I had to pick one hotel in Japan, the Fujiya would be it. It's a kind of Japanese Victorian folly, if you can imagine the combination – odd, personal, full of curious corners and recesses and vast bedrooms filled, or should one say, dotted with charmingly useless eastern-western furniture. The staff simply never stop bowing from morning to night and wear a perpetual Japanese show of teeth. But here it is really the gardens that are impressive in the best traditional manner – gorgeous trees, both oversized and undersized, miniature lawns, cascades and pools, cherry blossom and a score of those little Japanese bridges and interesting stones that are complemented by running water. The whole place is truly enchanting, and lies in the middle of the Hakone National Park. Tokyo and its suicidal taxi-drivers looks even worse from here.

Kyoto

MIYAKO HOTEL, Sanjo Keage, Kyoto, 605

★ TELEPHONE: (075) 771-7111
★ CABLES: Miyako Kyoto
★ TELEX: 5422-132 Miyako J
★ IN OPERATION: since 1893
★ RESERVATIONS: affiliated with Western International Hotels/Robert F. Warner, New York/John A. Tetley Co, Inc, Los Angeles
★ ROOMS: 422 doubles 21 singles
★ SUITES: 10
★ RESTAURANTS: 7
★ BARS: 1
★ DISCOTHEQUE: live music nightly
★ SHOPS: 27
★ CONFERENCE ROOMS: 15 (40 to 900)
★ BANQUETING ROOMS: 15 (20 to 750)
★ STANDARD BEDROOM SIZE: 33 m²
★ PRIVATE BALCONIES: yes
★ SWIMMING POOL: yes – 4, fresh water
★ GARDENS: yes
★ NO. OF STAFF: 540
★ ROOM SERVICE: 07.15–23.00
★ ORIENTATION: some rooms face the street, others face gardens and hills
★ CREDIT CARDS: American Express, Diners Club, Carte Blanche, Bankamericard and Master Charge
★ OWNING COMPANY: Westin Hotels Inc
★ GENERAL MANAGER: S. K. Kawana
★ DISTANCE TO SHOPS: 5 minutes by car
★ DISTANCE FROM AIRPORT: 50 km

Kyoto is rather like the Tower of London or Stratford-upon-Avon – the tourist js led there as to an abyss, and the clever travellers stay at the Miyako which is even better because here one can have the new Japan (rather like everywhere else) or the old Japan – quite unique and unlike anywhere else. The new wing is certainly equipped with enough gadgets to take off into space but you will find the Japanese wing, with its authentic Japanese rooms – sliding windows opening up on vast banks of azaleas and a superb 16-acre Japanese garden – a far more rewarding place to stay. If I had to pick on two things that are special to the Miyako, I would bestow the accolade on the extraordinary cleanliness of the place and the cheerful and omnipresent service, complete with so many bows and salutations that one feels embarrassed. One has a vast variety of choices of things to eat but, of course, the best is the Japanese cuisine.

Osaka

THE PLAZA, 2-49, Oyodo-Minami 2-chome, Oyodo-ku, Osaka 531

★ TELEPHONE: (06) 453-1111
★ CABLES: Plazahotel Osaka
★ TELEX: 524-5557 Plaosa J
★ IN OPERATION: 12 years
★ RESERVATIONS: Hotel Representatives Inc
★ ROOMS: 559
★ SUITES: 16
★ RESTAURANTS: 6 – Rendez-vous Grill, Belvedere, Hanagiri, Sui-En, Yodo and The Plaza Pantry
★ BARS: 3 bars, 1 cocktail lounge
★ DISCOTHEQUE: live music in Vista Lounge and Belvedere Restaurant
★ SHOPS: 18 including watches and clocks, electrical goods, china, furniture, clothes, books, beauty salon, barber, food and chemist
★ CONFERENCE ROOMS: 14
★ BANQUETING ROOMS: 14
★ STANDARD BEDROOM SIZE: 23 m²
★ PRIVATE BALCONIES: no
★ SWIMMING POOL: yes – fresh water
★ RECREATIONAL ACTIVITIES: Japanese tea ceremony room
★ GARDENS: yes
★ NO. OF STAFF: 700
★ ROOM SERVICE: around the clock
★ ORIENTATION: rooms face east and west
★ CREDIT CARDS: all major credit cards
★ OWNING COMPANY: Asahi Broadcasting Corporation
★ GENERAL MANAGER: Michio Nagaoka
★ DISTANCE TO SHOPS: 1 km
★ DISTANCE FROM AIRPORT: 13 km

On my first visit to the Plaza, I recall a charming Japanese young lady coming forward as I checked in, bowing and saying: 'Mr. Lecler, you have a French name and a British passport. Would you please prefer to be addressed in French or in English?' Well, well. I immediately wondered what other highlights lay in store. Quite a few – the biggest lobby I have ever seen, a delicious stone garden such as only Japanese can create, a gorgeous swimming pool (right in the middle of Osaka . . .), clean, good-looking furniture, a Japanese orchestra whose members can play Mendelssohn as if born to it and one of the finest European restaurants in the Far East where most of the dishes were created by Paul Bocuse and Louis Outhier and a wedding ceremony room which even at my advanced age I would have been tempted to use had it not meant risking a jail sentence.

In Japan, nowadays the country of the perfectionist, the Plaza is known as the hotel with everything and I for one could certainly not find anything missing in this splendid example of hotelmanship. One can no longer joke about Japanese hotels. One develops respect and admiration.

ROYAL HOTEL, 3-68, Nakanoshima 5-chome, Kita-Ku, Osaka

* TELEPHONE: (06) 448-1121
* CABLES: Royalhotel, Osaka
* TELEX: J63350 Royalhtl
* IN OPERATION: 47 years
* RESERVATIONS: Steigenberger Reservation Service/Japan Airlines/Japan Travel Bureau International Inc
* ROOMS: 835 doubles 600 singles
* SUITES: 65
* RESTAURANTS: 17
* BARS: 4
* DISCOTHEQUE: live music and dancing nightly in Sky Lounge and musical entertainment in the Cellar Bar
* SHOPS: 60
* CONFERENCE ROOMS: 30 (10 to 1,500)
* BANQUETING ROOMS: 30 (25 to 3,000)

* STANDARD BEDROOM SIZE: 30 m^2
* PRIVATE BALCONIES: no
* SWIMMING POOL: yes – fresh water, heated, indoor 25 m
* RECREATIONAL ACTIVITIES: sauna, gym and health club. Cultural school in hotel
* GARDENS: yes
* NO. OF STAFF: 1,100
* ROOM SERVICE: 06.00–02.00
* ORIENTATION: faces all directions
* CREDIT CARDS: American Express, Diners Club, Carte Blanche, Bankamericard and Master Charge
* OWNING COMPANY: The Royal Hotel Ltd
* GENERAL MANAGER: Minoru Watanabe
* DISTANCE TO SHOPS: 10 minutes by car
* DISTANCE FROM AIRPORT: 16 km

One of the most surprising hotels in the world. Certainly one of the biggest – 1,600 rooms, 58 banqueting rooms, 17 restaurants and half a hundred shops. On my first visit to the Royal I wondered how could people run a hotel this size? Well, the Japanese can and do with a style all of their own. In one corner I even discovered some pottery by Bernard Leach next to the Japanese counterpart. The gardens are an absolute poem – a twenty-four syllable haiku perhaps – created by someone with more than the usual Japanese green finger. I approached the French restaurant with trepidation only to find that the onion soup was as good as in Montmartre. There are five Japanese restaurants and one of those marvellous beef places one finds only in Japan. Of the public rooms I much preferred the Japanese lounge, with its marvellous panels, to the main lobby – about the size of the Place de la Concorde. What was a revelation was the personalised service in such an enormous caravanserai – even the floor staff greeted us by name, missing all the 'r's, of course. When modernity is like this, tempered with good taste, I have no objection.

Tokyo

IMPERIAL HOTEL, 1-1-1, Uchisaiwai-cho, Chiyoda-ku, Tokyo 100

* TELEPHONE: 03-504-1111
* CABLES: Impho Tokyo
* TELEX: 222-2346 IMPHO J
* IN OPERATION: since 1890
* RESERVATIONS: Steigenberger Reservation Service/Japan Travel Bureau International Inc/Japan Airlines/ Preferred Hotels Association

* ROOMS: 770
* SUITES: 55
* RESTAURANTS: 5 – Fontainebleau, Prunier, Grill Room, Rainbow Room and Coffee House 'Cycles'
* BARS: 4
* DISCOTHEQUE: no – but live music in the Rainbow Room

★ SHOPS: shopping arcade
★ CONFERENCE ROOMS: 24 (30 to 3,000)
★ BANQUETING ROOMS: 24 (30 to 3,000)
★ STANDARD BEDROOM SIZE: 37 m²
★ PRIVATE BALCONIES: no
★ SWIMMING POOL: no
★ GARDENS: yes
★ NO. OF STAFF: 1,500
★ ROOM SERVICE: 07.00–24.00
★ ORIENTATION: overlooking the Imperial Palace grounds and Hibiya Park
★ FURTHER DEVELOPMENTS: Imperial Tower opening in March, 1983 – 363 luxury class rooms, 7 new restaurants, sauna, international boutiques and all-season swimming pool
★ CREDIT CARDS: Diners Club, American Express, Master Charge, Bankamericard, Carte Blanche and Eurocard
★ OWNING COMPANY: Imperial Hotel Ltd
★ GENERAL MANAGER: Ichiro Inumaru
★ DISTANCE TO BEACH: 2 km
★ DISTANCE TO SHOPS: 5 minutes
★ DISTANCE FROM AIRPORT: 65 km (Narita), 10 km (Haneda)

The Emperor of Japan lives next door and, although one can't see him, one is obviously close to the fount of power. When I first knew it, the Imperial used to be as reassuringly old-fashioned as I suspect the palace itself must be but not any more. Like most things in Japan it's the last word in size and appearance. One banqueting room is a mere 28,000 square feet and in the enormous marble lobby, you need a little Honda to get to the reception desk ninety feet away. Yet, it all works very smoothly, with lots of little bows and nowhere does it offend because Japanese architects are far too well educated – cultured – for that. The rooms are large, very simply and unostentatiously modern and the suites are big enough for a board meeting. What surprised me despite all this is that the service is delightfully personalised, quiet and efficient. There are six restaurants and you can gorge yourself on tempura or on French cuisine.

HOTEL OKURA, 10-4 Toranomon, 2-chome, Minato-ku, Tokyo 105

★ TELEPHONE: (03) 582-0111
★ CABLES: Hotelokura
★ TELEX: J 22790 Tokyo 242-2014
★ IN OPERATION: since 1962
★ RESERVATIONS: Hotel Representative Inc, worldwide/Hotel Okura Europe Office, Amsterdam/Robert F. Warner, London, New York/John A. Tetley Co, Inc, Los Angeles/Utell International (UK) Ltd, Sydney, Melbourne/Muriel Fleger International, Toronto
★ ROOMS: 980
★ SUITES: 68
★ RESTAURANTS: 8
★ BARS: 5
★ DISCOTHEQUE: no – but piano in French restaurant and music in bar
★ SHOPS: 41
★ CONFERENCE ROOMS: 37 (up to 3,000)
★ BANQUETING ROOMS: 37 (up to 3,000)
★ STANDARD BEDROOM SIZE: 32 m²
★ PRIVATE BALCONIES: yes – all rooms on fifth floor (main building)
★ SWIMMING POOL: yes – 2 fresh water
★ RECREATIONAL ACTIVITIES: health club and gymnasium, steam bath, Japanese massage, platform tennis and spa
★ GARDENS: yes – Japanese garden
★ NO. OF STAFF: 1,400
★ ROOM SERVICE: 06.00–01.00
★ ORIENTATION: rooms face various directions
★ CREDIT CARDS: Access, American Express, Bankamericard, Barclaycard, American Torch Club, Chargex, Diners Club, Visa, Carte Blanche, Eurocard and Master Card
★ OPERATING COMPANY: Okura
★ GENERAL MANAGER: T. Goto
★ DISTANCE TO SHOPS: central
★ DISTANCE FROM AIRPORT: 60 km

One thing I will never forget about the Okura is the first waiter I spoke to in the French restaurant. He spoke English with a French accent, had been trained in France and learnt English in Japan. When I switched over to French he was absolutely delighted and served my meal with total Gallic aplomb. Another thing I like about this very large hotel is that it is one of the quietest in Tokyo (only Rio is noisier). Modern as can be, the Okura manages to be all things to all travellers – there are eleven types of rooms (Japanese too) and in each case the decor fits in beautifully. It is convenient, well equipped and superbly managed and works with an efficiency which is by now a legend. The doorman keeps a little pad handy and, when you ask for a taxi (each one is driven by a younger kamikaze pilot), he notes where you want to go and hands it to the driver. There is the tea ceremony too if you insist. Plus fresh flowers everywhere, very beautiful Japanese paintings and though you cannot dial the Kremlin on the telephone yet, it surely won't be long.

JORDAN
Amman
JORDAN INTER-CONTINENTAL, P.O. Box 35014/15, Jabal Amman

- ★ TELEPHONE: 41361
- ★ CABLES: Inhotelcor/Amman
- ★ TELEX: 1207
- ★ IN OPERATION: 18 years
- ★ RESERVATIONS: Inter-Continental Hotels Corporation
- ★ ROOMS: 400
- ★ SUITES: 18
- ★ RESTAURANTS: 2
- ★ BARS: 1
- ★ DISCOTHEQUE: yes
- ★ SHOPS: 8
- ★ CONFERENCE ROOMS: 3 (60 to 250)
- ★ BANQUETING ROOMS: 3 (60 to 250)
- ★ STANDARD BEDROOM SIZE: 24 m^2

- ★ PRIVATE BALCONIES: yes – 250
- ★ SWIMMING POOL: yes – fresh water
- ★ GARDENS: yes
- ★ NO. OF STAFF: 423
- ★ ROOM SERVICE: around the clock
- ★ ORIENTATION: rooms face south, north, east and west
- ★ CREDIT CARDS: all major ones
- ★ OWNING COMPANY: Jordan Hotels & Tourism Co Ltd, operated by Inter-Continental Hotels Corporation
- ★ GENERAL MANAGER: L. Marc Hamel
- ★ DISTANCE TO SHOPS: 500 m
- ★ DISTANCE FROM AIRPORT: 10 km

This hotel exemplifies one of the statements made in the foreword to this edition. It began life as a fairly undistinguished chain hotel in a small capital city which badly needed reasonable hotel accommodation. Then, year after year, the Jordan Inter-Continental improved and so markedly that at the last visit I concluded that it was now one of the best hotels in the Middle East. The utter niceness of the Jordanian or Bedouin personality has something to do with it – the staff can't do enough for you. Management has become more involved, more personal and far more quality conscious. The hotel is spacious, well designed and decorated with pleasant local touches but does not go out of its way to impress. It is very clean, beautifully maintained. The rooms are a good size, the bathrooms work and room service is quick and efficient – everything you want is done without a murmur. A splendid buffet is available every day for lunch and in the evening I found the food in the top floor restaurant to be well above the average for the area and served with real expertise. The hotel is a good centre too – rose-red Petra is three hours away by road and in 45 minutes you can fly to the sub-tropical shores of Aqaba.

KENYA
Lamu
PEPONI HOTEL, P.O. Box 24, Lamu

- ★ TELEPHONE: Lamu 29
- ★ CABLES: Peponi Lamu
- ★ TELEX: no
- ★ IN OPERATION: 15 years
- ★ RESERVATIONS: direct
- ★ ROOMS: 21
- ★ SUITES: 1

- ★ RESTAURANTS: 1
- ★ BARS: 1
- ★ DISCOTHEQUE: no
- ★ SHOPS: 1 – selling local jewellery, beach wear and toiletries
- ★ CONFERENCE ROOMS: none
- ★ BANQUETING ROOMS: 1 (up to 20)

★ STANDARD BEDROOM SIZE: 21 m²
★ PRIVATE BALCONIES: yes
★ SWIMMING POOL: no
★ RECREATIONAL ACTIVITIES: deep sea
fishing, water skiing, windsurfing,
dhaow sailing, goggling, spear fishing
and limited diving
★ GARDENS: yes – coconut and date palms
and bougainvillaea in abundance

★ NO. OF STAFF: 45
★ ROOM SERVICE: 07.00–22.00
★ ORIENTATION: east
★ CREDIT CARDS: American Express
★ OWNING COMPANY: private
★ GENERAL MANAGER: Mrs. Wera Korschen
★ DISTANCE TO BEACH: walking distance
★ DISTANCE TO SHOPS: 3 km
★ DISTANCE FROM AIRPORT: 5 km

When, in the last edition of this book, I first listed this hotel, I did so with trepidation. I love it, but would others? The first reader's letter to reach me made it plain that I had taken leave of my senses. Then by and by, other letters came: 'Unique', 'Absolutely divine', 'We will never forget Peponi's . . .'. One lady from Sweden wrote: 'Thank you for convincing me that there were still places like this in the world . . .' I am so glad.

Of course Peponi's is not like the Paris Ritz or the Pierre in New York. For one thing, it is way out there on a crazy, time-forgotten place, an old Swahili port in the very North of Kenya and still a stopping place for those marvellous Arab dhows and with houses – and their huge Zanzibari doors – going back a thousand years. Peponi's is simple, fresh, natural. From its terrace you can see your own beach, all eight miles of it, with scarcely anyone in sight and you can go sailing up and down the fascinating channels of a coastline hardly mapped properly. Then you can come back to an eight-pound lobster for dinner. Yes, there are still places like Peponi's in this world.

Masai Mara

MARA SERENA LODGE, P.O. Box 48690, Nairobi

★ TELEPHONE: Radiocall 3757
★ CABLES: Serena Nairobi
★ TELEX: 22878 Nairobi
★ IN OPERATION: 8 years
★ RESERVATIONS: Serena Lodges & Hotels,
P.O. Box 48690, Nairobi
★ ROOMS: 52
★ SUITES: none
★ RESTAURANTS: 1
★ BARS: 1
★ DISCOTHEQUE: no
★ SHOPS: 1 – boutique
★ CONFERENCE ROOMS: none
★ BANQUETING ROOMS: none

★ STANDARD BEDROOM SIZE: 19 m²
★ PRIVATE BALCONIES: no
★ SWIMMING POOL: yes – fresh water
★ RECREATIONAL ACTIVITIES: Masai dancing
★ GARDENS: yes
★ NO. OF STAFF: 80
★ ROOM SERVICE: 08.00–22.00
★ ORIENTATION: rooms face game reserve
★ CREDIT CARDS: Diners Club, American
Express, Visa and Barclaycard
★ OWNING COMPANY: Safari Lodge
Properties of Kenya Ltd
★ GENERAL MANAGER: Mr. Freddie Kiuru
★ DISTANCE FROM AIRPORT: own airstrip

Kenya was fortunate in the aristocratic settler from Britain who invented this hotel (and its companion on the coast). He took the local mud-hut architecture and adapted it to make it safe for aristocrats who wanted to hunt in comfort. The result is one of the best of Kenya's modern game lodges. This being Masai country, the architecture is that of a Masai 'manyatta' or village – rough texture hut-like buildings for rooms, all huddled together in the traditional manner. Decor is simple but good and comfort standards as high as are both service and food. Above all, it is the situation that impresses – on a bluff high over one of the finest game reserves – 700 square miles of larger-than-life Africa, with Masai warriors, lots of lion, hippo and other wild creatures. Highly recommended.

Mombasa

SERENA BEACH HOTEL, P.O. Box 90352, Mombasa

★ TELEPHONE: 45721/2/3/4
★ CABLES: Serena Mombasa
★ TELEX: 21220 Mombasa
★ IN OPERATION: 7 years
★ RESERVATIONS: direct
★ ROOMS: 120
★ SUITES: 2
★ RESTAURANTS: 2
★ BARS: 3
★ DISCOTHEQUE: yes
★ SHOPS: 2 – boutique and handicrafts/curios
★ CONFERENCE ROOMS: none
★ BANQUETING ROOMS: none
★ STANDARD BEDROOM SIZE: 22 m²
★ PRIVATE BALCONIES: yes
★ SWIMMING POOL: yes – fresh water
★ RECREATIONAL ACTIVITIES: tennis, volleyball, boating and windsurfing school
★ GARDENS: yes
★ NO. OF STAFF: 205
★ ROOM SERVICE: around the clock
★ ORIENTATION: most rooms have a sea view
★ FURTHER DEVELOPMENTS: squash courts and water-sports centre
★ CREDIT CARDS: Diners Club and American Express
★ OWNING COMPANY: Safari Lodge Properties of Kenya Ltd
★ GENERAL MANAGER: Mr. Mahmud Janmohamed
★ DISTANCE TO BEACH: 40 m
★ DISTANCE TO SHOPS: 20 km
★ DISTANCE FROM AIRPORT: 30 km

All East African beach hotels should look like Serena Beach – with a few variations, of course. The fact that they do not, reflects on the unique quality of the hotel and its architects. Serena Beach is an idealised version of a Swahili village – with little streets winding in and out of clusters of charming cottages, with walls and doors just as they used to be in Zanzibar. Everywhere there are masses of mangrove wood beams, fine carpets, old chests and colourful hangings in the Arab manner. The rooms are simple, cool and attractive which is what one wants in this climate and the beach, Shanzu, is one of the finest tropical beaches anywhere.

The hotel has a central village square, with little shops, an almost permanent market, a coffeemaker and such like. The staff are one huge Maclean-smile from ear to ear and the food they serve is fresh, tasty and attractive – enormous lobsters, firm vegetables and masses of fruit.

Nairobi

INTER-CONTINENTAL NAIROBI, P.O. Box 30353, City Hall Way, Nairobi

★ TELEPHONE: 335550
★ CABLES: Inhotelcor Nairobi
★ TELEX: 22631
★ IN OPERATION: 13 years
★ RESERVATIONS: Inter-Continental Reservations Offices, worldwide
★ ROOMS: 372 doubles/twins
★ SUITES: 27
★ RESTAURANTS: 3 – Le Chateau, Coffee Banda and Pool Terrace Restaurant
★ BARS: The Big Five and Le Chateau Lounge
★ DISCOTHEQUE: live international band six nights a week
★ SHOPS: 19 – plus 2 lobby desks – news stand, tour operator, travel agent, cameras, cosmetics, garments, jewellery, paintings, curios, florist, hairdresser and safari office
★ CONFERENCE ROOMS: 1 (665)
★ BANQUETING ROOMS: 1 (450)
★ STANDARD BEDROOM SIZE: 24.40 m²
★ PRIVATE BALCONIES: yes – most rooms
★ SWIMMING POOL: yes – fresh water, oval shape 17.70 m long and 11.85 m wide, heated
★ RECREATIONAL ACTIVITIES: children's paddling pool and massage
★ GARDENS: yes
★ NO. OF STAFF: 530
★ ROOM SERVICE: around the clock
★ ORIENTATION: surrounded by Uhuru Park, Parliament Building, Post Office and the Holy Family Cathedral
★ CREDIT CARDS: American Express, Diners Club, Carte Blanche, Visa and Interbank
★ OPERATING COMPANY: Inter-Continental Hotels

★ GENERAL MANAGER: Mr. J. P. Lanz ★ DISTANCE FROM AIRPORT: 18 km
★ DISTANCE TO SHOPS: 5 minutes' walk

In a city which fairly bristles with new hotels – and the operative word is 'bristle' – I would choose the Inter-Continental as the best of the new generation if only because here there has been no massive effort to overawe the guest, no attempt to impress just for the sake of impressing. It is a modern hotel of very good international standard and that in Africa is, alas, quite rare. The rooms and suites are quite excellent – beautifully furnished with good, solid pieces, nice textiles and also plenty of room to move about. Bathrooms are a dream and the floor service never seems to stop working. The menu in the Le Chateau French restaurant is dazzling and the food matches it. One is never disappointed, especially with the Kenya-grown ingredients. I was very impressed by the swimming pool area which is most attractive.

NORFOLK HOTEL, P.O. Box 40064, Nairobi

★ TELEPHONE: 335422
★ CABLES: Norfolk
★ TELEX: 22559
★ IN OPERATION: 78 years
★ RESERVATIONS: Hotel Representatives Inc, worldwide/Horis Reservations Systems/United Touring Overseas, London
★ ROOMS: 120
★ SUITES/COTTAGES: 10 suites 8 cottages
★ RESTAURANTS: Delamere Terrace, Delamere Restaurant, Ibis Grill
★ BARS: 3 plus a Mini Bar in each bedroom
★ DISCOTHEQUE: no
★ SHOPS: 2
★ CONFERENCE/BANQUETING ROOMS: 4 rooms (5 to 500)
★ PRIVATE BALCONIES: many have, some do not
★ SWIMMING POOL: yes – fresh water

★ RECREATIONAL ACTIVITIES: golf and horse riding nearby
★ GARDENS: central courtyard only: shaded, two aviaries housing various species of African birds
★ NO. OF STAFF: 340 approximately
★ ROOM SERVICE: around the clock
★ ORIENTATION: overlooks University Way and the Kenya National Theatre
★ FURTHER DEVELOPMENTS: A new centrally heated pool will be ready early 1983
★ CREDIT CARDS: American Express, Diners Club, Barclaycard, Eurocard and Access
★ OWNING COMPANY: Kulia Investments Ltd
★ GENERAL MANAGER: Nigel Arensen
★ DISTANCE TO SHOPS: 10 minutes walking, 2 minutes taxi
★ DISTANCE FROM AIRPORT: 16 km

It is hard to say which came first – the Norfolk Hotel or the city of Nairobi and when, some time back, a devastating fire gutted the old place, many habitual Africa hands were seen to shake their heads sadly. No, things would never be the same again. Yet, happily, they are – or almost. Miracles happened and the Norfolk rose again and, just as in the past, you might expect to see Hemingway's or Robert Ruark's ghosts come striding out of the famous bar, and the Lord Delamere Terrace is still the meeting place for anyone who is anyone in this fast-changing African capital. Let's face it – perhaps it was all for the best since some of the old Norfolk did need a change. But it has all been kept much along the same lines: the interior gardens, the state of big game information over the desk, the smiling faces of staff people who've been there for years. The food remains as good as it always was, plentiful and healthy, service and items like plumbing and communications are naturally much improved, the rooms are a good size and still simply and intelligently furnished. I for one would never dream of abandoning the Norfolk legend.

Nanyuki

MOUNT KENYA SAFARI CLUB, P.O. Box 35, Nanyuki, Kenya

★ TELEPHONE: 33.32.32   Reservations Nanyuki Club 2241
★ CABLES: Satcluo
★ TELEX: 22016   Reservations 28120

★ IN OPERATION: 22 years
★ RESERVATIONS: Inter-continental Hotels, worldwide
★ ROOMS: 30

★ SUITES: 10 plus 12 cottages with sunken baths
★ RESTAURANTS: 2
★ BARS: 2
★ DISCOTHEQUE: yes – and live music
★ SHOPS: 3
★ CONFERENCE ROOMS: 3 (40 to 115)
★ BANQUETING ROOMS: 3 (up to 100)
★ STANDARD BEDROOM SIZE: 28 m²
★ PRIVATE BALCONIES: yes – some rooms
★ SWIMMING POOL: yes – fresh water, heated, 20 × 6 m
★ RECREATIONAL ACTIVITIES: horse riding, golf, tennis, sauna, pond and river fishing, bowling and putting green

★ GARDENS: yes
★ NO. OF STAFF: 230
★ ROOM SERVICE: 07.00–23.00
★ ORIENTATION: 7,000 ft high facing Mount Kenya
★ CREDIT CARDS: American Express, Diners Club, Visa and Master Charge
★ OWNING COMPANY: Mt. Kenya Safari Club Ltd, operated by Inter-continental Hotels Corporation
★ GENERAL MANAGER: Gerald Etter
★ DISTANCE TO SHOPS: 125 miles
★ DISTANCE FROM AIRPORT: 225 km from international airport and 20 km from domestic airport

'Oh my Hemingway and my Blixen long ago.' This is one of the most beautiful and most amusing hotels in the whole of Africa – strictly for rich and well-tended bwanas and their ladies. A few rather elderly white hunters are still to be found in the long bar and some of the trophies on the walls look as though they could jump off and savage you at any moment. The Mount Kenya Safari Club is a place apart – lush, plush, romantic and quite unique. The noises of the African night, the haughty, snowy profile of Mount Kenya and the thrilling grandeur of the country cannot fail to excite you. You can have claret with your dinner, watch the exotic birds strutting on the manicured lawns, enjoy a logfire in your room (which bears no resemblance to a safari tent) or just read the guest book which in itself is a source of endless gossip. Founded by, among others, William Holden, it is now expertly run by one of the world's great hotel chains. The Mount Kenya Safari Club is to Africa as Cartier is to Bond Street.

Samburu

SAMBURU GAME LODGE, P.O. Box 47557, Nairobi

★ TELEPHONE: Radiocall 2051
★ CABLES: Blocotels, Nairobi
★ TELEX: 22146 Blocotels
★ IN OPERATION: since 1961
★ RESERVATIONS: United Touring International, London/Sergat France, Paris/Sergat Italia, Rome/United Touring International, Germany
★ ROOMS: 60 doubles   9 singles
★ SUITES: none
★ RESTAURANTS: 1
★ BARS: 2 – one 'Crocodile Bar' affording close view of river and crocodiles
★ DISCOTHEQUE: no
★ SHOPS: 1
★ CONFERENCE ROOMS: none
★ BANQUETING ROOMS: none
★ STANDARD BEDROOM SIZE: 25 m²

★ PRIVATE BALCONIES: yes
★ SWIMMING POOL: yes – fresh water, 50 ft × 20 ft
★ RECREATIONAL ACTIVITIES: viewing drives in safari vehicles, bird-watching walks and badminton
★ GARDENS: yes – large river frontage on Uaso Nyiro River
★ NO. OF STAFF: 114
★ ROOM SERVICE: 06.00–21.00
★ ORIENTATION: all rooms face south overlooking the river
★ CREDIT CARDS: American Express, Barclaycard and Diners Club
★ OWNING COMPANY: Block Hotels Ltd
★ GENERAL MANAGER: D. W. Stogdale
★ DISTANCE FROM AIRPORT: 350 km (Nairobi)

In a country where the natives are not too restless, the Samburu Game Lodge is evidence that life in Kenya is at least throbbing; the crocodiles lying in wait in the river just below the bar, the elephants across the water and the dancing at the nearby villages (a non-tourist pas-de-deux) are just what the missionary ordered. One of the best game lodges, the traveller who comes here gets a real feel of Africa. His cottage is African-style, thatched and simple but comfortable and clean. His food, despite the remoteness, is among the best Kenya can offer – the game is, of course, excellent – and that goes a long way. Despite the unending stream of tourists day after day, the staff still greet you as if you were Stanley or Livingstone. These days the 'safari' has been devalued as much as many currencies – but not at Samburu. Everything here is larger than life and contains all the elements you had expected from your African adventure. This is Hemingway Africa as she should be. What a pity Karen Blixen cannot write any more about her beloved Kenya or the district of Karen named after her.

Tsavo National Park

TAITA HILLS LODGE, c/o Hilton International Nairobi, P.O. Box 30624, Nairobi

★ TELEPHONE: Radio Call 2011
★ CABLES: Hiltels Nairobi
★ TELEX: 22252
★ IN OPERATION: 10 years
★ RESERVATIONS: Hilton Reservation Service
★ ROOMS: 60
★ SUITES: 2
★ RESTAURANTS: 1
★ BARS: 2
★ DISCOTHEQUE: yes
★ SHOPS: 1
★ CONFERENCE ROOMS: 2 (up to 110)
★ BANQUETING ROOMS: 2 (up to 110)
★ STANDARD BEDROOM SIZE: 16 m^2
★ PRIVATE BALCONIES: yes
★ SWIMMING POOL: yes – fresh water

★ RECREATIONAL ACTIVITIES: tennis, mini-golf, camel riding, darts, game-viewing safaris, boat rides on Lake Jipe, traditional dancers, lectures and film shows
★ GARDENS: yes
★ NO. OF STAFF: 80
★ ROOM SERVICE: 0700–23.00
★ ORIENTATION: rooms overlook the Taita Hills
★ CREDIT CARDS: Diners Club, American Express, Carte Blanche, Master Charge and Hilton Hotels Corp
★ OWNING COMPANY: Hilton International Co
★ GENERAL MANAGER: Mr. Brian Burrows
★ DISTANCE FROM AIRPORT: own airstrip

I must confess that neither nature nor circumstance meant me to be a boy scout. So, much as I love the tented camps I must also admit that after a day's game viewing – and you'd be surprised how tiring and dusty it is – it is pleasant to come back to a hotel like Taita Hills – clean, modern, efficient and not at all unpleasant to look at. It is a good-looking wood and stone building which goes well with its wild surroundings. Rooms are practical and beautifully equipped for a few days' stay and the bathrooms work like a dream. In such a place I do not even dislike the rather synthetised African decor – at least it does not offend. Taita Hills is what is called a base camp. From there you go anywhere in the vast Tsavo Game Park and only a few miles away is Taita's little sister, Salt Lick Lodge, with its thatched roundavels on stilts and its walkways. The elephants, by the way, are just down below you. Food and drink in both places are excellent.

LIECHTENSTEIN
Vaduz

PARK HOTEL SONNENHOF, 9490 Vaduz, Fürstentum Liechtenstein

★ TELEPHONE: (075) 2 11 92
★ CABLES: Sonnenhofhotel
★ TELEX: 77 78 1
★ IN OPERATION: since 1962
★ RESERVATIONS: direct or Relais de Campagne/Chateaux Hotels
★ ROOMS: 21
★ SUITES: 12
★ RESTAURANTS: 1

★ BARS: none
★ DISCOTHEQUE: no
★ SHOPS: none
★ CONFERENCE ROOMS: one (15 to 20)
★ BANQUETING ROOMS: none
★ STANDARD BEDROOM SIZE: 22 m^2
★ PRIVATE BALCONIES: yes
★ SWIMMING POOL: yes – fresh water

★ RECREATIONAL ACTIVITIES: hiking, riding, sauna, golf (24 km away)
★ GARDENS: yes
★ NO. OF STAFF: 18
★ ROOM SERVICE: 07.00–23.00
★ ORIENTATION: faces the Rhine valley

★ CREDIT CARDS: Visa, Master Charge, Eurocard, American Express
★ OWNING COMPANY: private
★ GENERAL MANAGER/OWNER: Emil Real
★ DISTANCE TO SHOPS: 1 km
★ DISTANCE FROM AIRPORT: (Zurich) 120 km

One has to go to one of Europe's smallest countries to discover one of the continent's finest hotels. In terms of quality, personalised management, food and above all general appointments, the Sonnenhof is an admirable hotel. Set on a wooded slope just outside Vaduz, the Sonnenhof's rooms, and particularly suites, are among the finest I have ever stayed in; beautifully fitted, with handsome lighting and unusually fine real wood fittings – everything made to measure and certainly designed by people who know the best. Everything works to perfection, silently and efficiently. There is a refrigerator-bar, good sitting space, wardrobes and bathrooms. The hotel is well furnished with local antiques and charming rustic wooden pieces, the flowers are forever fresh and the whole place is spotless. The food simply cannot be matched in this part of the world – even the table d'hôte is excellent, light and beautifully served by a bevy of smiling, dirndl-skirted girls. It is a family-run hotel and one must give the highest possible praise to an enterprise which is a model of a small, new, family-run and owned venture.

MALAYSIA

Kuala Lumpur

KUALA LUMPUR HILTON, P.O. Box 577, Jalan Sultan Ismail, Kuala Lumpur

★ TELEPHONE: 422122/422222
★ CABLES: Hiltels
★ TELEX: MA 30495
★ IN OPERATION: since November, 1972
★ RESERVATIONS: Hilton Reservation Service
★ ROOMS: 190 doubles   404 singles
★ SUITES: 84
★ RESTAURANTS: 6
★ BARS: 7
★ DISCOTHEQUE: yes – Tin Mine
★ CONFERENCE ROOMS: 10 (10 to 1,350)
★ BANQUETING ROOMS: 10 (10 to 1,100)
★ SHOPS: 82 – shopping arcade offering a large variety of souvenir items, antiques, jewellery, hairdressing salon, doctor's clinic and airline offices
★ STANDARD BEDROOM SIZE: 20 m²

★ PRIVATE BALCONIES: yes
★ SWIMMING POOL: yes – fresh water
★ RECREATIONAL ACTIVITIES: tennis, squash, saunas and indoor games. Golf, horse riding and bowling nearby
★ GARDENS: yes
★ NO. OF STAFF: 1,015
★ ROOM SERVICE: around the clock
★ ORIENTATION: rooms overlook racecourse, hills and city clock
★ CREDIT CARDS: American Express, Diners Club, Visa, Carte Blanche, Eurocard and Air Canada
★ OWNING COMPANY: Pernas International Hotels and Properties
★ GENERAL MANAGER: Willy Optekamp
★ DISTANCE TO SHOPS: 500 m
★ DISTANCE FROM AIRPORT: 22 km

One of the great mysteries of one's travelling life is that Malaysia, a superbly beautiful and varied country, has so few really good hotels and that is why, by default, the KL Hilton shines, which, in a way, is doing it an injustice. Here, the famous chain has done its best to introduce some interesting and very pleasant touches of individuality. Every balcony for instance – and there are hundreds of them – has its own bougainvillaea bush which is automatically water-sprinkled. In the bars and restaurants the Malaysian batiks are authentic. Happily, there is pleasing colour and good service – a smile comes naturally to those delightful people. The rest is what one would expect – Hilton functional, very well organised and dependable.

Trengganu

TANJONG JARA BEACH HOTEL, Kuala Dungun, Trengganu

- ★ TELEPHONE: (096) 41801-5
- ★ CABLES: Pemresort
- ★ TELEX: JARA MA 51449
- ★ IN OPERATION: since 1980
- ★ RESERVATIONS: direct or Pempena Consult, 17th Floor, Wisma MPI, Jalan Raja Chulan, P.O. Box 328, Kuala Lumpur
- ★ ROOMS: 84 doubles
- ★ SUITES: 6
- ★ RESTAURANTS: 1
- ★ BARS: 1
- ★ DISCOTHEQUE: yes
- ★ SHOPPING ARCADE: yes
- ★ CONFERENCE ROOMS: 12
- ★ STANDARD BEDROOM SIZE: 24 m²
- ★ PRIVATE BALCONIES: yes

- ★ SWIMMING POOL: fresh water
- ★ RECREATIONAL ACTIVITIES: water skiing, sailing, underwater swimming, jungle trips, tennis, squash
- ★ GARDENS: yes
- ★ NO. OF STAFF: 190
- ★ ROOM SERVICE: 07.00–23.00
- ★ ORIENTATION: most rooms have a sea view
- ★ CREDIT CARDS: most
- ★ OWNING COMPANY: T.D.C. (Tourist Development Corporation)
- ★ GENERAL MANAGER: Hans Steiger
- ★ DISTANCE TO BEACH: directly
- ★ DISTANCE TO SHOPS: 8 km
- ★ DISTANCE TO AIRPORT: 55 km

For years, in common with all travellers who love beautiful but little-known places, I have been waiting for a really good hotel on that divine East Coast of Malaysia. Now I have found it. Tanjong Jara is everything I could have wished for: a magnificent beach, totally unpolluted and seemingly without end, a hotel designed with imagination and good taste and people so charming that they can't do enough for you. The hotel is a cluster of attractive cottages built of rare timber of which this country has so much and some of them are actually built on stilts on the water. The lush gardens bloom everlastingly, there is no noise and no hustle and you can just be yourself on one of the world's truly most beautiful coastlines. There is a very good swimming pool (as if one needed it here . . .) and furnishings and decor are exotic enough to please the most demanding. Food is fresh: fish was brought ashore this morning and as for fruit, the staff just go along picking it off the trees for your breakfast tray. All around is Malay Malaysia (as against the Chinese community on the West Coast) – gentle people living in marvellously picturesque fishing villages built on stilts. The people welcome you as an honoured guest, with ceremony plus a hint of fun to come. A few miles to the north is the celebrated Beach of Passionate Love. Do go to Tanjong Jara.

MALTA
Gozo
HOTEL TA'CENC, Sannat, Gozo

- ★ TELEPHONE: 556819/556830/551520
- ★ CABLES: Tacencotal
- ★ TELEX: 479 Refinz MW
- ★ IN OPERATION: 10 years
- ★ RESERVATIONS: Gozo Holidays, London/Moteltour Milano, Italy/Holiday Maker, Zurich/Airtours International, Frankfurt
- ★ ROOMS: 38
- ★ SUITES: 12
- ★ RESTAURANTS: 2 including 1 on terrace in summer
- ★ BARS: 2 including 1 on beach
- ★ DISCOTHEQUE: yes
- ★ SHOPS: 2 – boutique and bookshop
- ★ CONFERENCE ROOMS: 1 (up to 80)
- ★ BANQUETING ROOMS: 1 (up to 80)
- ★ STANDARD BEDROOM SIZE: 25 to 30 m²
- ★ PRIVATE BALCONIES: yes
- ★ SWIMMING POOL: yes – fresh water, 300 m²
- ★ RECREATIONAL ACTIVITIES: 2 floodlit tennis courts, table tennis and billiards
- ★ GARDENS: yes
- ★ NO. OF STAFF: 96
- ★ ROOM SERVICE: 07.00–24.00
- ★ ORIENTATION: rooms face sea and gardens
- ★ CREDIT CARDS: American Express, Diners Club and Barclaycard
- ★ OWNING COMPANY: Hotel Operators Ltd
- ★ GENERAL MANAGER: Dr. Italico Rota
- ★ DISTANCE TO BEACH: 8 minutes by car (free minibus service)
- ★ DISTANCE TO SHOPS: 10 minutes by car
- ★ DISTANCE FROM AIRPORT: 90 minutes by car and ferry

Intelligent and sophisticated simplicity – that's the keynote here and I believe Ta'Cenc to be one of the most interesting holiday hotels in the Mediterranean. Many of my readers agree. On this gorgeous, cliffy island of Gozo, Ta'Cenc is a cluster of buildings, the colour of champagne, spread around a very large and beautifully clean swimming pool. There is a main building and lots of cottages where rooms are large and airy, kept scrupulously clean and furnished with simple but comfortable furniture, modern in character but good quality. The beds are particularly good and so is the storage space and bathrooms work like a dream. Most of the activity is outside – gardens, terraces, poolside and one al fresco restaurant where the food, basically Italian in character, is attractive. Service is cheerful and the staff quickly adapt to the wishes of individual guests. The sea is two miles away. You won't find hordes of cheap package tourists here.

MAURITIUS

LA PIROGUE, Flic-en-Flac

★ TELEPHONE: 5841/47041
★ CABLES: Pirogue Mauritius
★ TELEX: 4-255 1W
★ IN OPERATION: 5 years
★ RESERVATIONS: Landmark International Hotels Ltd, London/Sergat, Paris and Rome/Travamart Ltd, Johannesburg/Comfort Hotels International, Washington D.C.
★ ROOMS: 198
★ SUITES: 4
★ RESTAURANTS: 2
★ BARS: 3 – also a casino with a bar
★ DISCOTHEQUE: none
★ SHOPS: 2
★ CONFERENCE ROOMS: 1 (up to 200)
★ BANQUETING ROOMS: 1 (up to 150)
★ STANDARD BEDROOM SIZE: 28 m^2 – air conditioned and private bathroom
★ PRIVATE BALCONIES: yes

★ SWIMMING POOL: yes – fresh water
★ RECREATIONAL ACTIVITIES: extensive water sports including windsurfing and water skiing, tennis, volleyball and crazy golf. Golf course at Curepipe 15 km away
★ GARDENS: yes – over 20 acres of tropical landscape leading to beach
★ NO. OF STAFF: 320
★ ROOM SERVICE: around the clock
★ ORIENTATION: all rooms face the sea
★ CREDIT CARDS: American Express, Diners Club and Barclaycard
★ OWNING COMPANY: City and Beach Hotels (Mauritius) Ltd
★ GENERAL MANAGER: John Oxley
★ DISTANCE TO BEACH: immediate
★ DISTANCE TO SHOPS: 15 km (Curepipe) and 20 km (Port Louis)
★ DISTANCE FROM AIRPORT: 50 km

Fame is the penalty of success: that gentle island of Mauritius, a speck way down in the dark blue yonder of the Indian Ocean is a prime holiday destination these days, which means that there are would-be hotel developers lurking behind every tree. But there is still La Pirogue, and the reason is simple: while most holiday hotels tumble out of some concrete mould, La Pirogue is different, amusing, designed by architects who had respect for nature and humanity.

Its central building is a vast and daring structure with a roof like the sail of a pirogue in full spread. The rooms are little round cottages, with thatched roofs, walls of stone and pretty terraces lining a sensational beach – one of the finest in the tropics. The service is as cheerful as Mauritius itself – shy and smiling and genuine. The food, whilst inevitably geared to tourist needs, is not at all unpalatable. In the Indian Ocean countries, which do not shine with good hotels, La Pirogue continues to be one of the acceptable ones.

MEXICO

Puerto Vallarta

HOTEL GARZA BLANCA, P.O. Box 58, Puerto Vallarta, Jalisco

- ★ TELEPHONE: 2-10-23 & 2-10-83
- ★ CABLES: no
- ★ TELEX: 06518
- ★ IN OPERATION: 14 years
- ★ RESERVATIONS: John A. Tetley Co, Los Angeles/Robert F. Warner or direct
- ★ ROOMS: none
- ★ SUITES: 40 and 31 villas
- ★ RESTAURANTS: 1
- ★ BARS: 1
- ★ DISCOTHEQUE: live music
- ★ SHOPS: 2
- ★ CONFERENCE ROOMS: none
- ★ BANQUETING ROOMS: none
- ★ STANDARD BEDROOM SIZE: 32 m²
- ★ PRIVATE BALCONIES: yes
- ★ SWIMMING POOL: yes – 1 main pool 23 × 6 m, and 40 private pools, fresh water
- ★ RECREATIONAL ACTIVITIES: water skiing, scuba diving, fishing, tennis and city and jungle tours
- ★ GARDENS: yes
- ★ NO. OF STAFF: 110
- ★ ROOM SERVICE: 07.45–23.30
- ★ ORIENTATION: all rooms face the Pacific
- ★ FURTHER DEVELOPMENTS: plans to build 44 suites and 27 villas
- ★ CREDIT CARDS: Master Charge, American Express and Visa
- ★ OWNING COMPANY: Garza Blanca, S.A.
- ★ GENERAL MANAGER: Salvador E. Fernandez, C.P.
- ★ DISTANCE TO BEACH: walking distance
- ★ DISTANCE TO SHOPS: 7.5 km
- ★ DISTANCE FROM AIRPORT: 15 km

Since 'The Night of the Iguana' everybody wanted to see the odd-looking place where they made the film and whereas Acapulco was getting overrun, Puerto Vallarta became 'the' place which it still is. Alas, it too suffers from the Acapulco disease, except for Garza Blanca which I think is a super small holiday hotel on this legendary coast. The small white beach is quite gorgeous and if you want to be very close to it, choose one of the beachside suites. But if you want to be on your own, cross the road and climb up the hillside to one of the ineptly called chalet suites – a little Mexican house all to yourself in its own tiny garden and its own tiny swimming pool – quite divine and very private. There is a sunken, tiled bathtub and a very pleasant sitting room. The hotel is small so everybody congregates on that quite lovely dining terrace, made famous by Ava Gardner, for meals and the food ranges from the acceptable to the very good. Mercifully, the dreadful tourists known in the film never come here – Richard Burton must have scared them off.

San Juan Del Rio

HYATT GALINDO, P.O. Box 16, San Juan del Rio, Queretaro, Mexico

- ★ TELEPHONE: (91-467) 20050
- ★ CABLES: no
- ★ TELEX: 12804
- ★ IN OPERATION: 10 years
- ★ RESERVATIONS: Hyatt Reservations, worldwide
- ★ ROOMS: 160
- ★ SUITES: 7
- ★ RESTAURANTS: 3 – Florentino, Bosque Grande and Garden Restaurant
- ★ BARS: Lobby bar
- ★ DISCOTHEQUE: live music
- ★ SHOPS: gift shops and boutiques
- ★ CONFERENCE ROOMS: grand ballroom – 110 m²
- ★ BANQUETING ROOMS: 13 – seating from 35 to 854
- ★ STANDARD BEDROOM SIZE: 26 m²
- ★ PRIVATE BALCONIES: 18 rooms have private terraces
- ★ SWIMMING POOL: yes – fresh water
- ★ RECREATIONAL ACTIVITIES: tennis courts, horseback riding, putting green, 18-hole championship golf course a few minutes away
- ★ GARDENS: yes
- ★ NO. OF STAFF: 175
- ★ ROOM SERVICE: 07.00–22.00
- ★ ORIENTATION: all directions – some facing interior courtyards

★ CREDIT CARDS: American Express, Carte Blanche, Diners Club, Master Charge and Visa

★ OWNING COMPANY: Hyatt Hotels Corporation

★ GENERAL MANAGER: Jacques Andre Hamburger

★ DISTANCE TO SHOPS: 10 km

★ DISTANCE FROM AIRPORT: 90 minutes' drive from Mexico City

One of the rarest things in my type of work is discovering a good hotel totally by accident and this is what happened in the case of Galindo. Touring around the Bajio – Mexico's colonial heartland where (poor fellow) Emperor Maximilian met his end, I came across this magnificent old hacienda turned into a hotel, had a look around, loved it and stayed. I have never regretted it since this is without doubt one of the finest country hotels in this magnificent country. Legend has it that it was Hernan Cortes himself who built Galindo for his Indian wife – possibly hard to prove – but it looks as if it was that genuine: a beautiful, mellow and lovingly kept hacienda with great processions of interior courtyards filled with flowers and fountains, superb public rooms, especially the main restaurant which looks great and serves delicious food, and yes, even the original chapel of the estate. Bedrooms are period of course, beautifully serviced and since the hotel has been taken over by a reliable worldwide company the formerly 'mañana' attitude has gone – for good one hopes. In feeling and atmosphere, Galindo is so far from raucous Mexico City that it is worth the trip just to see the difference.

MONACO

Monte Carlo

HOTEL DE PARIS, Place du Casino

★ TELEPHONE: (93) 50 80 80

★ CABLES: Parisotel

★ TELEX: 469925 Parihotcarlo

★ IN OPERATION: since 1866

★ RESERVATIONS: Nicholas Lawson Ltd, London/Harmut C. Wegener, Frankfurt/Jean Morieux, Paris

★ ROOMS: 260 doubles 10 singles

★ SUITES: 30

★ RESTAURANTS: 2

★ BARS: 2

★ DISCOTHEQUE: live music and piano in bar

★ SHOPS: 7

★ CONFERENCE ROOMS: 2 (up to 30)

★ BANQUETING ROOMS: 2 (100 to 400)

★ STANDARD BEDROOM SIZE: 25 m^2

★ PRIVATE BALCONIES: yes

★ SWIMMING POOL: yes – salt water, 25 × 15 m

★ RECREATIONAL ACTIVITIES: saunas with tennis and squash at the Monte Carlo Country Club and also 18-hole golf course

★ GARDENS: yes

★ NO. OF STAFF: 400

★ ROOM SERVICE: around the clock

★ ORIENTATION: rooms face the sea, gardens and shopping street

★ CREDIT CARDS: American Express, Diners Club, Visa, Master Charge, Access and Eurocard

★ OWNING COMPANY: Société des Bains de Mer

★ GENERAL MANAGER: Fred Laubi

★ DISTANCE TO BEACH: 1 km

★ DISTANCE TO SHOPS: walking distance

★ DISTANCE FROM AIRPORT: 24 km

This hotel (well over a century of it) is for plutocrats, oilcrats, aristocrats and any other crats and is about as reticent as King Kong. Yet, what it does to keep the show on the road is carried out with such consummate panache, such skilled showmanship that it can be forgiven anything. If you dine on that terrace at night (admission is about as tough as the Royal Enclosure at Ascot), nibble at your langouste and sip your Dom Perignon, you are part of the show. Ordinary mortals pass by, drop one or two comments about your plate (or your jewels) and go on and if you can sit there unblushingly, the Hotel de Paris is for you. And, of course, one should add – as if this were necessary – that this is a very great hotel indeed, with a guest list longer and more illustrious than most royal palaces.

Everything here is larger than life – the sugar-icing architecture, the nymphs climbing up every column, the chandeliers dripping with light. Rooms range from the fairly plain to the outlandishly lush – it's the kind of hotel where the concierge is worth any highly paid secretary, he'll make your appointments for you if you wish. The best suites are on the harbour side, so that you can see what the Greek tycoons are doing on their floating battleships. The Empire Restaurant has not changed a bit since the days of Nick the Greek and the fin d'everything demi mondaines – it is overpoweringly superb.

HOTEL HERMITAGE, Square Beaumarchais

★ TELEPHONE: 56 67 31
★ CABLES: Hermit Monte Carlo
★ TELEX: 479 432
★ IN OPERATION: 87 years
★ RESERVATIONS: Nicholas Lawson Ltd, London/Harmut C. Wegener, Frankfurt/Jean Morieux, Paris
★ ROOMS: 211
★ SUITES: 11
★ RESTAURANTS: 1
★ BARS: 1
★ DISCOTHEQUE: no
★ SHOPS: none
★ CONFERENCE ROOMS: 2 (50 to 80)
★ BANQUETING ROOMS: 3 (30 to 250)
★ STANDARD BEDROOM SIZE: 25 m²

★ PRIVATE BALCONIES: yes – most rooms
★ SWIMMING POOL: yes – salt water, 25 × 15 m
★ GARDENS: no
★ NO. OF STAFF: 175
★ ROOM SERVICE: 07.00–24.00
★ ORIENTATION: south
★ CREDIT CARDS: American Express, Diners Club, Master Charge and Eurocard
★ OWNING COMPANY: Société des Bains de Mer
★ GENERAL MANAGER: M. Georges Maillet
★ DISTANCE TO BEACH: walking distance
★ DISTANCE TO SHOPS: walking distance
★ DISTANCE FROM AIRPORT: 24 km

An architect could not have built a hotel like this, it must have been a pastry chef. A Viennese pastry chef at that, perhaps in partnership with a Bohemian painter from the court of mad King Ludwig of Bavaria. The Hermitage is the only hotel I know where they have to put security guards on the washrooms, lest people should come in with hammer and chisel and steal the washbasins. Here, in a hotel which is less famous and less cosmopolitan than its stablemate, are endless vistas of vast corridors with painted ceilings, bouquets of cherubs climbing up every wall and ceilings literally dripping with rococo plaster and crystal candelabras. A monument to the scandalous good times of the Edwardian era. Women clients love the Hermitage because, like candlelight, it is intensely flattering. Rooms and suites are like aristocratic lovenests, the kind that go with Dom Perignon, red roses and a telephone off the hook. Service is unlikely to disturb you – it only comes when called – and when you walk into the Belle Epoque Restaurant, you know instinctively that the Prince of Wales must have sat, upstage, by the second column on the left.

MOROCCO

Fès

HOTEL PALAIS JAMAI, Bab-el-Guissa, Fès

★ TELEPHONE: 343-31, 32, 33 & 35
★ CABLES: Hotransat
★ TELEX: 519-74
★ IN OPERATION: since 1920
★ RESERVATIONS: direct
★ ROOMS: 140
★ SUITES: 8

★ RESTAURANTS: 2
★ BARS: 1
★ DISCOTHEQUE: yes
★ SHOPS: 2
★ CONFERENCE ROOMS: 1 (200)
★ BANQUETING ROOMS: 1 (150)
★ STANDARD BEDROOM SIZE: 28 m²

★ PRIVATE BALCONIES: yes

★ SWIMMING POOL: yes – fresh water

★ GARDENS: yes

★ NO. OF STAFF: 160

★ ROOM SERVICE: around the clock

★ ORIENTATION: facing old city and the mountain

★ CREDIT CARDS: American Express and Diners Club

★ OWNING COMPANY: O.N.C.F., Rabat

★ GENERAL MANAGER: M. Pique

★ DISTANCE TO SHOPS: 200 m

★ DISTANCE FROM AIRPORT: 15 km

Once it was the Grand Vizier's palace in this most beautiful of all Moroccan cities and his own room is still there for one to see. Now, as a traveller, you are the Grand Vizier and may all your dreams be peopled with veiled ladies scurrying about carrying trays of sweet whatnots. Of course, the Palais Jamai, like most things in this world, has changed – not always for the better and I don't care much for the overstuffed chairs in the otherwise lovely sitting room with its mosaic walls. Rooms have got smaller too – inevitably – but on the whole this is still one of the shining hotel stars of Morocco, with extremely good service, sensationally good Moroccan food served in the right setting and those little touches of extravagance which please so much. The gardens have hardly been touched by the new planners – the birds sing, the fountains fount and the lush trees give pleasant shade. Right there, opposite the white medina where thousands of craftsmen still work on silver, gold, leather and textiles, you are in a very special world.

Marrakech

HOTEL LA MAMOUNIA, Avenue Bab Jdid, Marrakech

★ TELEPHONE: 323-81

★ CABLES: Mamounia Marrakech

★ TELEX: 730-18

★ IN OPERATION: since 1920

★ RESERVATIONS: Hotel Representative Inc

★ ROOMS: 175

★ SUITES: 20

★ RESTAURANTS: 4

★ BARS: 2

★ DISCOTHEQUE: yes

★ SHOPS: yes

★ CONFERENCE ROOMS: none

★ BANQUETING ROOMS: none

★ STANDARD BEDROOM SIZE: 30 m²

★ PRIVATE BALCONIES: yes

★ SWIMMING POOL: yes – fresh water, heated in winter

★ RECREATIONAL ACTIVITIES: golf, riding and skiing close by

★ GARDENS: yes – 17 acres of secluded gardens, olive and orange groves

★ NO. OF STAFF: 400

★ ROOM SERVICE: around the clock

★ ORIENTATION: south and west

★ CREDIT CARDS: American Express, Diners Club, Visa and Master Charge

★ OWNING COMPANY: O.N.C.F.

★ GENERAL MANAGER: Claude Lemercier

★ DISTANCE TO SHOPS: 2 km

★ DISTANCE FROM AIRPORT: 5 km

As the liveried Moorish servant shows you into the tiled and latticed, colonnaded court that serves for a foyer in La Mamounia you step decisively into an illustration of the 1001 Arabian Nights. Your next contact with reality will come when you pay the bill on leaving. This was Winston Churchill's favourite haunt and from his balcony he painted the Atlas sunset time and again. As you sit there dreaming, looking over the fantastic red ramparts of Marrakech or down into those lush gardens, one gets a view of Islamic culture free of Ayatollahs. Like all great hotels, La Mamounia has modernised itself – I don't care much for the main restaurant or the bar but fell in love – again – with the sensational Bhaja Moroccan Restaurant where the food is out of this world. I, who do not like poolside barbecues on principle, was frankly amazed at the quality of the food dispensed out there in the noonday shade. Then there are those miles of glittering tiled Moorish corridors, the carved ceilings and above all the divine gardens.

LA RESIDENCE DE LA ROSERAIE, P.O. 769, Marrakech

★ TELEPHONE: Ouirgane 4 & 5

★ CABLES: Rosehotel Ouirgane

★ IN OPERATION: 12 years

★ RESERVATIONS: direct

★ ROOMS: 15
★ SUITES: 10 (bungalows)
★ RESTAURANTS: 2
★ BARS: 1
★ DISCOTHEQUE: yes
★ SHOPS: none
★ CONFERENCE ROOMS: 1 (50)
★ BANQUETING ROOMS: 1 (100)
★ STANDARD BEDROOM SIZE: 20 m²
★ PRIVATE BALCONIES: yes – terraces
★ SWIMMING POOL: yes – fresh water,
   20 × 10 m

★ RECREATIONAL ACTIVITIES: mule riding
   and excursions in the high Atlas
   Mountains
★ GARDENS: yes
★ NO. OF STAFF: 30
★ ROOM SERVICE: 07.00–23.00
★ ORIENTATION: south
★ CREDIT CARDS: Diners Club
★ OWNING COMPANY: privately owned
★ GENERAL MANAGER: A. Fenjiro
★ DISTANCE TO SHOPS: 60 m
★ DISTANCE FROM AIRPORT: 60 km

Driving down from the Atlas Mountains to Marrakech one day, I discovered La Roseraie quite by accident – the most memorable way of finding a new hotel – and fell in love with it. It is a small, French-style resort hotel, spread over a very pretty valley, with flower gardens and some lovely old trees. One thing that particularly took me was the inventive genius that created the little cottages. There is a very good swimming pool which is necessary in those parts to maintain equilibrium in the summer months. Against a backdrop of the dramatic, if a little sinister, Atlas Mountains, the al fresco cooking and its Arab presentation do much to whisk one securely away from the present century. Not here the meaningless display of tooth that passes for friendship but efficient, quiet, Mahgreb dignity and all the convenience of a modern hotel.

Rabat

HILTON INTERNATIONAL RABAT, P.B. 450 R.P. Souissi, Rabat

★ TELEPHONE: 721-51
★ CABLES: Telegramme Hiltels
★ TELEX: 31913-32026
★ IN OPERATION: since 1967
★ RESERVATIONS: Hilton Reservation
   Service
★ ROOMS: 218 doubles 32 singles
★ SUITES: 9
★ RESTAURANTS: 4 – Chellah Grill, Bab Es
   Sama, coffee shop and pool restaurant
★ BARS: 2
★ DISCOTHEQUE: live music – Moroccan
   orchestra, belly dancer, tea dancer and
   guitarist
★ SHOPS: 10 – barbers, beauty parlour,
   library, minerals, bank, car rental,
   handicraft shop, ladies kaftan dress
   shop, travel agency and art gallery
★ CONFERENCE ROOMS: 6 (up to 700)
★ BANQUETING ROOMS: 6 (up to 700)

★ STANDARD BEDROOM SIZE: 24 m²
★ PRIVATE BALCONIES: yes
★ SWIMMING POOL: yes – fresh water,
   25 × 20 m and a children's pool
★ RECREATIONAL ACTIVITIES: tennis, sauna,
   3-hole golf course and driving range
★ GARDENS: yes
★ NO. OF STAFF: 300
★ ROOM SERVICE: around the clock
★ ORIENTATION: west and east
★ CREDIT CARDS: American Express, Diners
   Club, Visa, Master Charge, Carte
   Blanche, Carte Bleue and Hilton Credit
   Card
★ OPERATING COMPANY: Hilton
   International Co
★ GENERAL MANAGER: Jurg J. Zimmermann
★ DISTANCE TO BEACH: 10 km
★ DISTANCE TO SHOPS: 2 km
★ DISTANCE FROM AIRPORT: 15 km

As far as Hiltons go I tend to prefer the smaller ones to the bigger ones since they seem to offer the Hilton-best without the Hilton-grandiose. Rabat is one of these and it is also probably the quietest of them all, standing some way out of the city. You can actually doze by the swimming pool without any rude awakenings from musack or motor cars. It is a well-behaved hotel – charming staff, good service and the decor is much less manufactured than usual in this group. Colours are fresh and there are some nice handicrafts around as well as some of the loveliest carpets in North Africa. Rooms are Hiltonish – a good size and very functional and room service is particularly fast and discreet. I found the Moroccan food to be somewhat toned down for transatlantic digestive tracts but the French variety was perfectly acceptable.

Taroudant

LA GAZELLE D'OR, P.O. Box 60, Taroudant

- ★ TELEPHONE: (085) 20-39/20-48
- ★ CABLES: Gazelor Taroudant
- ★ TELEX: 22 751 M
- ★ IN OPERATION: since 1960
- ★ RESERVATIONS: direct
- ★ ROOMS: 21 bungalows
- ★ RESTAURANTS: 1 main restaurant and terrace by pool for snack lunches
- ★ BARS: 1
- ★ DISCOTHEQUE: yes
- ★ SHOPS: none
- ★ CONFERENCE ROOMS: none
- ★ BANQUETING ROOMS: none
- ★ STANDARD BEDROOM SIZE: 24 m²
- ★ PRIVATE BALCONIES: all the bungalows have terraces
- ★ SWIMMING POOL: yes – fresh water, Olympic size
- ★ RECREATIONAL ACTIVITIES: tennis, table tennis and riding (4 horses)
- ★ GARDENS: yes – 20 acres
- ★ NO. OF STAFF: 50
- ★ ROOM SERVICE: 07.00–24.00
- ★ ORIENTATION: all bungalows face the gardens and Atlas Mountains
- ★ FURTHER DEVELOPMENTS: Turkish bath, massage facilities, billiard and card room and television and video room
- ★ CREDIT CARDS: American Express, Diners Club and Visa
- ★ OWNING COMPANY: privately owned
- ★ GENERAL MANAGER: Eribo G. Corona
- ★ DISTANCE TO BEACH: 80 km (Agadir Beach)
- ★ DISTANCE TO SHOPS: 1 km (Taroudant), 80 km (Agadir) and 250 km (Marrakech)
- ★ DISTANCE FROM AIRPORT: 80 km

Oldtime pashas would probably have designed this place for themselves, had they had Parisian taste, American plumbing and Italian panache. As it is, it's a hotel for the pashas of today – those who know what they want and are prepared to pay for it. Near this delicious little fortified city in the far south of Morocco, La Gazelle d'Or is literally an oasis of the good life – twenty acres of parkland blooming with orange blossom and bougainvillea, pools and whispering waters, desert dancers to entertain you in the evening while you are supping on the finest French and Moroccan food and that's only the beginning. La Gazelle d'Or, conceived years ago by a man of immense taste, offers twenty-one cottages of extreme beauty and comfort – mosaic ceilings, Berber carpets, handmade furniture and beautiful antiques and super silent service which glides along marble floors in Moroccan slippers. You can ride, swim, play tennis and imagine that you are an oil sheikh on holiday by playing at falconry in what is undoubtedly one of the most ravishing and extraordinary countries in the world. There are not many places like this any more – sheer folly – and very few have this hotel's amazing peace and quiet.

NEPAL

Kathmandu

HOTEL SOALTEE OBEROI, Tahachal, Kathmandu

- ★ TELEPHONE: 11211
- ★ CABLES: Soaltee or Obhotel, Kathmandu
- ★ TELEX: NP 203
- ★ IN OPERATION: since 1969
- ★ RESERVATIONS: Loews Representation International, New York and London/Oberoi Hotels (India), Frankfurt/P.R. International, Frankfurt/Odner Hotel Representatives Ltd, Hong Kong
- ★ ROOMS: 290
- ★ SUITES: 25
- ★ RESTAURANTS: 4 – The Al Fresco, Himalchuli, Garden Cafe and Gurkha Grill
- ★ BARS: 2 – Rodi Bar and Bamboo Bar
- ★ DISCOTHEQUE: live music
- ★ SHOPS: 10
- ★ CONFERENCE ROOMS: 3 (30 to 250)
- ★ BANQUETING ROOMS: 1 (200)
- ★ STANDARD BEDROOM SIZE: 20 m²
- ★ PRIVATE BALCONIES: no
- ★ SWIMMING POOL: yes – fresh water 36 × 27 m

★ RECREATIONAL ACTIVITIES: tennis, golf, saunas, health club and casino; excursions and treks in the mountains are also organised by the hotel
★ GARDENS: yes
★ FURTHER DEVELOPMENTS: a mini-golf course and additional swimming pool
★ CREDIT CARDS: American Express, Diners Club, Bankamericard and Visa

★ NO. OF STAFF: 600
★ ROOM SERVICE: around the clock
★ OPERATING COMPANY: Oberoi Hotels
★ GENERAL MANAGER: vacant at time of going to press
★ DISTANCE TO SHOPS: 2 km
★ DISTANCE FROM AIRPORT: 10 km

Once, Nepal was the home of the flower children and, as I know to my cost, suitable only for the bravest of the middle-aged. One took one's chances with the local hotels. Now that an experienced and versatile company have taken over the Soaltee you can see Nepal without any pain and because Nepal is Nepal – a quite unique country whose Himalayas are better and higher than anyone else's – the result is the best of all possible worlds. The Soaltee is a good hotel of international standards, modern, comfortable, well run and with the occasional touch of the exotic which makes all the difference. Rooms are ample in size, very well furnished with taste and some regard for the long-distance traveller's needs. Bathrooms work too which, all things being unequal, is something of a miracle up here and as for the service, there are two charming, smiling Nepalese boys and girls to every guest which means that your slightest wish is their command – they execute it with rare flourish and much good humour. The food, which rather spoilt my first visits to this distant kingdom, is now extremely palatable. And, if you like that sort of thing, you can play in the only casino for 3,000 miles around. For myself I much prefer to see Nepal, places like Pokkhara and Bhatgaon, or trek to some modest base camp.

NETHERLANDS

Amsterdam

AMSTEL HOTEL, 1 Professor Tulpplein, 1018 GX Amsterdam

★ TELEPHONE: (020) 226060
★ CABLES: Amstelotel
★ TELEX: 11004
★ IN OPERATION: since 1866
★ RESERVATIONS: Utell International
★ ROOMS: 65 doubles 43 singles
★ SUITES: none
★ RESTAURANTS: 1 – La Rive
★ BARS: 1
★ DISCOTHEQUE: no – but live music in the bar and restaurant
★ SHOPS: none – but showcases
★ CONFERENCE ROOMS: 7 (4 to 200)
★ BANQUETING ROOMS: 7 (4 to 200)
★ STANDARD BEDROOM SIZE: 25 m²
★ PRIVATE BALCONIES: no

★ SWIMMING POOL: no
★ GARDENS: yes
★ NO. OF STAFF: 125
★ ROOM SERVICE: 07.00–24.00
★ ORIENTATION: facing Amstel River and quiet square
★ CREDIT CARDS: American Express, Visa, Diners Club, Barclaycard, Grand Metropolitan
★ OWNING COMPANY: Inter-Continental Hotels
★ GENERAL MANAGER: N. T. van Heuveln
★ DISTANCE TO BEACH: 45 km
★ DISTANCE TO SHOPS: 1½ km
★ DISTANCE FROM AIRPORT: 20 km

This is the best hotel in Holland. The Amstel is so grand that even the Dutch Royal family use it for their special occasions and, over the last century, so have such diverse people as Gladstone and Paul Kruger, Isadora Duncan and Rachmaninoff, Henry Moore and Winston Churchill. This is not counting the crowned heads and all those cigar-loving Dutch tycoons. The Amstel is *the* social focus of glorious Amsterdam. The main restaurant, La Rive, is one of the most beautiful I have ever been in and the service and food are matchless. There is also a very, but very attractive bar – the kind of public room which is not always the best. Most rooms are large and palatial, very quiet and distinguished – splendid solid furniture – antique and last century – and lovely carpets. The all round expertise embodied in the Amstel is quite fantastic – nothing ever seems to go wrong and the hotel's location, right on the Amstel bank, could not be better.

HOTEL PULITZER, Prinsengracht 315-331, 1016 GZ Amsterdam

★ TELEPHONE: (020) 228333
★ CABLES: pulitzeramsterdam
★ TELEX: 16508 pulam
★ IN OPERATION: 11 years
★ RESERVATIONS: Nicholas Lawson Ltd, London/Utell International, Australia/Robert F. Warner, London, New York/Stinnes, Frankfurt/ MacLaughlan, Toronto/ Frantel, Paris
★ ROOMS: 193
★ SUITES: 2 senior 3 junior
★ RESTAURANTS: 2 – Pulitzer's coffee shop, Patio restaurant: De Goudsbloem
★ BARS: 1
★ DISCOTHEQUE: occasionally in bar
★ SHOPS: 1 – gift shop
★ CONFERENCE ROOMS: 4

★ BANQUETING ROOMS: 3 (10 to 180)
★ STANDARD BEDROOM SIZE: 25 m²
★ PRIVATE BALCONIES: some rooms with private terrace
★ SWIMMING POOL: no
★ RECREATIONAL ACTIVITIES: city sights within easy reach
★ GARDENS: yes
★ NO. OF STAFF: 80
★ ROOM SERVICE: 06.30–23.00
★ ORIENTATION: east and west
★ CREDIT CARDS: Bank Americard, Diners Club, American Express and Eurocard
★ OWNING COMPANY: Golden Tulip Hotels
★ GENERAL MANAGER: Theo Inniger
★ DISTANCE TO BEACH: 20 km
★ DISTANCE TO SHOPS: 500 m
★ DISTANCE FROM AIRPORT: 20 km

Take nineteen lovely gabled seventeenth-century houses along one of those marvellous canals in Amsterdam, touch them up outside to defy time (but not too much) and inside create a hotel of unique quality and you have the Pulitzer, surely one of the world's most unusual hostelries and also one of the most famous. Every one of the Pulitzer's rooms is different – it's a matter of pride and of policy. Some of them have superb old timbers, others mellow old brick walls and yet others have high, gabled ceilings. Bathrooms are bathrooms and they work. The great secret of course is Dutch thoroughness as well as respect for the past – and respect for the individual. Here you are never a number – everybody knows you by name. Nothing is too much trouble and the same goes for the food which is supremely beautiful to look at and good to eat. There is a sweet interior courtyard kept with personal pride and in my own mind there will never be any doubt that this is one of Europe's finest medium-sized hotels – one with a personality you will never forget.

The Hague

HOTEL DES INDES, Lange Voorhout 54-56, The Hague

★ TELEPHONE: 070-469553
★ CABLES: Indes-Haag
★ TELEX: 31196
★ IN OPERATION: 100 years
★ RESERVATIONS: Utell International Ltd, London/ Hotel Promotions, London/ Golden Tulip Hotels, New York/ NRC, Amsterdam/Crest Reservation, Europe
★ ROOMS: 67 doubles 10 singles
★ SUITES: 4
★ RESTAURANTS: a new restaurant has just been opened called Le Restaurant

★ BARS: 1
★ DISCOTHEQUE: live music for private parties and music in the restaurant
★ SHOPS: souvenirs and papers etc can be bought at the reception desk
★ CONFERENCE ROOMS: 6 (30 to 150)
★ BANQUETING ROOMS: 7 (10 to 250)
★ STANDARD BEDROOM SIZE: 20–40 m²
★ PRIVATE BALCONIES: yes – 5 rooms
★ SWIMMING POOL: no
★ GARDENS: no
★ NO. OF STAFF: 65
★ ROOM SERVICE: around the clock

★ ORIENTATION: main facade faces south overlooking a beautiful square
★ FURTHER DEVELOPMENTS: reconstruction of guest rooms into classical style is underway
★ CREDIT CARDS: American Express, Diners Club, Visa and Eurocard
★ OWNING COMPANY: Crest Hotels
★ GENERAL MANAGER: B. E. N. Felix
★ DISTANCE TO BEACH: 5 km
★ DISTANCE TO SHOPS: 200 m
★ DISTANCE FROM AIRPORT: 40 km

In the last edition of the guide I confessed, being a light sleeper, that my liking for this particular hotel went back to the night, years ago, when I noticed that after ten p.m., all upstairs staff wore felt-soled shoes. Inevitably I had a letter from an American lady six months ago stating that her room-service waiter did not use such footwear. Oops. Research revealed the reason which proved to be that all floors have been renovated and re-carpeted. Despite my kind correspondent I maintain that the Des Indes is still one of the continent's nicest, quietest and most comfortable hotels. The former baronial residence, it has a good pedigree, has been welcoming and charming guests for a century and though it has new owners they are sure to respect tradition. Rooms vary in size and some of them have been quietly modernised, often with very good, calm colour schemes and fine furniture. Public rooms are excellent, especially the main drawing-room with its famous rotunda ceiling and the restaurant where you never hear the tinkle of glassware or cutlery.

Carpet slippers or not, the staff are very quiet indeed, very well trained and obliging. Management is unobstrusive but always on hand. A very fine residence.

NORWAY

Bergen

HOTEL NORGE, Ole Bulls Plass 4, P.O. Box 662, N-5001, Bergen

★ TELEPHONE: (475) 233000
★ CABLES: Norge
★ TELEX: 42 129
★ IN OPERATION: since 1885, but was rebuilt in 1964
★ RESERVATIONS: KLM – Golden Tulip Hotels B.A. Reservation System
★ ROOMS: 129 doubles   90 singles
★ SUITES: 6
★ SHOPS: 2 – perfumery and souvenirs with bookstand
★ RESTAURANTS: 9 – the Grillen, Restaurant Ole Bull, the Corner Pub, the Baldakinen Restaurant, Norge Dancing and the Garden Room Restaurant etc
★ BARS: 2 in winter and 3 in summer
★ DISCOTHEQUE: yes – Corner Disco Pub, also dancing to the best orchestras in Norge Dancing and the Garden Room Restaurant (summer time only)
★ CONFERENCE ROOMS: 6 (50 to 140)
★ BANQUETING ROOMS: 7 (35 to 450)
★ STANDARD BEDROOM SIZE: 17 m²
★ PRIVATE BALCONIES: yes – some rooms
★ SWIMMING POOL: no
★ GARDENS: no
★ NO. OF STAFF: 400
★ ROOM SERVICE: 07.00–22.00
★ ORIENTATION: Ole Bulls Place and the City Park
★ CREDIT CARDS: American Express, Diners Club, Eurocard, Access, Master Charge and Visa
★ OWNING COMPANY: Hotel Norge – A/S De Forenede Hoteller
★ GENERAL MANAGER: Fridtjof Thirslund Berge
★ DISTANCE TO BEACH: 1 km
★ DISTANCE TO SHOPS: in the shopping centre
★ DISTANCE FROM AIRPORT: 20 km

In a dozen years' absence from Bergen it was a pleasure to rediscover this hotel – surely one of the two or three best in Scandinavia. The architecture may be undistinguished but the decor is not, as befits the home of so much fine design. Dining in the Grill one noticed how comfortable the chairs were. Why can't everybody design chairs like these or the ones in the bedrooms and the sparkling lobby and even in the coffee shop. In a busy, business city, the Norge is absolutely ideal – fast, efficient, clean and so helpful that it's like having a super secretary following you around. It is very popular locally and *'le tout Bergen'* throngs to the nine restaurants and the conference rooms are almost always booked. The rivers and fjords have salmon and there is a fishing fleet in the harbour, so the fish-eater is going to leave the Norge with the sad certainty that meals will not often be so good again.

Oslo

GRAND HOTEL, P.O. Box 9615, Egertorvet, Oslo 1

★ TELEPHONE: 33 48 70
★ CABLES: no
★ TELEX: 71683 grand n
★ IN OPERATION: since 1874
★ RESERVATIONS: Steigenberger Reservation Service, Frankfurt
★ ROOMS: 310
★ SUITES: 8
★ RESTAURANTS: 6 – the Speiler Room, Fritzner Grill Room, Etoile, Palmen, Bonanza and Rococo Room
★ BARS: 3 – Limelight Bar, Grand Plaisir Bar and Bonanza Bar
★ DISCOTHEQUE: Bonanza, and live music in the Mirror Room
★ SHOPS: none
★ CONFERENCE ROOMS: 9 (6 to 500)

★ BANQUETING ROOMS: 1 (500)
★ STANDARD BEDROOM SIZE: 17–30 m^2
★ PRIVATE BALCONIES: yes
★ SWIMMING POOL: yes – fresh water, 8 × 12.5 m
★ RECREATIONAL ACTIVITIES: sauna
★ GARDENS: no
★ NO. OF STAFF: 400
★ ROOM SERVICE: 07.00–23.00
★ ORIENTATION: towards main street
★ CREDIT CARDS: American Express, Visa and Eurocard
★ OWNING COMPANY: A/S Grand Hotel
★ GENERAL MANAGER: Helge Holgerson
★ DISTANCE TO SHOPS: walking distance
★ DISTANCE FROM AIRPORT: 8 km

Always the best hotel in Oslo, Ibsen lived here for a long time and for many decades the guests felt like some of his less-than-exuberant characters. The Grand was grand but sombre. But enterprise (and money) has brought this great dinosaur right down the evolutionary chain with more than a face-lift, a complete rejuvenation so that today it compares very favourably with first class metropolitan hotels elsewhere. It still has comforting reminders of past glories – the reception for instance and also the enormous wall paintings. But now the rooms have been transformed beyond recognition and the suites are especially spectacular – good design and great comfort. There is a new and quite superb penthouse restaurant where the food, Scandinavian-French-international, is worthy of praise and there is also the delicately-revamped Speilen period restaurant. Service is extremely efficient and, of course, this being Norway, the whole place is as clean as a whistle.

OMAN

Muscat-Muttrah

MUSCAT INTER-CONTINENTAL HOTEL, P.O. Box 7398, Muttrah, Sultanate of Oman

★ TELEPHONE: 600500
★ CABLES: Inhotelcor
★ TELEX: 3491 IHC MCT MB
★ IN OPERATION: since 30 November, 1977
★ RESERVATIONS: Inter-Continental Hotels
★ ROOMS: 178 doubles 74 singles 20 cabanas
★ SUITES: 12 – plus 2 Royal Suites
★ RESTAURANTS: 2 – Qurm Restaurant and Musandam Coffee Shop

★ BARS: Al Ghazal Bar, Sur Bar and Sohar Snack Bar
★ DISCOTHEQUE: yes – in Sur Club
★ SHOPS: 12 – includes a flower shop, 3 gift shops, jewellery shop, news stand, bank, handicrafts shop, boutique etc
★ CONFERENCE ROOMS: 5 (20 to 700)
★ BANQUETING ROOMS: 5 (15 to 500) for cocktails up to 900
★ STANDARD BEDROOM SIZE: 26 m^2
★ PRIVATE BALCONIES: yes

★ SWIMMING POOL: yes – fresh water, 327.5 m²

★ RECREATIONAL ACTIVITIES: 3 tennis courts and 2 air conditioned squash courts

★ GARDENS: yes

★ NO. OF STAFF: 400

★ ROOM SERVICE: around the clock

★ ORIENTATION: faces all directions

★ FURTHER DEVELOPMENTS: health centre with Turkish and sauna baths, seafood restaurant, golf putting green

★ CREDIT CARDS: American Express, Visa, Master Charge, Carte Blanche, Diners Club and Eurocard

★ OWNING COMPANY: Government of Oman/Operator – Inter-Continental Hotels

★ GENERAL MANAGER: Mr. Gerhard R. Schmidt

★ DISTANCE TO BEACH: on the beach

★ DISTANCE TO SHOPS: 10 km

★ DISTANCE FROM AIRPORT: 25 km

From cut-throat pirates and pearl divers to the Inter-Continental in one generation is the story of both the Sultanate of Oman and this hotel. And providing you-know-who does not get there before you, we suggest that you go now to this rather grand and magnificent country and stay at this hotel – like that you can have the best of both worlds. Part of the new generation of American chain hotels, this one is not at all offensive – large, sun-coloured concrete and built around that new-fangled architectural gimmick – the interior atrium, a piece of planning which at least gives you a quiet room – in this case large and airy, furnished with good sound hotel pieces which, if not always beautiful, are at least practical. It always mitigates the fiercer effects of the sun. Beds and bathrooms are particularly good and the service is efficient. All the food is imported but is extremely well handled and prepared by a staff who have been well trained. There are nice gardens and a huge swimming pool. From here you could sail by dhow to that fantastic Musandam Peninsula which guards the Straits of Hormuz – like most out-of-this-world spots it seems destined to become the centre of this world's troubles very soon. Let us hope it overcomes them.

PAPUA NEW GUINEA

KARAWARI LODGE, P.O. Box 371, Mount Hagen, Papua New Guinea

★ TELEPHONE: 52-1438

★ CABLES: no

★ TELEX: 52012 Transng

★ IN OPERATION: 5 years

★ RESERVATIONS: United Touring International Ltd, London, Tokyo, Germany, Paris, Rome/Travel Consultants International, California/Trans Niugini Tours Pty Ltd, Papua New Guinea

★ ROOMS: 20 double

★ SUITES: no

★ RESTAURANTS: 1

★ BARS: 1

★ DISCOTHEQUE: no

★ SHOPS: variety of items sold in Lodge Office

★ CONFERENCE ROOMS: 1 (up to 40)

★ BANQUETING ROOMS: 1 (up to 40)

★ STANDARD BEDROOM SIZE: 22 m²

★ PRIVATE BALCONIES: all rooms

★ SWIMMING POOL: yes – fresh water

★ RECREATIONAL ACTIVITIES: chess, backgammon and cards. Good selection of books

★ GARDENS: yes

★ NO. OF STAFF: 20

★ ROOM SERVICE: 07.00–22.00

★ ORIENTATION: rooms overlook Karawari River and Amboin Station or overlook tropical rain forest

★ CREDIT CARDS: American Express and Diners Club

★ OWNING COMPANY: Karawari Lodge Pty Ltd

★ GENERAL MANAGER: N. Bevan

★ DISTANCE TO SHOPS: no shops within 100 miles

★ DISTANCE FROM AIRPORT: private airport 10 minutes away

Once again, readers of this book will think that I have taken leave of my senses. One of the 300 Best Hotels in the World in Papua New Guinea? A joke surely. I swear it is not and if you don't believe me, go and see for yourself. In this astonishingly beautiful country, at least half of which seems to be vertical and where they keep coming across people who have never seen a Western face, is a mountain top and on its lee is Karawari Lodge, one of the most unusual hotels in the world and the very end of what one might call civilisation. Sit on the terrace as the sun goes down and you'll convince yourself that the world was born yesterday. Down below is the wide Karawari River which flows into the now world-famous Sepik – dugout canoes, crocodiles, unknown orchids and the vast enveloping jungle with the occasional village on stilts of charming people who paint their faces and wear a bunch of leaves back and front and, let it not be forgotten, are also great artists at carving (their creations cost a fortune on Fifth Avenue).

Karawari is built just like a Sepik village – the 'haus tamburan', or spirit house, is the main building, made of tropical timber without a single nail and filled with fantastic artifacts. Your cottage is another wooden hut on stilts (no, there are no chandeliers) and after the first raised eyebrow you'll love it, especially when tropical birds wake you up by pecking on your roof. Food is better than one has any right to expect – they even have Australian wine – but what really counts is being here, at the edge of the world – a world untouched and unsullied. Wearing your floppy jungle hat, you get ready for another speedboat excursion into the Stone Age. In twenty-five years of travelling, this is almost certainly the most unusual hotel I have ever visited. Don't miss it.

PHILIPPINES

Manila

THE MANILA MANDARIN HOTEL, Makati Avenue, Paseo de Roxas, P.O. Box 1038 MCC, Makati, Metro Manila 3117

★ TELEPHONE: 85-78-11
★ CABLES: Mandahotel Manila
★ TELEX: MANDA PN 63756
★ IN OPERATION: since 1976
★ RESERVATIONS: Hotel Representative Inc, worldwide
★ ROOMS: 504
★ SUITES: 20
★ RESTAURANTS: 4 – L'Hirondelle, Tivoli, The Marquee Coffee Shop and Clipper Lounge
★ BARS: 3
★ DISCOTHEQUE: no – but dancing and live music in the bar
★ SHOPS: 3 – drugstore, souvenirs and delicatessen
★ CONFERENCE ROOMS: 7 (10 to 700)
★ BANQUETING ROOMS: 7 (10 to 700)
★ STANDARD BEDROOM SIZE: 27 m²

★ PRIVATE BALCONIES: no
★ SWIMMING POOL: yes – fresh water
★ RECREATIONAL ACTIVITIES: health club with exercise area and sauna and massage
★ GARDENS: no
★ NO. OF STAFF: 800
★ ROOM SERVICE: around the clock
★ ORIENTATION: three facades
★ CREDIT CARDS: American Express, Visa, Master Charge, Carte Blanche and Diners Club
★ OWNING COMPANY: Mandarin International Hotels Ltd
★ GENERAL MANAGER: Wolfgang K. Hultner
★ DISTANCE TO SHOPS: walking distance
★ DISTANCE FROM AIRPORT: 8 km

Having had the pleasure of revisiting the Manila Mandarin, I have nothing but praise for a company which opens a new hotel only when it knows it will be the best in the locality. This one is a magnificent, ultra-modern hostelry where one is hard put to find fault. Everything runs smooth as silk and, in this rather noisy city, it is quiet in the extreme. Rooms are large, very well planned and a pleasure to be in and the suites, especially the Mandarin Suite with its own swimming pool, worth booking ahead for. Food and drink are extremely sophisticated and, in the famous L'Hirondelle restaurant, quite stunning in both quality and cadre. The staff, lavishly numerous, are ever watchful, ever willing and dedicated to making you feel at least a twenty-one gong tycoon. Without a murmur, they even repaired a suitcase handle mangled by the airline.

THE MANILA HOTEL, P.O. Box 307, Rizal Park, Metro Manila

★ TELEPHONE: 470011

★ CABLES: MANILHOTEL

★ TELEX: ITT 40537 MHotel PM/ETPI
63496 MHotel PN/RCA 22479 MHC PH

★ IN OPERATION: since 1912

★ RESERVATIONS: John A. Tetley Co, Los
Angeles, San Francisco, Seattle/Robert
F. Warner Inc, New York, Sydney/Utell
International Ltd, Paris, Dusseldorf,
Benelux, Melbourne/Muriel Fleger
International Hotel Consultants,
Toronto/Stinnes Touristic
Representations, Frankfurt/Supereps
International, London/Far East
Enterprises, Tokyo/Cardinal Hotel
Booking Service, Hong Kong/Philippine
Airlines District Sales and Reservations
Offices, worldwide

★ ROOMS: 7 king-size   213 queen-size
273 twins

★ SUITES: 55

★ RESTAURANTS: 7 – Champagne Room,
Maynila, Cowrie Grill, Café Ilang-Ilang,
Sea Breeze Grill, Pool Bar, Lobby
Lounge (speciality restaurants have live
entertainment)

★ BARS: 3

★ DISCOTHEQUE: 'Après' open nightly,
except Mondays

★ SHOPS: 11 (including duty free shop)

★ CONFERENCE ROOMS: 9 (25 to 120)

★ BANQUETING ROOMS: 3 (150 to 1,400)

★ STANDARD BEDROOM SIZE: 18 m^2

★ PRIVATE BALCONIES: 3 suites with
verandahs leading to common balcony;
5 studios

★ SWIMMING POOL: yes – fresh water, plus
baby pool

★ RECREATIONAL ACTIVITIES: the Manila
Hotel Bay Club which has putting
greens, two tennis and squash courts,
sauna and massage services, men's and
ladies' gyms, jacuzzi whirlpools,
sporting goods shop, dietetic snack bar

★ GARDENS: yes

★ NO. OF STAFF: 1,060

★ ROOM SERVICE: around the clock

★ CREDIT CARDS: American Express, Carte
Blanche, Diners Club, Master Charge,
Visa and Eurocard

★ OWNING COMPANY: Philippine
Government

★ GENERAL MANAGER: Frans Schutzman

★ DISTANCE TO SHOPS: 1 km

★ DISTANCE FROM AIRPORT: 12 km (Manila
International Airport)

Travel broadens the mind. And makes you blink with surprise. Last year when I walked, for the first time, into the redecorated Manila Hotel, I gained the firm impression that this was the most beautiful hotel in the world. In retrospect I would not go as far as that but this is certainly a hotel of such splendour, such artistry, such magnificence that it must on no account be missed. The great marble lobby has kept its Filipino-Hispanic columns and its marble and is without any doubt this time, the most impressive hotel lobby I know. The same adjectives can be applied to the Champagne Room with its wrought metalwork, its cane and its crystal trees and I defy any designer to do better – it has had the attention of some Oriental Cecil Beaton. But it was when I inspected the suites, especially the historic MacArthur Suite and the Presidential Suite, that I realised what a genuine treasure-house the Manila is. The story goes that the Philippines First Lady took a personal interest in the doing-up of the hotel – obviously she is on good terms with every museum in the islands because the place simply gleams with the most marvellous antiques, carvings, paintings and furniture – and all this mixed extremely cleverly with a modernity which can't be bettered anywhere. The staff is an army – there are always six white-clad bellboys waiting at attention when you arrive and service everywhere in this vast hotel is super-efficient and smiling. The Dutch gentleman who runs the Manila is one of those people who has been everywhere and done everything, and he has the great good luck – and judgment – to run a hotel which is probably unique in the world.

PORTUGAL

Bussaco

PALACE HOTEL BUSSACO, 3050 Mealhada

- ★ TELEPHONE: 0031 93101
- ★ CABLES: Palace Bussaco
- ★ TELEX: no
- ★ IN OPERATION: since the beginning of the century
- ★ RESERVATIONS: direct
- ★ ROOMS: 80
- ★ SUITES: 4
- ★ RESTAURANTS: 1
- ★ BARS: 1
- ★ DISCOTHEQUE: no
- ★ SHOPS: 1
- ★ CONFERENCE ROOMS: 1 (80)
- ★ BANQUETING ROOMS: 1 (80 to 120)
- ★ STANDARD BEDROOM SIZE: 20 m²

- ★ PRIVATE BALCONIES: yes – some rooms
- ★ SWIMMING POOL: yes – fresh water, 50 × 20 m
- ★ RECREATIONAL ACTIVITIES: tennis
- ★ GARDENS: yes
- ★ NO. OF STAFF: 60/80
- ★ ROOM SERVICE: around the clock
- ★ ORIENTATION: south, east and north
- ★ CREDIT CARDS: Bankamericard and Barclaycard
- ★ OWNING COMPANY: private
- ★ GENERAL MANAGER: Jose R. Santos
- ★ DISTANCE TO SHOPS: 25 km (Coimbra)
- ★ DISTANCE FROM AIRPORT: 100 km (Oporto) and 220 km (Lisbon)

This unusual hotel is Portuguese Manueline architecture gone mad – curlicues decorate arches, crazy towers and improbable staircases and carved ceilings. Once, it was the King of Portugal's hunting lodge and now that the kings are all somewhere else, it is the visitor who has the chance to try this extraordinary way of life. All around are great, green, forested hills where no doubt, His Majesty hunted everything there was excluding peasants. The trees are among the largest and finest I have seen in Europe and a short stroll brings royal delight – there is always a fountain, or a pond or some folly at the end of a vista. Inside, the place is very ornate indeed but, happily, the furnishings are in extremely good taste and carpets particularly beautiful. As in all onetime palaces, rooms vary a lot in size and quality – so make sure you are not relegated to the servant's wing. The best are very good indeed even if the bathroom plumbing turns out to be a bit on the noisy side. As always in Portugal, the food is superabundant, so watch your waistline.

Estoril

HOTEL PALACIO, Estoril

- ★ TELEPHONE: 2680400
- ★ CABLES: Palacio
- ★ TELEX: 12757 Plage P
- ★ IN OPERATION: since 1930
- ★ RESERVATIONS: Hotel Representative Inc
- ★ ROOMS: 190
- ★ SUITES: 27
- ★ RESTAURANTS: 2
- ★ BARS: 2
- ★ DISCOTHEQUE: yes
- ★ SHOPS: none
- ★ CONFERENCE ROOMS: 7 (20 to 450)
- ★ BANQUETING ROOMS: 4 (30 to 350)
- ★ STANDARD BEDROOM SIZE: 30 m²
- ★ PRIVATE BALCONIES: yes – in most rooms
- ★ SWIMMING POOL: yes – thermal water

- ★ RECREATIONAL ACTIVITIES: golf course nearby belonging to the hotel
- ★ GARDENS: yes
- ★ NO. OF STAFF: 230
- ★ ROOM SERVICE: around the clock
- ★ ORIENTATION: rooms face west and east
- ★ CREDIT CARDS: American Express, Diners Club and Eurocard
- ★ OWNING COMPANY: Estoril-Plage S.A.R.L.
- ★ GENERAL MANAGER: Manuel Henrique Ai Quintas
- ★ DISTANCE TO BEACH: walking distance
- ★ DISTANCE TO SHOPS: 200 m
- ★ DISTANCE FROM AIRPORT: 30 km

One of the things which have changed for the better in Portugal is the Palacio and I suspect that this is due largely to its eminent general manager, one of the best in the business, who has managed to keep the Palacio where it was – at the top. It's a dreamy place, ageless, all regal corridors and superbly beautiful lobbies, a bar that is like a bar – cheerful and convivial and above all a staff so knowledgeable that they guess instinctively not only your nationality but your tastes and habits. One never has to ask for the same thing twice – it's there – right down to the ceremonial whiter-than-white tablecloth they put on if you order a cup of tea. I like the old, grand rooms, but one must admit that the air-conditioned duplex suites by the swimming pool are also a very good buy. It is a quiet, well brought up, distinguished hotel. Food and drink, a bit of a problem during 'the troubles', are now back to normal and perfectly acceptable.

Evora

POUSADA DOS LOIOS, Largo Conde de Vila Flor, P-7000 Evora

- ★ TELEPHONE: 24051 or 24052
- ★ CABLES: Pousada Evora
- ★ TELEX: 43288
- ★ IN OPERATION: 18 years
- ★ RESERVATIONS: direct or Portuguese National Tourist Offices
- ★ ROOMS: 32
- ★ SUITES: 1
- ★ RESTAURANTS: 1
- ★ BARS: 1
- ★ DISCOTHEQUE: no
- ★ SHOPS: 1
- ★ CONFERENCE ROOMS: none
- ★ BANQUETING ROOMS: none
- ★ STANDARD BEDROOM SIZE: 20–25 m²

- ★ PRIVATE BALCONIES: 2 terraces
- ★ SWIMMING POOL: no
- ★ GARDENS: 1
- ★ NO. OF STAFF: 49
- ★ ROOM SERVICE: none
- ★ ORIENTATION: views over city
- ★ CREDIT CARDS: Master Card, Visa, American Express and Diners Club
- ★ OWNING COMPANY: ENATUR-Empresa National de Turismo, E.P.
- ★ GENERAL MANAGER: Manuel Cardoso
- ★ DISTANCE TO SHOPS: walking distance
- ★ DISTANCE FROM AIRPORT: 145 km (Lisbon)

Anyone who cares for the past ought to go to Evora – the loveliest little provincial city in Portugal, with its own Roman temple. There is a charming, Government-owned hotel, the Pousada dos Loios which is bliss – an original, untouched sixteenth-century convent with cloisters (you dine in one of them), long flagstoned passages, convoluted columns and lots of splendid carvings. Rooms vary but the best are superb – some of them have four-poster beds and everywhere the furniture is a national treasure.
Because Evora is a bit out of the normal tourist beat, not so many people go there which means that the staff are not overwhelmed – they are nice, friendly and helpful and if not brimming over with the joy of life (no Portuguese ever is) they try their best. As everywhere else in this delightfully old fashioned country, the food is plentiful and perfectly acceptable.

Lisbon

HOTEL RITZ, Rua Rodrigo da Fonseca 88, Lisbon

- ★ TELEPHONE: 684131
- ★ CABLES: Ritzotel Lisbon
- ★ TELEX: 1258 RITZP
- ★ IN OPERATION: since 1959
- ★ RESERVATIONS: Inter-Continental Hotels
- ★ ROOMS: 306
- ★ SUITES: 20
- ★ RESTAURANTS: 3
- ★ BARS: 2
- ★ DISCOTHEQUE: yes – Disco Carrousel
- ★ SHOPS: 6 in the hotel and 6 in the gallery

- ★ CONFERENCE ROOMS: 7 (5 to 500)
- ★ BANQUETING ROOMS: 3 (up to 500)
- ★ STANDARD BEDROOM SIZE: 20 m²
- ★ PRIVATE BALCONIES: yes
- ★ SWIMMING POOL: no
- ★ GARDENS: yes
- ★ NO. OF STAFF: 530
- ★ ROOM SERVICE: around the clock
- ★ ORIENTATION: overlooking city or Tagus Estuary and park
- ★ CREDIT CARDS: all major credit cards

★ OWNING COMPANY: Sodim/operated by Inter-Continental
★ GENERAL MANAGER: Mr. B. Schutz

★ DISTANCE TO BEACH: 20 km
★ DISTANCE TO SHOPS: 300 km
★ DISTANCE FROM AIRPORT: 12 km

Since it first opened twenty odd years ago I must confess to having had a long love affair with this hotel. Managed by an extremely expert international chain it will now get the publicity it deserves. Everything at the Lisbon Ritz is worth looking at – the carpets (made specially for the hotel) – the furnishings, the bathrooms, the service, even the guests. If there is a fault I haven't seen it.

Rooms are vast and the best have that superb view of Lisbon. Every room and everything else has that ageless quality which is the hallmark of a great hotel. The staff are charming. The Portuguese are normally quiet and polite, and remain impassive even if you require them to make running repairs to a garment early on a Sunday morning. Bathrooms are palatial and superbly clean at all times – I know because I once left a 'secret' mark on a towel and on returning, it had been changed. Flowers are fresh, lobbies gleaming after the early morning work and from the lift man to the front office manager everyone greets you as if you were someone really important. The food, once the weak link in this Ritz, has now been improved beyond recognition.

Madeira

REID'S HOTEL, Estrada Monumental 139, Funchal

★ TELEPHONE: 2 30 01
★ CABLES: Reids Funchal
★ TELEX: 72139 Reids P
★ IN OPERATION: since 1890
★ RESERVATIONS: Hotel Representative Inc
★ ROOMS: 168
★ SUITES: 15
★ RESTAURANTS: 3
★ BARS: 2
★ DISCOTHEQUE: yes – live music and dancing in the main bar
★ SHOPS: 3
★ CONFERENCE ROOMS: 2 (20 to 50)
★ BANQUETING ROOMS: 1 (150)
★ STANDARD BEDROOM SIZE: 24 m^2

★ PRIVATE BALCONIES: yes
★ SWIMMING POOL: 3 – sea water, 2 of which are heated in winter
★ GARDENS: yes – 50,000 m^2
★ NO. OF STAFF: 330
★ ROOM SERVICE: around the clock
★ ORIENTATION: most rooms face the sea
★ CREDIT CARDS: American Express, Eurocard and Master Charge
★ OWNING COMPANY: Island Hotel (Madeira) Ltd
★ GENERAL MANAGER: G. Hangartner
★ DISTANCE TO BEACH: walking distance
★ DISTANCE TO SHOPS: 2 km
★ DISTANCE FROM AIRPORT: 17 km

Tradition being what it is one never knows whether people go to Madeira to stay at Reid's or the other way around. This grand old hotel, created so long ago for the British upper classes who liked their tea (with their milk in the cup first, of course) and also loved gardens, is still home from home for the island race but by now Reid's has become famous all over the world and no wonder. It is charming, beautifully kept, easy on the eye and also the last word when it comes to service and evening entertainment. Rooms are a good size, simple but very comfortable and many have large balconies where you can sit and contemplate this sweet, green and gold island. The staff cover many generations and they are literally everywhere and extremely willing. The food, once rather plain, is now above the average, but what makes Reid's are its gardens – the finest of any hotel on the island. In fact, you can forget all the other Madeira hotels – I wouldn't dream of going anywhere else but to Reid's.

Sintra

HOTEL PALACIO DOS SETEAIS, Rua Barbosa du Bocage, 8–12, Sintra

- ★ TELEPHONE: 293.3200
- ★ CABLES: Seteais
- ★ TELEX: 42314 HOTISI P
- ★ IN OPERATION: since October, 1955
- ★ RESERVATIONS: direct
- ★ ROOMS: 10 doubles 8 singles
- ★ SUITES: 1
- ★ RESTAURANTS: 1
- ★ BARS: 1
- ★ DISCOTHEQUE: no – there is a piano for the guests' use
- ★ SHOPS: none
- ★ CONFERENCE ROOMS: none – two lounges can be adapted
- ★ BANQUETING ROOMS: none – two lounges can be adapted

- ★ STANDARD BEDROOM SIZE: 25 m^2
- ★ PRIVATE BALCONIES: yes
- ★ SWIMMING POOL: no
- ★ GARDENS: yes
- ★ NO. OF STAFF: 60
- ★ ROOM SERVICE: 08.00–23.00
- ★ ORIENTATION: main facade faces south, but there are rooms facing every cardinal point
- ★ CREDIT CARDS: American Express, Diners Club, Master Charge and Visa
- ★ OWNING COMPANY: Hotel Tivoli Ltd
- ★ GENERAL MANAGER: Manuel Cardoso
- ★ DISTANCE TO BEACH: 10–13 km
- ★ DISTANCE TO SHOPS: 1 km
- ★ DISTANCE FROM AIRPORT: 45 km

When the Duke of Wellington was looking for a suitable place to sign an armistice with Napoleon's generals, he was fortunate that the 'Palace of the Seven Sighs' was at hand and there could not have been a more fitting place. I have always loved this grand, graceful place in lovely Sintra. It was built in the eighteenth century by a Dutch architect for a richer-than-rich Portuguese nobleman and only the best would do. Seteais has majesty, good looks, a magnificent park, unique tapestries up and down the monumental staircases and enough 'azulejos' to please any admirer of things Portuguese. When Seteais serves lunch or dinner, it does so – but of course – on the country's own Sèvres, the lovely and delicate Vista Alegre porcelain – an absolute delight. Rooms are vast, some of them so much so that one needs a bicycle to reach the bathroom which, in turn, is part of the gurgling period of European plumbing. Furniture and furnishings are worth a king's ransom and, one would say, so is the staff – two to every guest. The food which used to be one of this hotel's weakest points (the kitchens are miles away) has now been much improved.

SAUDI ARABIA

Taif

MASSARRAH INTER-CONTINENTAL HOTEL, P.O. Box 827, Taif

- ★ TELEPHONE: (966-02) 732 8333
- ★ CABLES: Inhotelcor Tif
- ★ TELEX: 450055 Masara SJ
- ★ IN OPERATION: 4 years
- ★ RESERVATIONS: Inter-Continental Hotel Corporation, New York and London
- ★ ROOMS: 205
- ★ SUITES: 35 and 24 villas
- ★ RESTAURANTS: 2 – the Massarrah and coffee lounge
- ★ BARS: 2 cafeterias (soft drinks)
- ★ DISCOTHEQUE: live music on Thursdays and Fridays
- ★ SHOPS: 3 – gift shop/news stand, barber shop and travel agency
- ★ CONFERENCE ROOMS: 4 (300 to 800)
- ★ BANQUETING ROOMS: 5 (200 to 600)

- ★ STANDARD BEDROOM SIZE: 28 m^2
- ★ PRIVATE BALCONIES: no
- ★ SWIMMING POOL: yes 2 – fresh water, one hexagonal dia. 22 m and one 18 × 9 m
- ★ RECREATIONAL ACTIVITIES: tennis, billiards, table tennis, health club with sauna and massage parlour and private mosque
- ★ GARDENS: yes
- ★ NO. OF STAFF: 250
- ★ ROOM SERVICE: around the clock
- ★ ORIENTATION: faces the Riyadh Highway
- ★ GENERAL MANAGER: Gabriel R. Khawam
- ★ CREDIT CARDS: Carte Blanche, Amexco, Diners Club, Visa and Lufthansa

★ OWNING COMPANY: Inter-Continental
  Hotels Corporation

★ DISTANCE TO SHOPS: 12 km
★ DISTANCE FROM AIRPORT: 16 km

This region was marked *Arabia Felix* in the early maps. Happy Arabia in Latin, it is fortunate in the existence of this hotel. Ironically, the oil from which the money came to pay for everything comes from that part known as *Arabia Infelix* – the old cartographers were doubtless aware of the unhappy results of having more money than taste but they would approve of the Massarrah. The summer residence of the Saudi kings, Taif is a lively little hill town. Obviously it would not do in Venice or Baden Baden but that's another story.

Built around a huge and cool atrium, with pool and plants and fountains, the five wings radiate off to offer rooms which, considering the location and Arab taste, are amazing and sober – the Dubai gold bazaar has played no part in the motif. Furniture is ageless and very well kept and room service (mostly Pakistanis, we suspect) is prompt and attentive whether your pocket is full of petrodollars or not. Considering the supply difficulties, the food is remarkably palatable and we particularly admired the very beautiful table settings which must have cost a bob or two. Suites are sheikh-sized and all the tribes of Araby could gather in the banqueting rooms without overcrowding.

SEYCHELLES

BIRD ISLAND LODGE, P.O. Box 404, Seychelles

★ TELEPHONE: 21038/21525
★ CABLES: BIRD SEYCHELLES
★ TELEX: 2334 SZ
★ IN OPERATION: 8 years
★ RESERVATIONS: direct
★ ROOMS: 25 bungalows
★ SUITES: none
★ RESTAURANTS: 1
★ BARS: 1
★ DISCOTHEQUE: no
★ SHOPS: 1 – souvenirs and toiletries
★ CONFERENCE ROOMS: none
★ BANQUETING ROOMS: none
★ STANDARD BEDROOM SIZE: 20 m²
★ PRIVATE BALCONIES: all rooms have
  verandas
★ SWIMMING POOL: no

★ RECREATIONAL ACTIVITIES: tennis,
  billiards, ping pong, beach fishing,
  game fishing, library and indoor games
★ GARDENS: yes – the whole island is
  private
★ NO. OF STAFF: 30
★ ROOM SERVICE: none
★ ORIENTATION: all rooms adjacent to
  main swimming beach of Bird Island
★ CREDIT CARDS: Diners Club, Visa and
  American Express
★ OWNING COMPANY: Bird Island Ltd
  (private company)
★ GENERAL MANAGER: George Norah
★ DISTANCE TO BEACH: on the beach
★ DISTANCE FROM AIRPORT: 100 km

Now that almost every hotel on these superlatively beautiful islands, the Seychelles, has become a package holiday supermarket, there is only one place left to go: Bird Island Lodge. Its slogan is 'Our guests come back every year . . . and three million birds can't be wrong'. The birds of course are the graceful noddies, unique to this part of the world and at home here since Bird Island is basically a nature preserve. It is also a small, divine island, green and richly tropical, surrounded on all sides by the whitest sand beaches one is likely to see anywhere. The sea is pale blue, the sky blue and gold and there is absolutely nothing to do except swim, sunbathe, eat and drink (quite civilised really) and make friends with Esmeralda, believed to be the largest tortoise in the world.

This is a world of small island enchantment, with only a few locally built cottages with terraces and gardens all over and a feeling of peace and isolation which is quite priceless these days. If you wish to escape (from the tax collector, the newspapers or even your wife/husband . . .) Bird Island is the place you are looking for.

SINGAPORE

GOODWOOD PARK HOTEL, 22 Scotts Road, 0922

★ TELEPHONE: 7377411
★ CABLES: Goodwood
★ TELEX: RS 24377
★ IN OPERATION: since 1929
★ RESERVATIONS: Steigenberger Reservation Service, worldwide/Southern Pacific Hotels Corporation, Australia/UTA French Airlines, worldwide/R. M. Brooker Ltd, Liverpool
★ ROOMS: 156 doubles   14 singles
★ SUITES: 105
★ RESTAURANTS: 4 – Gordon Grill, L'Espresso, Coffee Lounge and Japanese
★ BARS: 1 – Highland Bar
★ DISCOTHEQUE: yes
★ SHOPS: 5 – drugstore, gift shop, jewellery and watches, hairdresser and barber
★ CONFERENCE ROOMS: 2 (50 to 300)

★ BANQUETING ROOMS: 2 (140 to 400)
★ STANDARD BEDROOM SIZE: 35 m²
★ PRIVATE BALCONIES: yes – most rooms
★ SWIMMING POOL: yes – 2, fresh water, 22 × 13 m and 22 × 11 m
★ RECREATIONAL ACTIVITIES: squash courts
★ GARDENS: yes
★ NO. OF STAFF: 450
★ ROOM SERVICE: around the clock
★ ORIENTATION: all directions – the hotel stands on a hill
★ CREDIT CARDS: American Express, Visa, Diners Club, Master Charge and Goodwood Group
★ OWNING COMPANY: Goodwood Hotels Corporation
★ GENERAL MANAGER: Mrs. Mavis Oei
★ DISTANCE TO SHOPS: directly
★ DISTANCE FROM AIRPORT: 24 km

In the business which concerns us, the most difficult job is not building a new hotel – it is restoring an old one and in this context I have no hesitation in saying that Singapore's Goodwood Park is where everybody should go to take lessons because here enterprise, infinite good taste and superb management have taken an old hulk – circa 1900 – and transformed it into a hostelry of dazzling excellence. Here one sits amidst fourteen acres of some of the most expensive real estate in the world and the grand hotel syndrome plus the Eastern magic turns the whole place into an instant success story. The Goodwood Park is perfection: rooms are vast and suites vaster, especially that superb Brunei Suite and yet nowhere is there any hint of razzle-dazzle. Furniture is handsome and beautifully kept, carpets are splendiferous, decor so delicate and so beautifully blended that you wonder who could have worked such miracles. Even the Coffee Lounge (which anywhere else would surely be the state dining room) is magnificent. The food goes with it all – splendidly varied, fresh and good-looking and with both Oriental and Western touches. Next door is the East's answer to Fortnum & Mason or Fauchon's – the greatest food shop in this part of the world. The staff, legions of them, are super-efficient, gentle and attentive. One really feels that in a place where Noel Coward stayed and Pavlova danced, one has the best of both worlds. Goodwood Park is an astonishing hotel which deserves every adjective in the book. Don't miss it. Singapore would not be Singapore without it.

THE MARCO POLO, Tanglin Road, 1024

★ TELEPHONE: 474-7141
★ CABLES: Homarcpolo
★ TELEX: 21476
★ IN OPERATION: 9 years
★ RESERVATIONS: Steigenberger Reservations Service, worldwide/British Airways Assoc Hotels, London/Utell/Golden Tulip, worldwide
★ ROOMS: 574
★ SUITES: 29
★ RESTAURANTS: 5 – the Marco Polo

Restaurant, Brasserie la Rotonde, La Pinata, El Patio, and San Marco
★ BARS: 3
★ DISCOTHEQUE: yes – and live music in the restaurant
★ SHOPS: shopping arcade – boutiques, objets d'art, ladies' beauty salon, barbershop and drugstore
★ CONFERENCE ROOMS: 4 (50 to 150)
★ BANQUETING ROOMS: 4 (50 to 100)
★ STANDARD BEDROOM SIZE: 28 m²

★ PRIVATE BALCONIES: no – but 10 terrace rooms have individual sun porches leading to the swimming pool

★ SWIMMING POOL: yes – fresh water, two, semi-olympic size and children's pool

★ RECREATIONAL ACTIVITIES: fitness centre with fully equipped gym, sauna, massage and juice bar, a jogging track and also within walking distance of a golf course

★ GARDENS: yes

★ NO. OF STAFF: 770

★ ROOM SERVICE: around the clock

★ ORIENTATION: faces Tanglin and Grange Roads

★ CREDIT CARDS: American Express, Diners Club, Bankamericard and Master Charge

★ OWNING COMPANY: Hong Kong & Kowloon Wharf

★ GENERAL MANAGER: Mr. Dario Regazzoni

★ DISTANCE TO BEACH: 15 km

★ DISTANCE TO SHOPS: 800 m

★ DISTANCE FROM AIRPORT: 36 km

Apart from the gewgaws in the shops and the Chinese wallpanels in the main restaurant, the Marco Polo appears brand new. Yet, this sister ship of Hong Kong's famed Peninsula was the first purpose-built hotel in the perpetual motion that is Singapore. What counts here is service – absolutely superb, smiling, efficient and never, but never on a day off. If you are lucky enough (and rich enough) to stay in the Marco Polo Suite you get a lady's maid or valet thrown in. Not that my room needed either – the floor service was so good that I had no time to ask for anything. Rooms and suites are very large, perhaps a little impersonal – modern but highly enjoyable with fabulous views all around. The vast lobby is banked with orchids and other exotica and the welcome is beatific. It's the kind of hotel which offers so many facilities that one is never bored – not even with the food because all the Orient's specialities are here. Marco Polo himself, who brought Chinese noodles back to Italy where they now call them spaghetti, would be astonished at the hotel that bears his name.

SHANGRI-LA HOTEL, Orange Grove Road, 1025

★ TELEPHONE: 7373644

★ CABLES: Shangrila Singapore

★ TELEX: Shangla RS21505

★ IN OPERATION: 10 years

★ RESERVATIONS: Utell, Europe/Direct Reservations, Australia/Westin Hotels, worldwide

★ ROOMS: 650

★ SUITES: 50

★ RESTAURANTS: 5 – Tiara Supper Club, Golden Peacock, Shang Palace, Coffee Garden and Waterfall Cafe

★ BARS: 4 – including pool side

★ DISCOTHEQUE: Xanadu Discotheque and live music and entertainment in the Tiara Supper Club and Peacock Lounge

★ SHOPS: 18 – jewellery, watches, fabrics, ceramics, boutiques, cameras, antiques, drugstore, ladies' and gentlemen's hairdressers

★ CONFERENCE ROOMS: 11 (20 to 1,500)

★ BANQUETING ROOMS: 10 (40 to 1,100)

★ STANDARD BEDROOM SIZE: 32 m² and 41.3 m² in new garden wing

★ PRIVATE BALCONES: yes

★ SWIMMING POOL: yes – fresh water

★ RECREATIONAL ACTIVITIES: pitch and putt, tennis, squash, saunas and health club

★ GARDENS: yes

★ NO. OF STAFF: 1,200

★ ROOM SERVICE: around the clock

★ ORIENTATION: rooms face either gardens or city

★ CREDIT CARDS: American Express, Diners Club, Bankamericard and Master Charge

★ OPERATING COMPANY: Westin Hotels

★ GENERAL MANAGER: Michael C. Kalyk

★ DISTANCE TO BEACH: 9 km

★ DISTANCE TO SHOPS: 300 m

★ DISTANCE FROM AIRPORT: 18 km

I have known this hotel more or less since it opened but it was only last year after a somewhat longer stay than usual that I began to realise what a truly magnificent living machine it really is – and I say the word machine without any disrespect. Shangri La is superb, beautifully organised, magnificently designed and serviced, down to the smallest detail, with enthusiasm and knowhow. I believe it to be a tribute to the intelligence and knowhow of this particular chain. Rooms are immaculate and if you are lucky enough to have one of the garden-side ones, my belief is that you won't find better or more practical and elegant anywhere. Balconies open not onto a frenetic city but onto a vista of greenery and peace. On the other side, it opens onto an atrium filled with more than one hundred varieties of tropical plants. Every service in the hotel – a complicated business with this size – works like a charm. People smile, execute immediately and without demur. Even the proverbial coffee-shop (usually the hum-drum set-up where a hotel fails) is not only sumptuous but quick at offering tasty food. Those who love the old and mature should not be put off by the rather overpowering lobby or indeed the tomorrow architecture. Shangri La is a great hotel – one of the best I know.

SOUTH AFRICA

Cape Town

MOUNT NELSON HOTEL, P.O. Box 2608, Cape Town 8000

★ TELEPHONE: (021) 220012
★ CABLES: Hostel
★ TELEX: 572-7804
★ IN OPERATION: since 1899
★ RESERVATIONS: Canaries Hotels Ltd, Sussex/Loews Reservations Inc, New York, Montreal and Tokyo/Claude Duteil, Paris
★ ROOMS: 107 doubles   36 singles
★ SUITES: 20
★ RESTAURANTS: 3 – the Grill Room, the Garden Room and the Poolside Restaurant
★ SHOPS: 2
★ BARS: 3 – Lord Nelson, Grill Room Cocktail Bar and Poolside Bar
★ DISCOTHEQUE: no – but live music in the Grill Room
★ CONFERENCE ROOMS: 5 (up to 450)
★ BANQUETING ROOMS: 6 (24 to 350)
★ STANDARD BEDROOM SIZE: 30 m², but all rooms vary

★ PRIVATE BALCONIES: yes – some rooms
★ SWIMMING POOL: yes – fresh water, heated, 19 × 18½ m
★ GARDENS: yes
★ NO. OF STAFF: 320
★ ROOM SERVICE: around the clock
★ RECREATIONAL ACTIVITIES: tennis, squash, and a new swimming pool. Golf, mountain climbing, sailing and deep sea fishing within easy reach
★ ORIENTATION: rooms face Table Mountain and gardens
★ CREDIT CARDS: American Express, Diners Club, Barclaycard, Standard, Access, Master Charge and Eurocard
★ OWNING COMPANY: African Lands and Hotels Ltd
★ GENERAL MANAGER: Mr. K. Morton Chance
★ DISTANCE TO BEACH: 3 km
★ DISTANCE TO SHOPS: 500 m
★ DISTANCE FROM AIRPORT: 20 km

In a physically stunningly beautiful country where, alas modern vulgarity is creeping along, this is the only place to stay happily in any of the big cities. Mount Nelson is an institution – a hotel that has got grander and more elegant with the years, shows none of the usual South African moneymania and still offers peace, quiet and great serenity. The rooms vary a lot – many of them are being done up – but the best are shiningly clean and fresh, with pretty wallpapers and furnishings and lots of room to move about. There is no exaggerated luxury anywhere, just good planning and a choice of furniture that many hotels could copy. The staff – most of them have been there a long time – are quite charming and helpful and food and wine are better than the South African average. The crowning point of Mount Nelson, of course, is its situation – amid glorious gardens with flowers the size of soup plates, lots of green arbours and much tranquillity.

Constantia

ALPHEN HOTEL, P.O. Box 35, Constantia 7848

★ TELEPHONE: 021 74-1011
★ CABLES: Alphen
★ TELEX: 57 26195
★ IN OPERATION: since 1962
★ RESERVATIONS: direct or via Relais et Chateaux, Paris
★ ROOMS: 17 doubles 1 single
★ SUITES: 2
★ RESTAURANTS: 1
★ BARS: 2
★ DISCOTHEQUE: no
★ SHOPS: none
★ CONFERENCE ROOMS: 2 (15 and 120)
★ BANQUETING ROOMS: 2 (36 and 150)
★ STANDARD BEDROOM SIZE: 25 m²
★ SWIMMING POOL: yes – fresh water

★ RECREATIONAL ACTIVITIES: tennis, squash and sauna across the road, with golf and horse riding 15 minutes' drive from the hotel
★ GARDENS: yes
★ NO. OF STAFF: 40
★ ROOM SERVICE: 06.00–22.00
★ ORIENTATION: all directions
★ CREDIT CARDS: Diners Club, American Express, Barclaycard and Standard Bank
★ OWNING COMPANY: Constanti Valley Hotel Pty
★ GENERAL MANAGER: A. P. B. Rijks
★ DISTANCE TO BEACH: 10 km
★ DISTANCE TO SHOPS: 3 km
★ DISTANCE FROM AIRPORT: 25 km

South Africa is a long way away but it is worth going there just to stay at the Alphen. I have always thought so for many years and those readers who have been there more recently confirm this belief. This is a truly delicious place, a Cape Dutch-cum-Georgian house classified as a national monument, immaculately kept in perfect order, elegantly furnished and a delight to the eye. There is tradition and hospitality. Bedrooms are most attractive, with handsome beds and also good bathrooms. The grounds are magnificent and in this wine country of South Africa, one has a lot to see and, indeed, a lot to drink for this region produces some of the finest wines outside Europe and at the Alphen they go hand in hand with fine, fresh food.

Stellenbosch

LANZERAC RAWDON'S HOTEL, P.O. Box 4, Stellenbosch 7600

★ TELEPHONE: 71132, 71182/3/4
★ CABLES: Lanzerac Stellenbosch
★ TELEX: 57-0395 SA
★ IN OPERATION: 23 years
★ RESERVATIONS: direct
★ ROOMS: 31 doubles 5 singles
★ SUITES: 7
★ RESTAURANTS: 4
★ BARS: 2
★ DISCOTHEQUE: live music on Saturday and Sunday evenings
★ SHOPS: none
★ CONFERENCE ROOMS: none
★ BANQUETING ROOMS: none
★ STANDARD BEDROOM SIZE: 25 m²

★ PRIVATE BALCONIES: yes – most rooms
★ SWIMMING POOL: yes – fresh water
★ GARDENS: yes
★ NO. OF STAFF: 100
★ ROOM SERVICE: 06.00–24.00
★ ORIENTATION: rooms overlook courtyard
★ CREDIT CARDS: Standard Card, Barclaycard, Diners Club and Visa
★ OWNING COMPANY: Lanzerac Hotels (Pty) Ltd
★ GENERAL MANAGER: David Rawdon (owner)
★ DISTANCE TO BEACH: 25 km
★ DISTANCE TO SHOPS: 5 km
★ DISTANCE FROM AIRPORT: 30 km

This is by far the prettiest hotel in Southern Africa – gentle, mellow, beautiful and kept in pristine condition. In this historic little town of Stellenbosch, it is, of course, an old Cape Dutch house, complete with gables, standing in acres of gardens whose blooms have won many prizes. It is an old wine estate – vineyards have been tilled on this site for over 200 years – and Lanzerac still makes its own wine – very acceptable wine at that. Many of the rooms have been converted from wine cellars on the original estate and both they and the public rooms are prettily furnished with good antiques but it is no museum – it remains very much an authentic Dutch colonial house. The whole place shines with cleanliness and peace. The rooms run from the comfortable to the very special and the food – fresh and delicately cooked – goes hand in hand with the quality of the wine. Stellenbosch is a beautiful town and this hotel does it justice.

SOUTH AMERICA – BRAZIL
Rio de Janeiro
OURO VERDE HOTEL, 1456 Avenida Atlantica, 22021 Rio de Janeiro

★ TELEPHONE: 542-1887
★ CABLES: Ouverhotel
★ TELEX: 2123848 OVHT BR
★ IN OPERATION: since 1951
★ RESERVATIONS: direct
★ ROOMS: 51 double 5 single
★ SUITES: 5
★ RESTAURANTS: 1
★ BARS: 1
★ DISCOTHEQUE: no
★ SHOPS: none
★ CONFERENCE ROOMS: none
★ BANQUETING ROOMS: none
★ PRIVATE BALCONIES: yes – some rooms

★ STANDARD BEDROOM SIZE: 25 m², plus hall and private bathroom
★ SWIMMING POOL: no
★ GARDENS: no
★ NO. OF STAFF: 140
★ ROOM SERVICE: around the clock
★ ORIENTATION: facing Copacabana beach
★ CREDIT CARDS: American Express
★ OWNING COMPANY: privately owned
★ GENERAL MANAGER: H. G. Brandt
★ DISTANCE TO BEACH: on the beach
★ DISTANCE TO SHOPS: walking distance
★ DISTANCE FROM AIRPORT: 30 km

In this extraordinarily photogenic city, most hotels seem to be sitting on launching pads about ready to take off for outer space which, after all, is where they should be. That's why I like the little Ouro Verde on Copacabana and, apparently, the bankers who read *Fortune* agree with me. Ouro Verde, while modern, is not outrageous – small, rather intimate, very comfortable and serviced with old world excellence which is rare in Brazil. People take your messages as a matter of course and make up your room when you are not in it – which is as it should be. You are never, but never, disturbed and your room – perfectly large enough – is furnished in a way that won't give you nightmares. Bathrooms work and are nicely devoid of plumbing exaggerations and the public rooms are so quiet, in this noisy country, that you can actually converse without shouting. The food is one of Ouro Verde's strongest points – a vast and beautifully equipped kitchen serves the best hotel meals in Rio. The hotel incidentally does not welcome groups.

Salvador
BAHIA OTHON PALACE HOTEL, Avenue Presidente Vargas, 2456 – Salvador, BA

★ TELEPHONE: 247-1044
★ CABLES: Bahiaothon
★ TELEX: 711217
★ RESERVATIONS: Reservothon Rio de Janeiro; Telex: 02123265/Windotel Ltd, London
★ ROOMS: 231
★ SUITES: 37
★ RESTAURANTS: 2
★ BARS: 3
★ DISCOTHEQUE: yes
★ SHOPS: 10
★ CONFERENCE ROOMS: 3 (25 to 800)
★ BANQUETING ROOMS: 6 (20 to 450)
★ STANDARD BEDROOM SIZE: 30 m²

★ PRIVATE BALCONIES: yes
★ SWIMMING POOL: yes – fresh water
★ GARDENS: yes
★ NO. OF STAFF: 350
★ ROOM SERVICE: around the clock
★ ORIENTATION: all rooms have sea view
★ CREDIT CARDS: American Express, Master Charge, Bankamericard and Diners Club
★ OWNING COMPANY: Hotels Othon S.A.
★ GENERAL MANAGER: Guilherme A. Gomes
★ DISTANCE TO BEACH: on the beach
★ DISTANCE TO SHOPS: 10 km
★ DISTANCE FROM AIRPORT: 30 km

In Brazil the glamour is in Rio, the money in Sao Paulo but ask any Brazilian where the heart of the country really beats and he will answer 'in Bahia' – or rather Salvador dos Todos Os Santos to give this incredible city its full name. This is tropical Brazil, chocolate-coloured Brazil, with a great rhythm and fantastic markets. It's also the oldest city in Brazil with fine beaches on both sides and magnificent churches. For a long time it looked as if the hotels were a further arm of Portuguese colonialism. Now there is the Othon and one is glad to see a new Brazilian hotel that really functions properly. Rooms are gay and often amusingly furnished with local pieces. The staff mostly wear local costume which ripples as they move and goes well with the wide smiles. What is most remarkable here is the food. Bahia food is Brazil's finest and in the Lampiao Restaurant you get the full treatment. A very fine hotel in a most unusual city.

SOUTH PACIFIC
Fiji

THE FIJIAN HOTEL, Private Mail Bag, Nadi Airport, Fiji

- ★ TELEPHONE: 50155
- ★ CABLES: Resorts, Fiji
- ★ TELEX: FJ 4241 Fijian
- ★ IN OPERATION: since September, 1967
- ★ RESERVATIONS: John Tetley Co Inc, U.S.A./Supereps International, London/Utell International, Toronto, Melbourne, Sydney and New York
- ★ ROOMS: 316
- ★ SUITES: 13 plus 4 beach burés
- ★ RESTAURANTS: 4 – the Golden Cowrie, Ka Levu, Taliva Terrace and Takali Terrace
- ★ BARS: 5
- ★ DISCOTHEQUE: yes – on Friday and Sunday nights with live music nightly
- ★ SHOPS: 5
- ★ CONFERENCE ROOMS: 4 (40 to 350)
- ★ BANQUETING ROOMS: 4 (24 to 280)
- ★ STANDARD BEDROOM SIZE: 38 m^2
- ★ PRIVATE BALCONIES: yes

- ★ GARDENS: yes
- ★ SWIMMING POOL: yes – fresh water, 2, 15 × 8 m and 24.5 × 10.5 m
- ★ RECREATIONAL ACTIVITIES: tennis, golfing, bowling, snorkelling, water skiing, scuba diving, horse riding, guided reef walks, sailing, paddle boats, rowing boats, game fishing, reef fishing, para-sailing and coral viewing boat trips
- ★ NO. OF STAFF: 530
- ★ ROOM SERVICE: around the clock for drinks, 07.00–23.00 for food
- ★ ORIENTATION: all rooms face the lagoon or ocean
- ★ CREDIT CARDS: Diners Club, American Express and Visa
- ★ OWNING COMPANY: Fiji Resorts Ltd
- ★ GENERAL MANAGER: Alois Wymann
- ★ DISTANCE TO BEACH: walking distance
- ★ DISTANCE TO SHOPS: 12 km
- ★ DISTANCE FROM AIRPORT: 62.8 km

With mass tourism as it is, many holiday hotels tend to deteriorate in the natural order of things. One exception is the Fijian, the most complete resort in those lovely islands and one of the best in the Pacific. As a hotel, it saw architects and artists long before accountants turned up to make their ugly calculations to match the architecture and turn an ideal into the coldest of cold cash. The buildings, many of them shaped like Fijian 'burés' or huts, display lots of good local timber and stone and drape themselves along an incomparable bay with superfine sands and a fringe of coconuts. Gardens are well tended and rooms are unusually large, always with a double bed and a single and bathrooms are very good. This is a rambling hotel, with lots of places to go, good shops and many activities like fishing, snorkelling, coral-watching, golf and tennis. Public rooms are largely al fresco and the food, especially in the Golden Cowrie Restaurant, is an elegant Pacific surprise. You can have peace and quiet too – the hotel is on its own private island, linked to the shore by a causeway. What makes the Fijian are the Fijians – great mountains of manhood who look as if they had turned from cannibals to babysitters in two generations – and those who make up the staff are enormous, cheerful and amusing. Their smiles look like the keys of a piano.

TURTLE ISLAND LODGE, P.O. Box 9317, Nadi International Airport, Turtle Island, Fiji

★ TELEPHONE: (nadi) 72921
★ CABLES: no
★ TELEX: FJ5197
★ IN OPERATION: since 1979
★ RESERVATIONS: Fiji Vacation Service, Sydney, Australia/C.C. Evanson & Co, Washington, U.S.A.
★ ROOMS: 8 (cottage-style on beach)
★ SUITES: 4 (cottage-style on beach)
★ RESTAURANTS: covered dining area and on beach
★ BARS: 2 – 1 on the beach and one inside
★ DISCOTHEQUE: no – but live musical entertainment provided
★ SHOPS: no – but toiletries and books available
★ CONFERENCE ROOMS: none
★ BANQUETING ROOMS: none
★ STANDARD BEDROOM SIZE: 25 m^2
★ PRIVATE BALCONIES: all rooms open onto beach

★ SWIMMING POOL: no
★ RECREATIONAL ACTIVITIES: exclusive use of island. Sailing, windsurfing, snorkelling, shelling, canoes, glass bottom paddle boating, fishing, riding, guided hiking tours, village trips and private beach
★ GARDENS: 500 acres
★ NO. OF STAFF: 25
★ ROOM SERVICE: 07.00–23.00
★ ORIENTATION: all rooms on beach overlooking lagoon
★ CREDIT CARDS: American Express
★ OWNING COMPANY: Richard Evanson
★ GENERAL MANAGER: Richard Evanson
★ DISTANCE TO BEACH: on beach
★ DISTANCE TO SHOPS: 25 minutes by seaplane
★ DISTANCE FROM AIRPORT: 75 km

If you like islands and you wonder where paradise is, I have got the address for you – it's Turtle Island Lodge. My own memories of the Yasawas off the coast of Viti Levu go back some twenty years when you went there for a day or two and hoped that people hadn't forgotten the food. Now there is Turtle Island: five hundred acres, with twelve beaches and never more than fifteen other guests besides yourself, the nearest approach you might ever get to an island of your own. You sleep in a typical 'buré', that's a Fijian hut, and these are cooled by the breezes all the way around (plus a ceiling fan). You eat where it sounds nice to eat that day, inside, outside, on the beach, anywhere and what you eat is what the fisherman caught that day – could be lobsters or crabs or fish, chicken, quail or duck. The bar is well stocked and service is smiling (Fijians are the smilingest people on earth . . .)

You don't spend money on Turtle because everything is included. Also, you don't know what you will be doing this or that day (if anything) because everything is spontaneous. There is no noise, no bustle, no dress requirements. Just you and Turtle and its absolutely unique, beautiful white beaches surrounded by lagoons. The whole thing is the dream of an intelligent American who just likes it that way. Incidentally, this is where Hollywood filmed the movie *The Blue Lagoon* a couple of years back. Fortunately, they left. Bula Bula – welcome to you.

French Polynesia

KAINA VILLAGE, B.P. 2460, Papeete, Tahiti, French Polynesia

★ TELEPHONE: 2-75-53 Papeete
★ CABLES: KainaTahiti
★ TELEX: no
★ IN OPERATION: since January, 1979
★ RESERVATIONS: Sofitel – UTH, Paris/Sofitel, California
★ ROOMS: 16 overwater bungalows
★ SUITES: 2 'family suites'
★ RESTAURANTS: 1
★ BARS: 1 (overwater)

★ DISCOTHEQUE: yes – twice a week. Polynesian songs and guitars in the evening
★ SHOPS: 1
★ CONFERENCE ROOMS: none
★ BANQUETING ROOMS: none
★ STANDARD BEDROOM SIZE: 24 m^2
★ PRIVATE BALCONIES: each overwater bungalow has a terrace

- ★ SWIMMING POOL: no – but there is the lagoon
- ★ RECREATIONAL ACTIVITIES: billiard room, pearl diving demonstration, picnics on beach, reef excursions, snorkelling, scuba diving, waterskiing and deep sea fishing·
- ★ GARDENS: yes
- ★ NO. OF STAFF: 21
- ★ ROOM SERVICE: none
- ★ ORIENTATION: on the lagoon
- ★ CREDIT CARDS: American Express, Diners Club and Visa
- ★ OWNING COMPANY: S.A.R.L. Kaina Village
- ★ GENERAL MANAGER: André Teriimana Chaze
- ★ DISTANCE TO BEACH: on the lagoon
- ★ DISTANCE TO SHOPS: Manihi 520 m from Tahiti
- ★ DISTANCE FROM AIRPORT: 90 minutes by air from Tahiti

Once upon a time, if you went to Tahiti that was the blessed end of the world. Then travel agents discovered Gauguin's island and its immediate neighbours, lady tourists with blue-rinsed hair came along and bang went your dream. Now you have to go further. Where? The Tuamotous. The what? you may ask. Quite – your travel agent isn't likely to know too much about this heavenly archipelago of tiny atolls way out there in the blue Pacific and that is why you should go now, while there is still time. Kaina Village is on Manihi atoll – nothing but tall coconut trees, sandy beaches that look peroxided and a pale blue lagoon with your 'faré' or hut on top. Dreamland? It certainly is and it is so far off the beaten track that the Joneses don't go there. Too much trouble. You do what comes naturally – eat, sleep, have a drink under the trees, go fishing or move over to Manihi's famous underwater farm where lustrous black pearls are cultivated. But do believe this old traveller: the real pearl is Kaina Village and the chance to live a lifestyle which has almost disappeared.

Western Samoa

AGGIE GREY'S HOTEL, P.O. Box 67, Apia, Western Samoa

- ★ TELEPHONE: 22-880
- ★ CABLES: Aggies
- ★ TELEX: Aggies SX 257
- ★ IN OPERATION: 40 years
- ★ RESERVATIONS: direct/Instant Hotels, Australia and New Zealand/Utell International
- ★ ROOMS: 40 doubles 40 twins 22 singles
- ★ SUITES: 5 family rooms and 10 individual bungalows
- ★ RESTAURANTS: 1
- ★ BARS: 2
- ★ DISCOTHEQUE: live music every evening
- ★ SHOPS: 1
- ★ CONFERENCE ROOMS: 1 (50)
- ★ BANQUETING ROOMS: 1 (up to 200)
- ★ STANDARD BEDROOM SIZE: 25 m²
- ★ PRIVATE BALCONIES: yes
- ★ SWIMMING POOL: yes – fresh water, 25 × 12 m
- ★ RECREATIONAL ACTIVITIES: tennis and golf close by and horse riding by arrangement
- ★ GARDENS: yes
- ★ NO. OF STAFF: 120
- ★ ROOM SERVICE: 08.30–20.30
- ★ ORIENTATION: north-west
- ★ CREDIT CARDS: American Express, Diners Club, Carte Blanche, Visa and Master Charge
- ★ OWNING COMPANY: Aggie Grey's Hotel Ltd
- ★ GENERAL MANAGER: Alan Grey
- ★ DISTANCE TO BEACH: 1 km
- ★ DISTANCE TO SHOPS: walking distance
- ★ DISTANCE FROM AIRPORT: 35 km

This is undoubtedly one of the two funniest, most unconventional hotels I have ever come across in my travels. For a long time, it was 'the pub' for beachcombers, writers and remittance men washed ashore in beautiful Samoa and has figured in books and movies. Then, things being what they are, Aggie Grey's became a 'proper' hotel – more's the pity – but it still retains a natural, unrehearsed atmosphere which enlivens the visit and Aggie is still there herself – a dignified old lady who's seen the world go by. It's largely al fresco, with a bunch of bananas hanging outside your window, huts called 'falé' here spread about some gorgeous gardens and a staff of gentle and smiling Polynesians for whom life seems to be one long 'South Pacific'. Service is odd, erratic and absolutely charming and as for food, you take what's coming – it's mostly good though you don't always know what it is. There are evenings of song and dance in the biggest 'falé' in the South Pacific, the original beach of 'Return to the Islands' is not far away and the place is alive with memories. At night, the bar hums with tall stories from far away. If I am in these parts, I would not dream of missing Aggie Grey's.

SPAIN

Jaen

PARADOR NACIONAL DEL CASTILLO DE SANTA CATALINA, Apartado 178, Jaen

- ★ TELEPHONE: 232287-232288
- ★ CABLES: Paral
- ★ TELEX: no
- ★ IN OPERATION: since 1965
- ★ RESERVATIONS: direct
- ★ ROOMS: 37 doubles 6 singles
- ★ SUITES: no
- ★ RESTAURANTS: 2
- ★ BARS: 1
- ★ DISCOTHEQUE: no
- ★ SHOPS: none
- ★ CONFERENCE ROOMS: 1 (26)
- ★ BANQUETING ROOMS: 2 (100 to 250)
- ★ STANDARD BEDROOM SIZE: 30 m^2
- ★ PRIVATE BALCONIES: yes
- ★ SWIMMING POOL: yes – fresh water, 15 × 10 m
- ★ GARDENS: yes
- ★ NO. OF STAFF: 57
- ★ ROOM SERVICE: 08.00–24.00
- ★ ORIENTATION: north-west
- ★ FURTHER DEVELOPMENTS: tennis courts
- ★ CREDIT CARDS: Visa, American Express, Diners Club and Eurocard
- ★ OWNING COMPANY: Ministerio Informacion Y Turismo
- ★ GENERAL MANAGER: Manuel Galvez Garcia
- ★ DISTANCE TO BEACH: 120 km
- ★ DISTANCE TO SHOPS: 5 km
- ★ DISTANCE FROM AIRPORT: 97 km

Presiding over this interesting city whose name only a Spanish tongue can pronounce properly is this excellent parador – one of the most interesting in the Government-run chain. It is an old castle – very Spanish and extremely interesting from the visual point of view – ancient stones, great windows, marvellous views. Rooms are large and slightly monastic in style but there is nothing monkish in the comfort and the decor – the latter ranking very high for being simple and the real thing. The bathrooms work which makes a change in Spain and the staff are quite good though, as always in paradors, a little distant. Probably they see too many awkward foreigners. Public rooms are quite beautiful, including the magnificent vaulted dining room. The food is not quite so magnificent. If one has one criticism to level at paradors, it is the somewhat institutional character of their cuisine.

Leon

HOTEL SAN MARCOS, Plaza de San Marcos 7, Leon

- ★ TELEPHONE: 23 73 00
- ★ CABLES: Hostal
- ★ TELEX: 89809
- ★ IN OPERATION: 17 years
- ★ RESERVATIONS: Iberian Service Ltd, London/Securotel, Frankfurt/Atesa, Paris
- ★ ROOMS: 258
- ★ SUITES: 15
- ★ RESTAURANTS: 3
- ★ BARS: 1
- ★ DISCOTHEQUE: no
- ★ SHOPS: none
- ★ CONFERENCE ROOMS: 3 (15 to 600)
- ★ BANQUETING ROOMS: 2 (180 to 500)
- ★ STANDARD BEDROOM SIZE: 24 m^2
- ★ PRIVATE BALCONIES: yes
- ★ SWIMMING POOL: no
- ★ GARDENS: patios
- ★ NO. OF STAFF: 180
- ★ ROOM SERVICE: around the clock

★ ORIENTATION: faces main square
★ CREDIT CARDS: Diners Club, American Express, Bankamericard, Eurocard and Carte Blanche
★ OWNING COMPANY: Empresa Nacional de Turismo, S.A.
★ GENERAL MANAGER: Luis Garcia Fernandez
★ DISTANCE TO SHOPS: 100 m
★ DISTANCE FROM AIRPORT: 100 km

One of the most beautiful hotels in the whole of Europe. Behind that fantastic facade, it is like living in a museum but one that is warm, gentle and forever uplifting. The best of Spain is here – art, history, tradition, all translated into magnificent furniture, priceless carpets and genuine works of art in every corner where you care to look. Even what is new is worth looking at – the best design and the finest materials. Many readers might say: 'That's all very well, but does the plumbing work?' Hand on heart, it does, since the hotel now belongs to a very experienced hotel company.

It still has to do some work on the food, which is vaguely Spanish international but the rest of the hotel operation is well within our terms of reference. Even the smallest rooms are quite acceptable – handsomely furnished and well maintained.

Madrid

MONTE REAL HOTEL, Ciudad Puerto de Hierro, Madrid 35

★ TELEPHONE: 216 2140
★ CABLES: Realmontel
★ TELEX: 22089 Mavel E
★ RESERVATIONS: direct
★ IN OPERATION: since 1970
★ ROOMS: 84
★ SUITES: 14
★ RESTAURANTS: 2
★ BARS: 2
★ DISCOTHEQUE: yes
★ SHOPS: none
★ CONFERENCE ROOMS: 8 (40 to 200)
★ BANQUETING ROOMS: 4 (20 to 200)
★ STANDARD BEDROOM SIZE: 20 m²
★ PRIVATE BALCONIES: yes
★ SWIMMING POOL: yes – fresh water
★ GARDENS: yes
★ NO. OF STAFF: 165
★ ROOM SERVICE: around the clock
★ ORIENTATION: south
★ CREDIT CARDS: American Express, Diners Club, Eurocard, Carte Blanche
★ OWNING COMPANY: Mavel
★ GENERAL MANAGER: Francisco Lopez Hernandez
★ DISTANCE TO SHOPS: 7 km
★ DISTANCE FROM AIRPORT: 20 km

One of the most remarkable hotels in any capital city – far enough from the centre of noisy Madrid to be removed from the hurly-burly and yet so elegantly sophisticated that it makes you catch your breath as you go in. Monte Real, sandwiched between golf course and gardens, is an oasis of wellbeing and good taste, not to say extraordinary refinement. All the paintings you see are real (Matisse, Murillo, Dali and many Impressionists) and nowhere does one find a single touch that offends. The rooms are extraordinarily comfortable, very serene and beautifully serviced and furnished. I am told that everything is the lady owner's own choice – like all the best, it is for an audience of one. The food, both international and Spanish, is extremely soigné. If you are prepared to take a cab ride to the city or travel in your own car, Monte Real is an excellent choice.

VILLA MAGNA, Paseo de la Castellana, 22, Madrid 1

★ TELEPHONE: 2614900
★ CABLES: Villamagna
★ TELEX: 22914 vima e
★ IN OPERATION: since May, 1972
★ RESERVATIONS: direct
★ ROOMS: 174 doubles 16 singles
★ SUITES: 10
★ RESTAURANTS: 1
★ BARS: 2
★ DISCOTHEQUE: no
★ SHOPS: 6
★ CONFERENCE ROOMS: 1 (100)
★ BANQUETING ROOMS: 2 (30 to 250)
★ STANDARD BEDROOM SIZE: 34 m²
★ PRIVATE BALCONIES: no

★ SWIMMING POOL: no
★ RECREATIONAL ACTIVITIES: sauna
★ GARDENS: yes
★ NO. OF STAFF: 300
★ ROOM SERVICE: around the clock
★ ORIENTATION: east overlooking Serrano Street and west overlooking Castellana Avenue
★ FURTHER DEVELOPMENTS: colour T.V.
★ CREDIT CARDS: American Express
★ OWNING COMPANY: Nerja S.A.
★ GENERAL MANAGER: Eduardo Martin
★ DISTANCE TO SHOPS: a few minutes' walk
★ DISTANCE FROM AIRPORT: 15 km

No latter-day returning conquistador could have done better than this. In a large garden right in the centre of Madrid, the Villa Magna is sumptuous, elegant, eye-filling and I cannot think of any hotel chain that would dare operate a hotel like this. Accountants would not like it. This is a grand gesture, Spanish style and there is no imitation. The plants are real, the leather is leather and the acres of marble were not produced overnight. Bedrooms are vast (suites are airfield size) and excellently furnished with good, sound pieces all kept scrupulously spotless. I would very much like to roll one of the carpets up and take it home. Even the lifts are attractive and the public rooms are done up with a style which only top-drawer Spaniards can manage. The staff are multi-lingual, very urbane and helpful. I have often tried hard to find fault with this hotel – so have our readers – and so far we have nothing but praise. Food is elegantly international and served with great decorum. In a capital city which is not now short of good hotels, the Villa Magna is superlative.

Mallorca

HOTEL FORMENTOR, Puerto de Pollensa, Formentor, Mallorca

★ TELEPHONE: 531300
★ CABLES: Formentorotel
★ TELEX: 68523
★ IN OPERATION: since 1930
★ RESERVATIONS: Robert Reid Associates, London/Robert F. Warner Inc, U.S.A./Claude L. C. Duteil, France
★ ROOMS: 106 doubles 7 singles
★ SUITES: 17
★ RESTAURANTS: 3 – General Restaurant, Beach Restaurant and Grill Room
★ BARS: 2 – one at the beach and one in the hotel
★ DISCOTHEQUE: yes
★ SHOPS: 1
★ CONFERENCE ROOMS: 1 (80 to 150)
★ BANQUETING ROOMS: 3 (100, 150 and 300)
★ STANDARD BEDROOM SIZE: 27 m²
★ PRIVATE BALCONIES: yes – in 12 rooms and 10 suites

★ SWIMMING POOL: yes – 2, fresh water
★ RECREATIONAL ACTIVITIES: mini golf, 5 tennis courts (2 floodlit), riding, water skiing, fishing, boat excursions, cinema etc
★ GARDENS: yes
★ NO. OF STAFF: 200
★ ROOM SERVICE: around the clock
★ ORIENTATION: most rooms face the sea, the rest face the mountains
★ CREDIT CARDS: American Express, Diners Club, Visa and Eurocard
★ OWNING COMPANY: Inmobilaria Formentor, S.A.
★ GENERAL MANAGER: Juan Carlos Mascaro
★ DISTANCE TO BEACH: 150 m
★ DISTANCE TO SHOPS: 9 km
★ DISTANCE FROM AIRPORT: 70 km

If you are Mediterranean bound, one of the ways of avoiding tourist pollution (and other kinds too) is to take plenty of travellers' cheques with you, fly to Palma and get your taxi to drive you to this hotel. Once on its peninsula, behind the curtain of pines, you are undoubtedly where you deserve to be – at one of the finest resort hotels in the Mediterranean, one that has been going for a long time, has tradition, good looks and only the 'right' people between its walls. Nothing here is cheap or skimped. Decor is handsome but muted and the whole 'feel' of the place is one of gentle relaxation. Rooms are sizeable and very well equipped as well as extremely well serviced and the public rooms, particularly the magnificent lobby are well worth living in. There are gardens everywhere, lots of private spots, a very good beach, two swimming pools and if you want anything, why, just raise your finger. Everybody who is anybody has been at Formentor, including the King of Spain and for comfort one could not do better. Since I was there last I have heard a few reports about the food not being what it used to be. But for the time being I don't believe them.

Marbella

HOTEL LOS MONTEROS, Carretera de Cadiz, Marbella

- ★ TELEPHONE: (52) 77-17-00
- ★ CABLES: Monteros
- ★ TELEX: 77059
- ★ IN OPERATION: since July, 1962
- ★ RESERVATIONS: Robert F. Warner Inc, New York/Robert Reid Associates, London
- ★ ROOMS: 152 doubles 16 singles
- ★ SUITES: 4
- ★ RESTAURANTS: 3 – 'La Cabane' beach club, 'El Corzo' grill and the main hotel
- ★ BARS: 4
- ★ DISCOTHEQUE: dancing nightly to a live band in the Bar Club. Also piano music in the 'El Corzo' grill
- ★ SHOPS: 3 – ladies and men's boutiques and drugstore with perfumery and beauty products
- ★ CONFERENCE ROOMS: 1 and also a conference room which is suitable for small, private reunions
- ★ BANQUETING ROOMS: none
- ★ STANDARD BEDROOM SIZE: 30 m²
- ★ PRIVATE BALCONIES: yes

- ★ SWIMMING POOL: yes – 4, fresh water, 2 outdoor, 1 children's pool and a new indoor pool at 'La Cabane' beach club
- ★ RECREATIONAL ACTIVITIES: 10 tennis courts and 5 squash courts. Also Club Hipico with a choice of Andalusian ponies. Table tennis, sauna and massage
- ★ GARDENS: yes – sub-tropical, small decorative pools with Japanese-style bridges and pink flamingoes roaming freely
- ★ NO. OF STAFF: 300
- ★ ROOM SERVICE: around the clock
- ★ ORIENTATION: rooms face north, south, east and west
- ★ CREDIT CARDS: American Express, Diners Club and Eurocard
- ★ OWNING COMPANY: Hotel los Monteros S.A.
- ★ GENERAL MANAGER: Rafael de la Fuente
- ★ DISTANCE TO BEACH: walking distance
- ★ DISTANCE TO SHOPS: 5 km
- ★ DISTANCE FROM AIRPORT: 50 km

Los Monteros is like an old friend whose company you have always enjoyed – a hotel so civilised, so affluently generous, so varied in its pleasures that you just slip in, unpack and take it all up where you left off last time. Of course, it's one of the best resort hotels in the whole of Europe, superbly run by a conservative management which does not know the meaning of razzmatazz. Bedrooms and suites are generally palatial, large, comfortable and beautifully designed and there are quite a few types to choose from. Then there are the villas down the road on the way to the 'La Cabane' beach club where the tasty Technicolour buffets seem to run for ever and ever and where the food, rich and international, manages to have that little touch of Spanish 'olé' which makes all the difference. As for the 'El Corzo' grill, it's one of the two or three best restaurants on the coast. Last time I was there, I discovered that Los Monteros smokes its own salmon. But of course. Los Monteros is what you would wish it to be at any time – quiet and peaceful, jumping and gay and always in the most perfect of tastes. What I like most of all about it is that it never shows off. It is just what it is – grand, friendly, good-mannered and ready for anything. A very good hotel indeed.

HOTEL PUENTE ROMANO, Carretera de Cádiz Km 184, Marbella

★ TELEPHONE: 77-01-00
★ CABLES: Hotel Puente Romano, Marbella
★ TELEX: 77399
★ IN OPERATION: since July, 1978
★ RESERVATIONS: The Leading Hotels of the World – HRI, or directly
★ ROOMS: 150
★ SUITES: 45
★ RESTAURANTS: 3 – La Plaza, El Puente (Grill Room), La Tasca
★ BARS: 4 – La Cascada (with Piano Bar), Grill Bar, swimming pool snack bar and beach bar
★ DISCOTHEQUE: yes – 'Régine's'
★ SHOPS: 4 boutiques, 1 hairdresser, 1 drugstore, 1 real estate agency
★ CONFERENCE ROOMS: 4 (20 to 150)
★ BANQUETING ROOMS: 1 (100)
★ STANDARD BEDROOM SIZE: 57 m²

★ PRIVATE BALCONIES: yes
★ SWIMMING POOLS: 3 – fresh water, 1 heated, 1 for children, main pool 25 × 8 m
★ RECREATIONAL ACTIVITIES: tennis (Tennis Centre Bjorn Borg), aquatic sports, golfing facilities nearby
★ GARDENS: yes
★ NUMBER OF STAFF: 300
★ ROOM SERVICE: around the clock
★ ORIENTATION: south-east
★ CREDIT CARDS: American Express, Diners Club, Visa, Eurocard, Master charge and Carte Blanche
★ OWNING COMPANY: Al Rima S.A.
★ GENERAL MANAGER: Willi Dietz
★ DISTANCE TO THE BEACH: on the beach
★ DISTANCE TO SHOPS: 3 km to Marbella town, 2 km to Puerto Banus
★ DISTANCE FROM AIRPORT: 57 km

Money without taste is money. Money with taste is shining success. Prince Alfonso (the famed Marbella Club is next door) dreamt this one up in a moment of inspired recklessness – beginning with a tiny, old Roman Bridge in the centre and going on to build what one can only describe as an Andalusian village. No doubt you have seen developers' Andalusian villages before – but not one like this. I would call it one of the five most successful hotel creations I have ever seen. There are clusters of houses, vistas of sloping gardens, gurgling streams, an open-air amphitheatre, a Moorish restaurant (and others) and three swimming pools. But it is when one comes to the rooms and suites that one's eyes begin to open wide – everything is designed with such intelligent expertise that one wonders why it has not been done like this before. The furniture, much of it cane, is quite splendid and so are the extremely original colour schemes and the deceptive mirrors. Some rooms are split-level, others straightforward but all are the kind of room you would like to have for yourself. It is all very, very clever with no false ostentation and not a single wrong note. The food seemed excellent for Spain.

MARBELLA CLUB HOTEL, Carretera de Cadiz, Marbella

★ TELEPHONE: 771300
★ CABLES: Clubhotel
★ TELEX: 77319
★ IN OPERATION: 28 years
★ RESERVATIONS: Hotel Representative Inc, worldwide/Relais et Chateaux, Paris
★ ROOMS: 28
★ SUITES: 22 and 5 bungalows
★ RESTAURANTS: 2
★ BARS: 2
★ DISCOTHEQUE: yes
★ SHOPS: 4
★ CONFERENCE ROOMS: 1 (40)

★ BANQUETING ROOMS: 1 (35 to 40)
★ STANDARD BEDROOM SIZE: 45 m²
★ PRIVATE BALCONIES: yes
★ SWIMMING POOL: yes – fresh water, two, 150 m² and 220 m²
★ RECREATIONAL ACTIVITIES: sauna, massage and tennis, horse riding and golf nearby
★ GARDENS: yes
★ NO. OF STAFF: 153
★ ROOM SERVICE: around the clock
★ ORIENTATION: most rooms face the south

★ CREDIT CARDS: American Express, Diners
   Club and Eurocard
★ OWNING COMPANY: Marbella Club S.A.
★ GENERAL MANAGER: Count Rudolf von
   Schonburg

★ DISTANCE TO BEACH: on the beach
★ DISTANCE TO SHOPS: 3 km
★ DISTANCE FROM AIRPORT: 57 km

The Marbella Club was always good. Now that it has moved, without hiccups, from being a somewhat up-market club for a particular international set, it has automatically become one of the finest resort hotels in this part of the world. Age and maturity have given it a feeling of easy and elegant informality which are very difficult to achieve. It is still very private in the sense that it does not look like a hotel, more like a vast Andalusian garden with a few bits and pieces here and there. Those bits and pieces offer perfectly wonderful accommodation even in the more obvious buildings and if you are lucky enough to have a suite or better still one of the 'cottages' (Marie Antoinette would have liked them) you won't do better anywhere. The most apparent commodity is good taste – in furnishings, in colours, in everything. Privacy is a real and very valuable asset these days when false, cheery togetherness is so often the rule. The Marbella Club and its management know how to live well, graciously and intelligently. The food incidentally is very much better than it was. We would willingly hold up the Marbella Club as the 'right' kind of resort hotel – a place where People (upper-case P) congregate.

Oviedo

HOTEL DE LA RECONQUISTA, Gil de Jaz, 16, Oviedo

★ TELEPHONE: 985/241100, 241200,
   241300
★ CABLES: Reconquista
★ TELEX: 87328 – OASAE
★ IN OPERATION: 9 years
★ RESERVATIONS: direct or Keytel, S.A.,
   Madrid and Barcelona
★ ROOMS: 123 doubles 14 singles
★ SUITES: 4
★ RESTAURANTS: 4
★ BARS: 2
★ DISCOTHEQUE: yes – and live music
★ SHOPS: 12
★ CONFERENCE ROOMS: 6 (50 to 800)
★ BANQUETING ROOMS: 5 (70 to 800)
★ STANDARD BEDROOM SIZE: 22 m²

★ PRIVATE BALCONIES: yes
★ SWIMMING POOL: no
★ RECREATIONAL ACTIVITIES: sauna and
   gymnasium
★ GARDENS: no
★ NO. OF STAFF: 175
★ ROOM SERVICE: around the clock
★ ORIENTATION: main facade faces east
★ CREDIT CARDS: Diners Club, American
   Express, Visa, Master Charge and Carte
   Blanche
★ OWNING COMPANY: Hoteles Husa
★ GENERAL MANAGER: Rafael Vazquez
★ DISTANCE TO BEACH: 15 minutes
★ DISTANCE TO SHOPS: walking distance
★ DISTANCE FROM AIRPORT: 40 km

One of the trio of hotels in the smaller cities of Spain which always make foreign visitors catch their breath with surprise. This one is eighteenth century, built around a colonnaded square courtyard and its austere beauty is undeniable. Most of the bedrooms have been planned, in a modern idiom, by some of Spain's greatest experts – lighting is fine, the atmosphere cool and calm and the furnishings and especially the carpets extremely beautiful. For Spain, the bathrooms are quite lovely and practical. Public rooms are vast, not too ornate this time and lined with great paintings and tapestries. Here and there, the modernity of a chair hits you where it hurts. I sometimes wonder if all modern chair designers are thin midgets. Service is calm and orderly and quite efficient and the food is remarkably authentic when it comes to the Spanish dishes and most of the country's good wines are available.

Santiago de Compostela

HOSTAL DE LOS REYES CATOLICOS, Plaza de Espana 1, Santiago de Compostela

★ TELEPHONE: 58 22 00
★ CABLES: Hostal
★ TELEX: 86004
★ IN OPERATION: 27 years
★ RESERVATIONS: Iberian Service Ltd, London/Securotel, Frankfurt/Atesa, Paris
★ ROOMS: 157
★ SUITES: 3
★ RESTAURANTS: 3
★ BARS: 1
★ DISCOTHEQUE: no
★ SHOPS: 1
★ CONFERENCE ROOMS: 2 (50 to 200)
★ BANQUETING ROOMS: 3 (100, 150 and 250)
★ STANDARD BEDROOM SIZE: 18 m²

★ PRIVATE BALCONIES: no
★ SWIMMING POOL: no
★ GARDENS: yes
★ NO. OF STAFF: 180
★ ROOM SERVICE: around the clock
★ ORIENTATION: faces main square
★ CREDIT CARDS: Diners Club, American Express, Bankamericard, Eurocard and Carte Blanche
★ OWNING COMPANY: Empresa Nacional de Turismo, S.A.
★ GENERAL MANAGER: Luis Garcia Fernandez
★ DISTANCE TO SHOPS: 100 m
★ DISTANCE FROM AIRPORT: 15 km

In the last edition it stated that we knew of two American tycoons who tried to buy this hotel. Now there have been at least three more bids. The enterprising company that runs Los Reyes Catolicos is not letting go this jewel of a place – surely one of the most beautiful and architecturally striking hotels in Spain. It was built by Ferdinand and Isabella as a hospital for pilgrims to the famous shrine of St. James. Now, just to stand looking at its facade you will be much moved. Of course, it is usually full, especially in the season since it is a destination in itself. Despite this tourist popularity, Los Reyes manages to remain a very good hotel indeed with unbelievably beautiful public rooms (especially the main restaurant) filled with many fine antiques and some great paintings and carpets. Rooms vary a lot in size – so ask to see them first. The best are imperial in both size and furnishings and even the marble floors in some of the bathrooms are heated. Whether you are a passing-through tourist or a proper resident, this hotel is where you must stay.

SRI LANKA

Colombo

LANKA OBEROI, 77 Steuart Place, Colombo

★ TELEPHONE: 20001
★ CABLES: Obhotel
★ TELEX: CMB-1201
★ IN OPERATION: since 1975
★ FULLY COMPUTERISED: by October, 1982
★ RESERVATIONS: Loews Representation International, New York and London/Oberoi Hotels (India), Frankfurt/Odner Hotel Representatives Ltd, Hong Kong
★ ROOMS: 500
★ SUITES: 60
★ RESTAURANTS: 5 – the Supper Club, Ran Malu, London Grill and Coffee Shop (addition 'Araliya' restaurant)
★ BARS: 3
★ SHOPS: 30 – offering traditional

Ceylonese specialities, gems, batiks, handloom textiles and handicrafts
★ CONFERENCE ROOMS: 1 (up to 1,000)
★ BANQUETING ROOMS: 1 (up to 1,000)
★ STANDARD BEDROOM SIZE: 20 m²
★ PRIVATE BALCONIES: no
★ SWIMMING POOL: yes, fresh water – 25 × 25 m
★ RECREATIONAL ACTIVITIES: tennis and fully equipped health club, 2 squash courts
★ GARDENS: yes
★ NO. OF STAFF: 650
★ ROOM SERVICE: around the clock
★ ORIENTATION: faces four directions
★ CREDIT CARDS: American Express, Diners

Club, Bankamericard, Eurocard, Access
and Master Charge
★ OWNING COMPANY: Asian Hotels
  Corporation
★ GENERAL MANAGER: Mr. Stefan Pfeiffer
★ DISTANCE TO BEACH: 8 km
★ DISTANCE TO SHOPS: 2 km

★ DISTANCE FROM AIRPORT: 40 km
★ ADDITIONAL FEATURE: by September,
  1982 – an exclusive 'Businessman's
  Club' with separate dining and bar
  facilities, 4 meeting rooms, 1
  conference room and library

If ever there was a city that deserved a good hotel, it was Colombo – that gentle exotic Bournemouth of the Orient. Colombo has the relics of high civilisation aplenty – it just needed perking up and the Lanka Oberoi has done much towards this end. It is one of the original central atrium-style hotels. You go in and are greeted by an enormously tall central lobby, draped with huge batik hangings and splashed with tropical flowers. All rooms are approached through the corridors ringing this atrium and they are, as a result, extremely quiet. Here too, modern style has been softened by some nice local touches – rare woods, good hangings, lovely carpets and surprisingly good lighting for a new hotel. Wardrobes are huge and beautifully fitted by real joiners. There are verdant gardens and the grass grows right up to the edge of the original swimming pool built in the shape the old Kandy kings liked. The international food – always difficult in Sri Lanka – is very acceptable as is the service.

SUDAN
Khartoum

HILTON INTERNATIONAL KHARTOUM, P.O. Box 1910; Mogran, Khartoum

★ TELEPHONE: 74100 & 78930
★ CABLES: Hiltels – Khartoum
★ TELEX: KM. 250
★ IN OPERATION: 5 years
★ RESERVATIONS: Hilton Reservation
  Service
★ ROOMS: 256
★ SUITES: 18
★ RESTAURANTS: 3 – Ivory Club, Mogran
  Coffee Shop and Garden Restaurant
★ BARS: 2
★ DISCOTHEQUE: no – live music in Ivory
  Club nightly
★ SHOPS: 6 – books, hairdressers, African
  handicrafts, leathergoods, duty-free
  goods and airways booking office
★ CONFERENCE ROOMS: 2 (5 to 500)
★ BANQUETING ROOMS: 2 (70 to 350)
★ STANDARD BEDROOM SIZE: 30 m²

★ PRIVATE BALCONIES: no
★ SWIMMING POOL: yes – fresh water
★ RECREATIONAL ACTIVITIES: tennis, health
  club with sauna and massage, four-lane
  bowling alley and billiards
★ GARDENS: yes
★ NO. OF STAFF: 400
★ ROOM SERVICE: around the clock
★ ORIENTATION: rooms overlook either the
  Blue or the White Nile
★ CREDIT CARDS: American Express, Visa,
  Diners Club, Access, Master Charge,
  Eurocard, Air Canada and Lufthansa
  Courtesy Card
★ OWNING COMPANY: Sudan Kuwait
  Hotels Co
★ GENERAL MANAGER: Norbert Spichtinger
★ DISTANCE TO SHOPS: 3 km
★ DISTANCE FROM AIRPORT: 9 km

Strange as it may seem to some the Sudan – Africa's largest country – is one of my firm favourites and I'll go back to Khartoum at the drop of a credit card. Especially now that the Khartoum Hilton is there. And if this sounds like a bit of a joke, ask any old hand what it was like before this legendary city was Hiltonised. The hotel stands on a historic spot, the Mogran, where the Blue and White Niles meet and just across the great river is Omdurman where Young Winston – with some help from Kitchener – defeated the hellish plots of the Mahdi and you can still see the dancing dervishes there. The Khartoum Hilton has one thing in common with all its brothers and sisters – it works – which here, frankly, is nothing short of a miracle, especially in the bathrooms. Bedrooms, a trifle 'international', are nevertheless spacious and nicely equipped. There is a very good swimming pool – which one needs badly – and some sensational views of the two Niles. The food in the Ivory Club is better than one has any right to expect and as for the staff, the Sudanese have the widest smiles in Africa.

SWEDEN
Malmö
SAVOY HOTEL, P.O. Box 880, S-201 Malmö (Norra Vallgatan 62)

* TELEPHONE: 40 702 30
* CABLES: Savoy
* TELEX: 32383 Savoy S
* IN OPERATION: since 1914
* RESERVATIONS: Steigenberger Reservation Service
* ROOMS: 38 doubles 33 singles
* SUITES: 7
* RESTAURANTS: 3
* BARS: 2
* DISCOTHEQUE: no
* SHOPS: none
* CONFERENCE ROOMS: 3 (10 to 30)
* BANQUETING ROOMS: 6 (15 to 150)
* STANDARD BEDROOM SIZE: 30 m²

* PRIVATE BALCONIES: yes – some rooms
* SWIMMING POOL: no
* GARDENS: no
* NO. OF STAFF: 170
* ROOM SERVICE: 07.00–20.00
* ORIENTATION: facing the harbour
* CREDIT CARDS: American Express, Eurocard, Visa and Diners Club
* OWNING COMPANY: Lars Lendrop Restauranter AB
* GENERAL MANAGER: Mr. Lars Lendrop
* DISTANCE TO BEACH: 2 km
* DISTANCE TO SHOPS: 200 m
* DISTANCE FROM AIRPORT: 20 km (100 m from air terminal)

Swedes have the reputation of being a trifle stand-offish, prone to Strindbergian gloom and to have perfect manners. The latter trait is the hallmark of this hotel – the only one outside Stockholm which achieves the very best in the context of, say, a really good French or German hotel. Well-heeled locals who have travelled and are not short of a krone or two know this and patronise the Savoy extensively. This hotel has grown over the years – a bit here and a bit there – and has great charm. Its rooms are extremely well appointed, furnished with a good eye for the small detail that counts and the bathrooms are a dream. Staff are courteous, knowing instinctively what the guest wants and most of them are multi-lingual. I found the food both in the grill and in the restaurant to be quite outstanding – a very happy mixture of Scandinavian and French served with quiet ceremony and obviously a sound practice of the culinary art. Highly recommended.

Stockholm
GRAND HOTEL, P.O. Box 16424, S-103 27 Stockholm

* TELEPHONE: 08/22 17 20
* CABLES: Grand
* TELEX: 19500
* IN OPERATION: since 1874
* RESERVATIONS: Hotel Representatives Inc
* ROOMS: 166 doubles 184 singles
* SUITES: 11
* RESTAURANTS: 3 – the French Dining Room, the Café and the Royal Winter Garden

* BARS: 2
* DISCOTHEQUE: no – but dancing to live music every night
* SHOPS: 1 – newspapers, books, souvenirs, jewellery, china, silk ties etc
* CONFERENCE ROOMS: 15 (15 to 1,000)
* BANQUETING ROOMS: 15 (20 to 1,200)
* STANDARD BEDROOM SIZE: 28 m²

★ PRIVATE BALCONIES: yes – some rooms
★ SWIMMING POOL: no
★ RECREATIONAL ACTIVITIES: sauna
★ GARDENS: no
★ NO. OF STAFF: 300
★ ROOM SERVICE: around the clock
★ ORIENTATION: facing the Royal Palace and by the River Strommen
★ CREDIT CARDS: American Express, Visa, Eurocard, Master Charge and Access

★ FURTHER DEVELOPMENTS: the Royal Winter Garden has been rebuilt to make it suitable for conferences and also for shows
★ OWNING COMPANY: AB Nya Grand Hotel
★ GENERAL MANAGER: Mr. Sölve Persson
★ DISTANCE TO SHOPS: 300 m
★ DISTANCE FROM AIRPORT: 40 km

In Sweden where everybody is supposed to be both rich and equal, this unlikely double event has been achieved only at the Grand Hotel. It is better than any other and has been like that on and off for over a century. Right now, it is definitely on, one of those massive landmarks which the traveller would surely miss if someone turned it into the limpest member of an international chain. The Grand is what a big city hotel should be – all things to all men: good looking, practical, very clean and beautifully laid out within the old shell and kept up to date in the tiniest detail. If you want to see the latest plumbing or the latest design it's bound to be here. Rooms and suites are large, but elegantly stark. One would call it restrained luxury. The only showpiece is the fantastic turn-of-the-century Mirror Hall – only slightly smaller than Versailles. Service is urbane, perhaps a little distant but very efficient and the food everywhere is worth a bank manager's frown, especially the smorgasbord in the riverside verandah.

SWITZERLAND
Basel

HOTEL DREI KOENIGE, Blumenrain 8, 4001 Basel

★ TELEPHONE: 061/25 52 52
★ CABLES: Troisrois Bale
★ TELEX: 62937
★ IN OPERATION: since 1026
★ RESERVATIONS: Hotel Representative Inc
★ ROOMS: 41 doubles 34 singles
★ SUITES: 3
★ RESTAURANTS: 2 – Rotisserie des Rois and Restaurant Rhy-Deck
★ BARS: 1
★ DISCOTHEQUE: yes
★ SHOPS: none
★ CONFERENCE ROOMS: 2 (6 to 200)
★ BANQUETING ROOMS: 2 (6 to 200)
★ STANDARD BEDROOM SIZE: 20 m²
★ SWIMMING POOL: no

★ PRIVATE BALCONIES: yes – some rooms, also terrace with seating equipment
★ GARDENS: no
★ NO. OF STAFF: 60
★ ROOM SERVICE: 06.30–24.00
★ ORIENTATION: most rooms overlook the river, some rooms overlook the city
★ CREDIT CARDS: American Express, Diners Club, Eurocard, Bankamericard, Carte Blanche
★ OWNING COMPANY: Société d'Exploitation et Gestion Hotelière
★ GENERAL MANAGER: P. Bougenaux
★ DISTANCE TO SHOPS: walking distance
★ DISTANCE FROM AIRPORT: 10 km

Forty years before William the Conqueror crossed to Hastings, there was already a hotel on this bank of the Rhine at Basel. It was called 'At the Sight of the Flower'. Then three crowned heads met there to put their seal on one of Europe's greatest carve-ups and The Three Kings it remained. They have stopped counting kings here now – so many have slept here, at this oldest hotel in Switzerland, that singling them out would be invidious. Some people have lately made rude comments about the hotel's modern improvements. I rather like them because, like so many things in Switzerland they are in irreproachable taste and solidity. I still prefer the old period rooms, of which there are quite a few, all of them beautifully furnished and superbly cared for. The Three Kings is comfortable, beautifully run and one would be hard pressed to find fault.

There certainly isn't any either in the service – in the finest Swiss tradition – or in the food which is spectacular and memorable.

Buergenstock

THE BUERGENSTOCK ESTATE (PALACE HOTEL, GRAND HOTEL),
CH-6366, Buergenstock

★ TELEPHONE: Grand: 041/64 12 12,
  Palace: 041/64 11 22
★ CABLES: Freyhotel Buergenstock
★ TELEX: CH 78462
★ IN OPERATION: since 1874
★ RESERVATIONS: Hotel Representative Inc
★ ROOMS: 152
★ SUITES: 11
★ RESTAURANTS: 6
★ BARS: 2
★ DISCOTHEQUE: live music
★ SHOPS: 5
★ CONFERENCE ROOMS: 8 (10 to 350)
★ BANQUETING ROOMS: 8 (10 to 400)
★ STANDARD BEDROOM SIZE: 25 m²

★ PRIVATE BALCONIES: yes
★ SWIMMING POOL: yes – fresh water
★ GARDENS: yes
★ NO. OF STAFF: 160
★ ROOM SERVICE: around the clock
★ ORIENTATION: rooms face north
  overlooking lake and south overlooking
  the Alps
★ CREDIT CARDS: American Express and
  Visa
★ OWNING COMPANY: (privately owned)
  Fritz Frey
★ GENERAL MANAGER: Elmar K. Greif
★ DISTANCE FROM AIRPORT: 75 km (Zurich)

For that top-of-the-world – nothing-but-the-best feeling, I know of nowhere that equals the Buergenstock Estate. It is mad, extravagant, totally unrealistic, obviously megalomaniac and at the same time so wonderful that it makes you feel better just being there. Sitting on top of a verdant mountain overlooking Lake Lucerne (you get there via Europe's fastest vertical transport) this is the private empire of the legendary Mr. Fritz Frey whom everybody knows because there is only one like him. There are three hotels – Palace, Park and Grand – plus a variety of private villas, very Swiss chalets and lots of little follies hidden away. Here you leave the ordinary world aside and enter a magnificent domain hung with Van Dycks and Tintorettos, Brueghels and Titians. Your room – palatial – may well show off a Gobelins tapestry but you won't get a refund if it does not because the room next door has a Sèvres table service. Priceless period furniture, finest silk Qum carpets, food that is of the highest order go with all that and, when you go out, there is at least half Switzerland at your feet. It is not the cheapest place in the world but one of the most unusual: the management are remarkably selective about who stays and who does not.

Geneva

HOTEL BEAU-RIVAGE, 13 Quai du Mont-Blanc, 1201 Genève

★ TELEPHONE: (022) 31 02 21
★ CABLES: Beaurivage
★ TELEX: 23 362
★ IN OPERATION: since 1865
★ RESERVATIONS: Steigenberger Reservation Service
★ ROOMS: 70 doubles 50 singles
★ SUITES: 7
★ RESTAURANTS: 1 – Le Chat-Botté
★ BARS: 2
★ DISCOTHEQUE: no – but pianist in the bar
★ SHOPS: none
★ CONFERENCE ROOMS: 6 (15 to 85)
★ BANQUETING ROOMS: 6 (20 to 130)
★ STANDARD BEDROOM SIZE: 20 m²
★ PRIVATE BALCONIES: yes
★ SWIMMING POOL: no
★ GARDENS: no – open air terrace overlooking lake
★ NO. OF STAFF: 110
★ ROOM SERVICE: around the clock
★ ORIENTATION: south – Lake Geneva, Mont-Blanc and the water fountain
★ CREDIT CARDS: American Express, Diners Club, Master Charge, Access, Eurocard and Visa
★ OWNING COMPANY: Famille Mayer
★ GENERAL MANAGER: Jacques Mayer
★ DISTANCE TO BEACH: 100 m
★ DISTANCE TO SHOPS: 400 m
★ DISTANCE FROM AIRPORT: 5 km

It is said that all habitual travellers know instinctively which hotel they will stay at in any given city. Quite. For me, if it's Geneva it must be the Beau Rivage. There are bigger hotels in this home of Swiss perfection and also more flashy ones. But for me, this one has something special. First, it's in the very centre of the city, so you can walk everywhere. Second, it's been in the hands of the same genial family for over a century and, like good wines, it has grown mellow and acquired the patina of time. Yet, it also seems to get cleaner and better and more up to date every time I visit it. It seems to have that special genius whereby things are changed – but not upset – just to keep up with the times, and all this apparently without effort. Some rooms are possibly a trifle small but the lakefront ones are superb and the bathrooms are legendary. The staff in this Swiss hotel are Swiss (not Serbo-Croats or Turks) marvellously discreet and efficient and the food is often stratospheric in the 'Chat-Botté' restaurant. In the summertime, you can sit on that marvellous terrace facing the lake and not worry too much about the Stock Exchange. It's a good life at the Beau Rivage.

Gstaad

GSTAAD PALACE HOTEL, 3780 Gstaad

★ TELEPHONE: (030) 83131
★ CABLES: Palace
★ TELEX: 922222
★ IN OPERATION: since 1930
★ RESERVATIONS: Hotel Representative Inc
★ ROOMS: 160
★ SUITES: 20
★ RESTAURANTS: 2
★ BARS: 2
★ DISCOTHEQUE: yes
★ SHOPS: 4
★ CONFERENCE ROOMS: 4 (10 to 200)
★ BANQUETING ROOMS: 2 (150 to 220)
★ STANDARD BEDROOM SIZE: 18 m²
★ PRIVATE BALCONIES: yes – in most rooms
★ SWIMMING POOL: yes – fresh water
★ GARDENS: yes
★ NO. OF STAFF: 220
★ ROOM SERVICE: around the clock
★ ORIENTATION: rooms face all directions
★ CREDIT CARDS: none
★ OWNING COMPANY: Royal Hotel Winter & Gstaad Palace A.G.
★ GENERAL MANAGER: Ernst A. Scherz
★ DISTANCE TO SHOPS: 300 m
★ DISTANCE FROM AIRPORT: 150 km (Geneva)

This castle-like hotel dominating one of Switzerland's best winter resorts is famous for many things and not the least of them is its guest list. They are all here – names that come straight from the Almanach de Gotha or have lots of zeros after the first digit – the rich, the influential, the beautiful and, oddly enough, the young. The Palace has been like this forever largely thanks to a management that knows how to attract clients and also how to entertain them. I don't like the main restaurant much but I do like the other one that has a bar attached to it. The bedrooms vary a lot in size – some have super new bathrooms with his-and-hers – but what does not vary is the quality of the hotel and the service – very, very soigné and personalised. The swimming pool is truly one of the most beautiful in Europe and, with the high Alps outside during the day, the nights are filled with good-natured jollity. A very good place for a grand holiday.

Lausanne

BEAU RIVAGE HOTEL, 1000 Lausanne 6, Ouchy

- ★ TELEPHONE: (021) 26 38 31
- ★ CABLES: Beaurivage Lausanne
- ★ TELEX: 24 341 Boriv
- ★ IN OPERATION: since 1906
- ★ RESERVATIONS: Hotel Representative Inc
- ★ ROOMS: 240
- ★ SUITES: 6
- ★ RESTAURANTS: 2
- ★ BARS: 2
- ★ DISCOTHEQUE: yes – dancing to live music six nights each week
- ★ SHOPS: 6
- ★ CONFERENCE ROOMS: 9 (50 to 500)
- ★ BANQUETING ROOMS: 10 (50 to 800)
- ★ STANDARD BEDROOM SIZE: 35 m²
- ★ PRIVATE BALCONIES: yes
- ★ SWIMMING POOL: yes – salt water, heated

- ★ RECREATIONAL ACTIVITIES: 18-hole golf course within 15 minutes of the hotel and all other outdoor sports facilities close by
- ★ GARDENS: yes – 10 acre private park
- ★ NO. OF STAFF: 250
- ★ ROOM SERVICE: 07.00–24.00
- ★ ORIENTATION: main façade faces south – also other directions
- ★ CREDIT CARDS: Eurocard, Master Charge and Access
- ★ OWNING COMPANY: Beau Rivage Palace S.A.
- ★ GENERAL MANAGER: Bodo von Alvensleben
- ★ DISTANCE TO SHOPS: 5 minutes by car
- ★ DISTANCE FROM AIRPORT: 60 km

Since the last edition of the guide, the Lausanne Beau Rivage has managed the impossible – it has brought salt water to Switzerland (in the swimming pool of course) and if you have visions of armies of Swiss gentlemen shaking out the salt cellars every morning, be warned – this is genuine sea water. Don't ask me how they do it. Other things have changed too since at last it has successfully blended its three wings of different periods into one fantastic pad without losing any of its age-old charm, and what else would you expect from a hotel that was the original setting for Noel Coward's *Private Lives*? The Beau Rivage is one of the grand old hotels of the world. The huge wedding cake palace stands in its own forty-acre park facing the lake with a marvellously beautiful terrace, half in and half out of the hotel which is its great asset. Rooms are vast and quietly palatial without any ostentation and the service is so smooth that one hardly has time to aspirate for help. The food in the beautiful French restaurant with its fin de siècle decor is among the best in any Swiss hotel. Its famous general manager has gone now but his successor is also one of the great names of the hotel business around the world. The Beau Rivage is in good hands.

LAUSANNE PALACE HOTEL, 7–9 Grand Chene, 1002 Lausanne

- ★ TELEPHONE: (021) 20 37 11
- ★ CABLES: Palace Lausanne
- ★ TELEX: 24 171
- ★ IN OPERATION: since 1912
- ★ RESERVATIONS: Hotel Representative Inc
- ★ ROOMS: 175
- ★ SUITES: 25
- ★ RESTAURANTS: 1

- ★ BARS: 2
- ★ DISCOTHEQUE: nightclub
- ★ SHOPS: 7
- ★ CONFERENCE ROOMS: 4 (70 to 350)
- ★ BANQUETING ROOMS: 4 (70 to 260)
- ★ STANDARD BEDROOM SIZE: 26 m²
- ★ PRIVATE BALCONIES: yes – terrace with seating equipment

★ SWIMMING POOL: no
★ GARDENS: yes
★ NO. OF STAFF: 180
★ ROOM SERVICE: around the clock
★ ORIENTATION: most rooms overlook the lake

★ OWNING COMPANY: Lausanne Palace S.A.
★ CREDIT CARDS: American Express, Diners Club, Carte Blanche and Bankamericard
★ GENERAL MANAGER: André Háuri
★ DISTANCE TO SHOPS: walking distance
★ DISTANCE FROM AIRPORT: 60 km

In a small country where hotel standards are usually of the highest, the Lausanne Palace is no laggard – one of those old palace hotels that keeps renewing itself without disturbing anyone. The latest offering in the newly refurbished rooms (not all of them are) is a bedside control panel which adjusts almost everything around, the lighting, which by the way is far above the average, the curtains, the television, your life too, maybe. Bathrooms are the last word and you can choose music from three channels while you shave. Breakfast arrives, gleaming silver and immaculate napery, with a fresh red rose in a vase. The marbled, pillared lobby is so quiet that it is hard to realise one is in a public place – staff move with a noiseless glide which is a pleasure to watch. The great dining room is splendid '*Belle Epoque*', the food quite perfect. The very experienced management is there to ensure that the highest standards never fall.

Lucerne

GRAND HOTEL NATIONAL, Haldenstrasse 4, CH-6002 Lucerne

★ TELEPHONE: 041/50 11 11
★ CABLES: National
★ TELEX: 78130 Natlu-Ch
★ IN OPERATION: since 1871
★ RESERVATIONS: Steigenberger Reservation Service
★ ROOMS: 72 doubles 17 singles
★ SUITES: 4 Attika Suites, 2 Salons
★ RESTAURANTS: 4 – Promenade with Bar, Viennese Cafe, Von Pfyffer-Stube and Le Trianon
★ BARS: 1 – Carousel Bar (in the lobby)
★ DISCOTHEQUE: no – but Night Club San Francisco opposite the Grand National
★ SHOPS: 2 – beauty salon and travel agency
★ CONFERENCE ROOMS: rooms for 12 to 350 persons
★ BANQUETING ROOMS: rooms for 12 to 350 persons
★ STANDARD BEDROOM SIZE: 20 m²

★ PRIVATE BALCONIES: yes – some rooms
★ SWIMMING POOL: yes – fresh water, 72 m²
★ RECREATIONAL ACTIVITIES: sauna, solarium in the hotel with tennis and golf nearby. Horse riding 5 km away
★ GARDENS: no
★ NO. OF STAFF: 120
★ ROOM SERVICE: 06.30–24.00
★ ORIENTATION: facing the lake and the Alps
★ CREDIT CARDS: American Express, Diners Club, Visa, Eurocard and Master Charge
★ OWNING COMPANY: Grand Hotel National AG
★ GENERAL MANAGER: M. Windlin
★ DISTANCE FROM BEACH: 1 km to Lido Beach
★ DISTANCE TO SHOPS: walking distance
★ DISTANCE FROM AIRPORT: 60 km

Cesar Ritz ran the Grand National for a dozen years while Escoffier devised ever new delights in the kitchen so the provenance could hardly be better. The hotel itself, standing like a statement of pride on the shores of Lake Lucerne, looks as if it has not changed for years – but study it carefully for here is one of those miracles of the hotel business – one that got better, and newer, and grander with age by the simple (but not inexpensive) process of taking the best from all periods. The result is luxury in the grand manner. Everything you see, everything you touch, is perfection – superb furnishings and carpets, beds so comfortable that no one needs sleeping pills and a service so smooth, so intelligently anticipating the guest's requirements that you only remember it afterwards. The Grand National's periodic facelifts are just what they mean: you leave the bone structure and improve the rest but here you never see the telltale lines of a poor face-lift.

Montreux

LE MONTREUX PALACE, 100 Grand-rue, CH 1820, Montreux

★ TELEPHONE: (021) 61-32-31
★ CABLES: PALACEMTX
★ TELEX: 453 101 mpm ch
★ IN OPERATION: since 1906
★ RESERVATIONS: Steigenberger Reservation System, worldwide/Hotel Representative Inc (HRI), worldwide/Robert F. Warner, New York
★ ROOMS: 181 twins 26 singles
★ SUITES: 10 full and executive suites 25 junior suites
★ RESTAURANTS: 4 – Restaurant français, Cave du Cygne, La Rôtisserie, Le Grand Café, a swiss coffee shop and a barbecue and snacks available at the swimming pool
★ BARS: 2 – the Golden Rose Bar and Le Tube
★ DISCOTHEQUE: no
★ SHOPS: various shops, including hairdresser, watch and jewellery shop, drugstore, Swiss embroideries, antiques
★ CONFERENCE ROOMS: 10 (20 to 1,400)

★ BANQUETING ROOMS: 10 (10 to 1,500)
★ STANDARD BEDROOM SIZE: 45 m²
★ PRIVATE BALCONIES: yes
★ SWIMMING POOL: yes – fresh water, outdoor, 260 m²
★ RECREATIONAL ACTIVITIES: tennis, mini golf, mountain climbing, horse riding, sailing, swimming, 18-hole golf course nearby
★ GARDENS: yes
★ NO. OF STAFF: 250
★ ROOM SERVICE: 07.00–24.00
★ ORIENTATION: south with view of Lake Geneva and the Swiss Alps
★ CREDIT CARDS: American Express, Diners Club, Visa, Eurocard and Master Charge
★ OWNING COMPANY: Montreux Palace S.A.
★ GENERAL MANAGER: Alfred J. Frei, Administrator
★ DISTANCE TO SHOPS: 100 m
★ DISTANCE FROM AIRPORT: 80 km

How the Swiss manage to produce such hotel miracles we will never know. And the Montreux Palace is an excellent example of an old grand hotel, one of the most famous in the world, which, at every visit, seems to have been re-decorated and refurnished yesterday. Everything is so fresh, so clean, so right that we think it is a very special genius. Now there is a new and impressive lobby but the plaster nymphs and angels still beautify other walls. The rooms are palatial – whatever their style – and we think that having breakfast on one's own terrace facing Lake Geneva and the French Alps beyond is one of the real pleasures left in one's travelling life.

Bathrooms are so elegant that one could splend a holiday in any of them, just for the sheer narcissistic enjoyment of so much good planning. In this hotel you will never see yesterday's flowers or a dirty ashtray and the minute you return from your stroll the receptionist gives you your key – without asking for your room number. As for the food, the only way to survive it is to go climb an alp.

St. Moritz

BADRUTT'S PALACE HOTEL, CH-7500, St. Moritz

★ TELEPHONE: (082) 2 11 01
★ CABLES: Palace
★ TELEX: 74 424 palsm ch
★ IN OPERATION: since 1896
★ RESERVATIONS: Hotel Representatives Inc
★ ROOMS: 250
★ SUITES: 20
★ RESTAURANTS: 5
★ BARS: 4
★ DISCOTHEQUE: yes – King's Club Disco and Le Grand Bar Night Club with live combo

★ SHOPS: 12 – jewellery, fashion, antiques etc
★ CONFERENCE ROOMS: 3 (30 to 320)
★ BANQUETING ROOMS: 3 (30 to 450)
★ STANDARD BEDROOM SIZE: 30 m²
★ PRIVATE BALCONIES: yes – most rooms
★ SWIMMING POOL: yes – fresh water, indoor 20 × 25 m, outdoor 8 × 25 m
★ RECREATIONAL ACTIVITIES: tennis, sauna, gym, ice rink in winter, hotel has its own ski-school and own kindergarten, all summer and winter sports nearby

★ GARDENS: yes

★ NO. OF STAFF: 400

★ ROOM SERVICE: around the clock

★ ORIENTATION: most rooms face south facing Lake St. Mortiz

★ FURTHER DEVELOPMENTS: 18 de luxe service flats, 3 indoor tennis courts, 2 squash courts and additional meeting facilities

★ CREDIT CARDS: Amexo, Diners Club, Visa, Eurocard and Master Charge

★ OWNING COMPANY: The Badrutt Family

★ GENERAL MANAGER: Max Keller

★ DISTANCE TO SHOPS: own shopping arcade

★ DISTANCE FROM AIRPORT: 250 km (Zurich)

Should anyone still wonder which came first, the Badrutt dynasty or St. Moritz, the answer is the first. Four generations ago, it was Caspar Badrutt who took St. Moritz, a tiny village in the Engadine and began transforming it into the stuff legends are made of. Since then, in the great and wonderful world of winter sports, this place has never really had any equals and of course Badrutt's Palace has been the focus of the chic, rich and beautiful people from January to April. To my way of thinking the hotel is the finest in Switzerland, one of the six best in Europe and a place at once so grand and so much fun that it has no real imitators. Its guest list reads like the Who's Who of the past eighty-odd years – anybody with any claim to fame, fortune or beauty has been there living it up. The place has such tradition, such aura that adjectives fail. Where else but at the Palace would you get 'fraises des bois' in mid winter? How else could you get there than with the private Rhaeto rail link? Cartier and Vuitton are there of course together with all those little whatnot shops from the greatest city centres of the world. So is the Chesa Veglia, one of Europe's finest restaurants, and the Corviglia Club, the continent's most exclusive. I have not so far said anything about the hotel itself and neither do I intend to except to say that it is the best there is and a good deal of it. If you need convincing, go see for yourself though you'll have to be lucky with your booking.

CARLTON HOTEL, CH-7500 St. Moritz

★ TELEPHONE: 082 11 41

★ CABLES: Carltonotel St. Moritz

★ TELEX: 74 454

★ IN OPERATION: since 1913

★ RESERVATIONS: Steigenberger Reservation Service, New York/Ernest J. Newman Inc, New York/Robert F. Warner, New York

★ ROOMS: 85 doubles 30 singles

★ SUITES: 5

★ RESTAURANTS: 3 – Romanoff, Tschine Grill and Chalet Prueveda

★ BARS: 2

★ DISCOTHEQUE: live music in the bar

★ SHOPS: 1 – several showcases

★ CONFERENCE ROOMS: 4 (40 to 200)

★ BANQUETING ROOMS: 2 (up to 200)

★ STANDARD BEDROOM SIZE: 25–30 m²

★ PRIVATE BALCONIES: yes – 50% of the rooms

★ SWIMMING POOL: yes – fresh water, 8 × 15 m

★ RECREATIONAL ACTIVITIES: tennis courts, sauna, golf course, sailing, surfing, windsurfing, summer skiing, skating, hiking and mountain climbing

★ GARDENS: yes

★ STAFF: 120

★ ROOM SERVICE: 07.00–24.00 and night service

★ ORIENTATION: south

★ CREDIT CARDS: American Express, Diners Club, Visa and Master Charge

★ OWNING COMPANY: Carlton Hotel St. Moritz AG

★ GENERAL MANAGER: B. Kilchenmann

★ DISTANCE TO SHOPS: 500 m

★ DISTANCE FROM AIRPORT: 250 km (Zurich)

The despair of those who run the Carlton must surely be that people the world over always make it their second choice in St. Moritz which is very unfair. If this hotel was situated anywhere else it would surely be number one and I have a special affection for it. A grand hotel in the grand Swiss manner, it is plush, dignified, extremely comfortable in every respect and beautifully situated. The minute one enters the panelled, thickly carpeted great hall, one has the feel of quality and as soon as one goes into the main restaurant it is obvious that dinner is going to be something of an event. Carlton food is renowned. Rooms are large and discreetly furnished and the bathrooms are superb. There is a beautiful indoor swimming pool and, apart from skiing, there are lots of interesting and convivial events. I have not been to the Carlton in the winter season but I am told that its clientele is younger and livelier than elsewhere.

Zurich

DOLDER GRAND HOTEL, Kurhausstrasse 65, 8032 Zurich-CH

- ★ TELEPHONE: (01) 251-62-31
- ★ CABLES: Doldergrand
- ★ TELEX: 53449
- ★ IN OPERATION: for about a century
- ★ RESERVATIONS: Hotel Representative Inc/Utell International Ltd/Preferred Hotels Association
- ★ ROOMS: 200
- ★ SUITES: 15 including Royal Suite with 2 bed and bathrooms and living room
- ★ RESTAURANTS: 2 – La Rotonde and in the bar
- ★ BARS: 1
- ★ DISCOTHEQUE: no – but piano music in the bar
- ★ SHOPS: 15 showcases (with purchasing at the newsstand)
- ★ CONFERENCE ROOMS: 6 (up to 500)
- ★ BANQUETING ROOMS: 6 (up to 250)

- ★ STANDARD BEDROOM SIZE: 28 m^2
- ★ PRIVATE BALCONIES: yes
- ★ SWIMMING POOL: yes – fresh water
- ★ RECREATIONAL ACTIVITIES: 9-hole golf course, 5 clay tennis courts, skating in winter, swimming in summer and horse riding nearby
- ★ GARDENS: yes
- ★ NO. OF STAFF: 260
- ★ ROOM SERVICE: around the clock
- ★ ORIENTATION: most rooms face the south overlooking the city, the lake and the distant Alps
- ★ CREDIT CARDS: Amexco, Master Charge, Visa and Eurocard
- ★ OWNING COMPANY: family-owned
- ★ GENERAL MANAGER: Raoul T. de Gendre
- ★ DISTANCE TO SHOPS: 7 to 10 minutes
- ★ DISTANCE FROM AIRPORT: 12 km

Switzerland has many charms and Zurich only a few (one being money) and perhaps the best thing about the patrician Dolder Grand is that it is far enough from the city centre – ten minutes at most – for the noise of bulls and bears bellowing or computers and calculators ticking not to penetrate its august walls, surrounded as they are by vast cushions of parkland. Of course it is one of the great hotels of Switzerland – a fact one realises at the first step inside. Apart from the size of the royal suite (only important crowned heads need apply), there is nothing at all flashy about the Dolder. It is solid, comfortable, beautifully and cleanly appointed and run like a Swiss timepiece. The staff are so expert at their job that one merely has to mention something for it to be done – instantly and without murmur. For exercise afterwards there is an interesting swimming pool with artificial waves, a very pretty nine-hole golf course and tennis courts. Though it is not cheap, you do not need a numbered bank account.

HOTEL BAUR AU LAC, Talstrasse 1, CH-8001 Zurich

★ TELEPHONE: 01/221 16 50
★ CABLES: Baurlac
★ TELEX: 813 567 bal
★ IN OPERATION: since 1848
★ RESERVATIONS: Hotel Representative Inc, U.S.A., London/Preferred Hotels Association
★ ROOMS: 80 doubles 70 singles
★ SUITES: 14
★ RESTAURANTS: 3 – French Restaurant, Grill-Room and Pavillon Restaurant
★ BARS: 3
★ DISCOTHEQUE: yes
★ SHOPS: 1 Newspaper stand
★ CONFERENCE ROOMS: 5 (10 to 180)

★ BANQUETING ROOMS: 5 (10 to 180)
★ STANDARD BEDROOM SIZE: 24 m^2 (single), 34 m^2 (double)
★ PRIVATE BALCONIES: yes
★ SWIMMING POOL: no
★ GARDENS: yes – private park
★ NO. OF STAFF: 330
★ ROOM SERVICE: 06.00–24.00
★ CREDIT CARDS: American Express
★ ORIENTATION: half the rooms face the lake or the canal
★ OWNING COMPANY: H. Kracht's Erben
★ GENERAL MANAGER: Georges Rey
★ DISTANCE TO SHOPS: 50 m
★ DISTANCE FROM AIRPORT: 14 km

If you hold petrodollars, gold bars from Dubai (or even sterling from North Sea oil) and you are business orientated, you will surely find kindred souls at the Baur au Lac, one of Switzerland's best-known hotels. Everything works with Swiss precision – laundry, telephone, messages, stock market news from everywhere and service so smooth one does not even know it is there. A very handsome hotel, with good-sized rooms furnished with superb beds and good though predictable furniture. Public rooms are just right for those big deals and there is now a (happily) soundproofed discotheque. It has a superb private park, right in the middle of Zurich where one can actually hear birds singing, presumably to bank managers. The food at the Baur au Lac is justly celebrated, very substantial and handsomely served to people who know what is value for money. The management is one of the most experienced in Switzerland.

SYRIA

Damascus

HOTEL MERIDIEN, Av Choukry Kouatly, B.P. 5531, Damascus

★ TELEPHONE: 229200
★ CABLES: Homer Damas
★ TELEX: 11379 SY
★ IN OPERATION: 5 years
★ RESERVATIONS: Meridien Reservation International/Air France
★ ROOMS: 372
★ SUITES: 33
★ RESTAURANTS: 4 – Les Années Folles, Le Cafe des Deux Mondes, Walima and La Ghouta

★ BARS: 3
★ DISCOTHEQUE: yes – and live music
★ SHOPS: shopping arcade – 14 boutiques, including handicraft centre, barber shop, beauty salon etc
★ CONFERENCE ROOMS: 7 (25 to 1,000)
★ BANQUETING ROOMS: 8 (25 to 650)
★ STANDARD BEDROOM SIZE: 25 m^2
★ PRIVATE BALCONIES: yes – all rooms
★ SWIMMING POOL: yes – fresh water, 32 × 12 m

★ RECREATIONAL ACTIVITIES: tennis, sauna and health club
★ GARDENS: yes – 2½ acres of park, planted with palm, pepper and eucalyptus
★ NO. OF STAFF: 380
★ ROOM SERVICE: around the clock
★ ORIENTATION: west
★ CREDIT CARDS: American Express and Diners Club
★ OWNING COMPANY: Meridien Hotels
★ GENERAL MANAGER: Gunther Schachtner
★ DISTANCE TO SHOPS: 5 minutes' walk
★ DISTANCE FROM AIRPORT: 23 km

Damascus is not yet lost to the tourist hordes but it soon will be and if you are going there go now and stay at the Meridien. The only place to stay, it is a French hotel cast in the American/international mould and managed by the very able Air France subsidiary. The bars are thriving, the laundry works such that a Russian grand duke could send his shirts here to be cleaned rather than Paris and your room is well up to big-city hotel standards anywhere, with the occasional touch of Franco-Arab decor. Bathrooms are excellent and the multilingual staff are very helpful and pleasant. Though the decor of the top floor restaurant is eminently forgettable it is even easier to forget when you have tried the food – Franco-Arab again – and seen far below the lights of Damascus, capital of the Ummayad caliphs, where the bazaar is still a bazaar and the tourist trapping is in close season all year round. Just to be able to call a cab and say 'Take me to The Street Called Straight' is sensation enough to match a chance encounter with St. Paul. And when you have seen the enormous mosque, the tomb of Saladin and all the rest, you will be glad the Meridien is there to welcome you back.

Palmyra

MERIDIEN HOTEL, Palmyra

★ TELEPHONE: (031) 37000
★ CABLES: no
★ TELEX: 441041
★ IN OPERATION: 1 year
★ RESERVATIONS: Air France Agencies, worldwide/all Meridien Hotels, worldwide
★ ROOMS: 240
★ SUITES: 10
★ RESTAURANTS: 2 – La Reine Zenobie and L'Oasis
★ BARS: 1
★ DISCOTHEQUE: yes
★ SHOPS: not yet in operation. There are plans for 6 shops selling suits, carpets, jewellery
★ CONFERENCE ROOMS: 5
★ BANQUETING ROOMS: 5 (10 to 250)
★ STANDARD BEDROOM SIZE: 26 m²
★ PRIVATE BALCONIES: yes
★ SWIMMING POOL: yes – fresh water
★ RECREATIONAL ACTIVITIES: tennis courts and horse riding
★ GARDENS: yes
★ NO. OF STAFF: 190
★ ROOM SERVICE: around the clock
★ ORIENTATION: east, south
★ CREDIT CARDS: Diners Club and American Express
★ OWNING COMPANY: Government Ministry of Tourism
★ GENERAL MANAGER: J. P. Chauhard
★ DISTANCE TO SHOPS: 2 km
★ DISTANCE FROM AIRPORT: 250 km

Once upon a time going to Palmyra was for the dedicated and the tough. You crossed the desert at high speed and ended up in this absolutely fascinating site of antiquity – it was the capital of the legendary Queen Zenobia who gave the Romans so much trouble – only to discover that the only place you could stay was a fly-ridden, none-too-clean 'local' hostelry. No longer. Air France's own hotel chain – one of the fastest growing in the world – has changed all that. Now you can stay at the Meridien Palmyra without having to reach for your medicine chest. The hotel is very new and needs time to adjust to the harsh conditions of this remote locality as well as to the more particular needs of its guests but the very fact that it is there, open and working, is a miracle indeed. It is cool and airy, very well planned and rather more American than French in outlook. Rooms are large and comfortable in an unostentatious way and when you have covered the seven or eight square miles of the site of ancient Palmyra –

very emotion-making but very tiring – it is a blessed relief to return to a hotel where you can breathe, eat and drink in a civilised manner. Full marks for trying.

THAILAND
Bangkok
THE ORIENTAL HOTEL, 49 Oriental Avenue, Bangkok 5

- ★ TELEPHONE: 234 8690-9
- ★ CABLES: Orienhotel
- ★ TELEX: TH 82997
- ★ IN OPERATION: 106 years
- ★ RESERVATIONS: Hotel Representatives Inc
- ★ ROOMS: 336 doubles   48 singles
- ★ SUITES: 22
- ★ RESTAURANTS: 4 – the Normandie, the Lord Jim's, the Verandah and the Riverside Terrace
- ★ BARS: 2
- ★ DISCOTHEQUE: Diana's
- ★ SHOPS: 23
- ★ CONFERENCE ROOMS: 3 (50 to 800)
- ★ BANQUETING ROOMS: 6 (50 to 500)

- ★ STANDARD BEDROOM SIZE: 38 m^2
- ★ PRIVATE BALCONIES: yes – suites and de luxe rooms
- ★ SWIMMING POOL: yes – 2, fresh water, 25 × 12 × 2 m
- ★ GARDENS: yes
- ★ NO. OF STAFF: 900
- ★ ROOM SERVICE: around the clock
- ★ CREDIT CARDS: American Express, Diners Club and Visa
- ★ OWNING COMPANY: Mandarin International Hotels Ltd
- ★ GENERAL MANAGER: Mr. Kurt Wachtveitl
- ★ DISTANCE TO SHOPS: walking distance
- ★ DISTANCE FROM AIRPORT: 27 km

As a professional traveller, people often ask which is my favourite hotel. An impossible question to answer, but I would not dare leave the Oriental out of the first six. This miraculous hostelry is a monument to those who care for quality.

It's really two hotels. One is the River Wing, towering and impressive, with rooms and suites which are among the most comfortable in the world with lovely views of the River of Kings on which, daily, the hotel's two boats – the Oriental Queen and the Orchid Queen – ply their trade. Down below is a truly magnificent lobby, chandeliered, sparkling and handsome. On top is the Normandie Grill, one of the two or three finest Western restaurants anywhere in the Far East. When I dined there, the little known French cheese I used to take with me to school just happened to be on the plateau.

Across the gardens is the period piece – the Oriental's Authors' Wing where, among others, Somerset Maugham and Joseph Conrad wrote and lived and listened, where now there are suites named after them. Downstairs is a unique and quite splendid interior courtyard, with white cane furniture and exotic bamboos. Everything happens at the Oriental – Thai dancing, exotic shops, music, buffets by the river. As for service, with one of the highest staff-to-guest ratios in the east, it is also so good that one does not even notice it. Above it all reigns a subtle and infinitely intelligent management whose modesty is endearing. All those who love great hotels should stay at the Oriental at least once in a lifetime.

TUNISIA
Tunis
TUNIS HILTON HOTEL, Avenue Salambo, P.O. Box 1160, Tunis

- ★ TELEPHONE: 282.000
- ★ CABLES: Hiltel Tunis
- ★ TELEX: 12 372
- ★ IN OPERATION: 16 years

- ★ RESERVATIONS: Hilton Reservation Service, worldwide
- ★ ROOMS: 249
- ★ SUITES: 19

★ RESTAURANTS: 2 – Grill Room and Coffee Shop
★ BARS: 2 – Khema Bar and Oasis Pool Club Bar in swimming season
★ DISCOTHEQUE: no – but live music in the Grill Room
★ SHOPS: 2 – souvenir shop and drugstore
★ CONFERENCE ROOMS: 3 (30 to 450)
★ BANQUETING ROOMS: 3 (30 to 350)
★ STANDARD BEDROOM SIZE: 21 m²
★ PRIVATE BALCONIES: yes
★ SWIMMING POOL: yes – fresh water, 17.5 × 10 × 2 m
★ GARDENS: yes
★ RECREATIONAL ACTIVITIES: golf, tennis and horse riding nearby

★ NO. OF STAFF: 280
★ ROOM SERVICE: around the clock
★ ORIENTATION: main facade faces the city, the other facade overlooks the valley and the Bay of Tunis
★ CREDIT CARDS: American Express, Hilton, Diners Club, Eurocard, Master Charge, Access, En Route and Carte Blanche
★ OWNING COMPANY: operated by Hilton International Co
★ GENERAL MANAGER: M. B. Stoecklein
★ DISTANCE TO BEACH: 16 km
★ DISTANCE TO SHOPS: 4 km
★ DISTANCE FROM AIRPORT: 7 km

Ever since the day I got back to Tunis from a rather mad, very dusty, muddy and mistaken Saharan adventure, I have never forgotten the Tunis Hilton – it gave exactly what was most wanted: courtesy and efficiency, cleanliness, practicality and an atmosphere that made me feel almost human again. In a charming country where, alas, most hotels have become package tour dormitories, this one is an exception. Unlike its bigger brothers in the chain, it is gently and intelligently decorated, with nice human touches and items that are not there just for show. A little away from the centre of town, it has peace and quiet, a lovely swimming pool and pleasant gardens. Rooms are what one would expect but the care taken of them is above average because here is a management who cares and a staff who really do their smiling best. The food, one of Tunisia's better points, is very good – both French and Tunisian – and served with attention to detail. The wine waiters know their stuff and the head waiter in the main restaurant is a model of what that functionary should be.

TURKEY
Istanbul

HILTON INTERNATIONAL ISTANBUL, Cumhuriyet Caddesi, Harbiye, Istanbul

★ TELEPHONE: 46 70 50
★ CABLES: Hiltels Istanbul
★ TELEX: 22379
★ IN OPERATION: 27 years
★ RESERVATIONS: Hilton Reservation Services
★ ROOMS: 417
★ SUITES: 18
★ RESTAURANTS: 3
★ BARS: 4
★ DISCOTHEQUE: no – but live music
★ SHOPS: 14
★ CONFERENCE ROOMS: 2 (150 to 450)
★ BANQUETING ROOMS: 3 (50 to 600)
★ STANDARD BEDROOM SIZE: 25 m²
★ PRIVATE BALCONIES: yes – all rooms
★ SWIMMING POOL: yes – fresh water
★ RECREATIONAL ACTIVITIES: four tennis courts

★ GARDENS: yes – 13 acres of lawn and private garden
★ NO. OF STAFF: 650
★ ROOM SERVICE: around the clock
★ ORIENTATION: rooms face Bosphorus and gardens
★ CREDIT CARDS: American Express, Diners Club, Carte Blanche, TWA Getaway and Ambassador, Eurocard, Master Charge, Hilton Credit ID Cards and Hilton Preferential Cards
★ OWNING COMPANY: Turkish Republic Pension Fund
★ GENERAL MANAGER: George W. Engelhardt
★ DISTANCE TO BEACH: 20 minutes by car
★ DISTANCE TO SHOPS: walking distance
★ DISTANCE FROM AIRPORT: 25 km

A quarter of a century is quite a long lifetime for a Hilton hotel. Too long for some I know but not for the Istanbul variety which I still rate among the two or three best in this worldwide chain. To be here, facing the beautiful Bosphorus and knowing that behind you the wheels are turning with high American efficiency seems to present the best of both worlds. Down below, the Grand Bazaar is not far away as are St. Sophia and Topkapi. What counts here is the very high standard of hotel-keeping. Charmingly decorated, in a Hilton-Islamic manner with lots of green plants and fresh flowers, the rooms are the usual Hilton size – very acceptable and the bathrooms work like a dream. As in most countries with high unemployment the services such as laundry are more or less instant and room service most efficient. In the top floor grill, the food is by far the best of any Istanbul hotel.

UNITED ARAB EMIRATES

Fujairah

HILTON INTERNATIONAL FUJAIRAH, P.O. Box 231, Fujairah

★ TELEPHONE: 22411
★ CABLES: Hiltels Fujairah
★ TELEX: 89018FU
★ IN OPERATION: 4 years
★ RESERVATIONS: direct or Hilton Reservation Service
★ ROOMS: 116
★ SUITES: 8
★ RESTAURANTS: 3 – Coffee Shop, Siji Restaurant, Pool Terrace Cafe
★ BARS: 1
★ DISCOTHEQUE: yes and occasional live music
★ SHOPS: 2 – 1 newsagent/pharmacy and 1 clothes/sports equipment
★ CONFERENCE ROOMS: 5 (up to 25)
★ BANQUETING ROOMS: 1 (up to 200)
★ STANDARD BEDROOM SIZE: 24 m²
★ PRIVATE BALCONIES: all rooms

★ SWIMMING POOL: yes – fresh water
★ RECREATIONAL ACTIVITIES: swimming, tennis, badminton, fishing, waterskiing, land surfing, mini golf, playground and 200 m beach
★ GARDENS: yes
★ NO. OF STAFF: 150
★ ROOM SERVICE: around the clock
★ ORIENTATION: facing east over Gulf of Oman
★ CREDIT CARDS: all major credit cards
★ OWNING COMPANY: operated by Hilton International
★ GENERAL MANAGER: Emanuel Matsakis
★ DISTANCE TO BEACH: on the beach
★ DISTANCE TO SHOPS: 1½ km
★ DISTANCE FROM AIRPORT: 128 km (Dubai)

If you have never heard of Fujairah, you are forgiven – neither have millions of other people. I discovered it some years ago and thought it was like one of those places one reads about in books about the French Foreign Legion: reddish-brown mountains, very spectacular, belts of palms, blue seas and a sheikh's palace with a flag on top. Nobody there, except the Sheikh and his subjects of course though it is only an hour's drive away from those nasty oil wells on the Gulf. Imagine my surprise a while later coming back and finding a Hilton in Fujairah! And not just any Hilton, but a charming baby-sized one, right on the beach, built with imagination and wit, with an interior garden and rooms that are superbly equipped, fresh and ideally suited to this often ferocious climate. A beach hotel à la Hilton. That's new and in my opinion well worth going to because it is the only one of its kind and its location is worth the journey – you drive over moonish mountains and deserts to the point where you think this must indeed be the end of the world. But there, on the free and clear Indian Ocean side is Fujairah, with its 119 varieties of fish, its dates and its ancient ways. I even had Greek food at the Fujairah Hilton. I also had total peace and quiet in a country one normally associates with banks, gold bars and unbearable jazziness. Good for Hilton – they can do anything when they set their minds to it.

U.S.A.

Amelia Island, Florida

AMELIA ISLAND PLANTATION, Amelia Island, Florida 32034

★ TELEPHONE: (904) 261-6161
★ CABLES: no
★ TELEX: 56-8424
★ IN OPERATION: 8 years
★ RESERVATIONS: direct
★ ROOMS: 900 + in 360 rented villas and over 100 oceanfront hotel rooms
★ RESTAURANTS: 5
★ BARS: 4
★ DISCOTHEQUE: yes
★ SHOPS: several including grocery, bicycle rental, ladies' apparel, crafts, hairdressers, plants and gifts
★ CONFERENCE ROOMS: 23 (15 to 500)
★ BANQUETING ROOMS: 16 (32 to 480)
★ STANDARD BEDROOM SIZE: 30 m^2
★ PRIVATE BALCONIES: yes
★ SWIMMING POOL: yes – 14, salt water and fresh water, 1 Olympic size at Beach club
★ RECREATIONAL ACTIVITIES: 27 holes of Peter Dye golf, 19 Har Tru tennis courts (3 floodlit), bicycling, jogging trails, health spa, horse back riding, sailing, fishing, paddleboats, electric cars, playgrounds, tours and youth programme
★ GARDENS: yes
★ NO. OF STAFF: 600
★ ROOM SERVICE: breakfast only in Inn Rooms
★ ORIENTATION: buildings face all directions, amongst the trees, behind the sand dunes and beside lagoons
★ FURTHER DEVELOPMENTS: Sandcastles – 86 oceanfront units to be completed in spring of 1982. Courtside village – a tennis village comprising 48 condominiums located near Racquet Park Tennis Centre. Linkside – 50 low-rise condominiums on the 27th fairway of Amelia Links Golf Course
★ CREDIT CARDS: all major credit cards
★ OWNING COMPANY: Amelia Island Plantation Co
★ GENERAL MANAGER: James M. Rester
★ DISTANCE TO BEACH: on the beach
★ DISTANCE TO SHOPS: small village located on property
★ DISTANCE FROM AIRPORT: 47 km

Amelia Island is the 1,800-acre tip of a wild and breezy island off the north coast of Florida – virtually untouched, untamed, completely natural and just right for all those who are tired of conventional resorts – it is partly tidal, the home of freewheeling seabirds. Beaches are vast and totally uncluttered and there is no hotel as such – only the centrepiece of the Amelia Island Beach Club. Most of the rooms are individual villas – some by the beach, some by the lagoon and others by the golf course. Each villa has between one and four bedrooms – very spacious indeed, most of them privately owned and decorated to satisfy a personal taste. There is maid-service but no room-service – everybody walks or usually cycles to one of four restaurants where all the good things of the sea await the gourmet. There is conviviality if you want it and perfect, but perfect solitude if that is what you are seeking.

Beverly Hills, California

BEVERLY WILSHIRE HOTEL, 9500 Wilshire Blvd, Beverly Hills, Ca. 90212

★ TELEPHONE: 213-275-4282
★ CABLES: Bevshire
★ TELEX: 698-220
★ IN OPERATION: since 1961
★ RESERVATIONS: Preferred Hotels Association/Hotel Representative Inc, worldwide
★ ROOMS: 432 – including suites
★ RESTAURANTS: 4 – La Bella Fontana, El Padrino Bar and Rotisserie, Don Hernando's and the Pink Turtle Cafe
★ BARS: 3 – Hideaway Bar, Zindabad Pub and El Padrino Bar
★ DISCOTHEQUE: dancing Wednesday to Saturday nights in Don Hernando's
★ SHOPS: 10
★ CONFERENCE ROOMS: 8 (25 to 1,200)
★ BANQUETING ROOMS: 8 (25 to 1,200)
★ STANDARD BEDROOM SIZE: 50 m^2
★ PRIVATE BALCONIES: yes

★ SWIMMING POOL: yes – fresh water, 14 × 17½ m
★ RECREATIONAL ACTIVITIES: sauna and gymnasium
★ GARDENS: no
★ NO. OF STAFF: 750–800
★ ROOM SERVICE: 07.00–01.30
★ ORIENTATION: rooms face all four directions

★ CREDIT CARDS: American Express, Bankamericard, Carte Blanche, Master Charge, Visa and Diners Club
★ OWNING COMPANY: Courtright Co
★ GENERAL MANAGER: George White
★ DISTANCE TO BEACH: 15 km
★ DISTANCE TO SHOPS: walking
★ DISTANCE TO AIRPORT: 35 km

One European traveller who arrived at the Beverly Wilshire looked at the place and asked: 'Who built this place – Nero?' In a city devoted to show, to ostentation, it is right that there should be nothing shy about the Beverly Wilshire – it is an overstatement of almost everything, money (lots of it), good taste and good manners, superb management skills and the tremendous impresario-like personality of the man who owns it – a legend everywhere. Built into and overflowing the shell of an old building once described as 'Rudolph Valentino baroque or Theda Bara regency', the Beverly Wilshire has simply everything – marble from Italy, carpets from Persia, chandeliers from France and indeed entire decor schemes imported in toto from all parts of the world. Even staircases and corridors are fantastic – there must be an emperor at least, if not Sam Goldwyn behind it. Rooms and suites are palatially vast and beautifully appointed and you can have them in any style you like – French, Spanish, Mexican, Californian, Italian and so on. The hotel entrance is a private driveway and the swimming pool is large enough for a water ballet. Two of its restaurants – the Grand Trianon and Bella Fontana – are probably the most beautiful hotel eating places anywhere and what is more, both food and wine reflect the decor – the cellar being one of the owner's great joys. Service, altogether, is matchless in efficiency and know-how, performed without effort or fuss in a hundred different ways.

Boca Raton, Florida

BOCA RATON HOTEL AND CLUB, Boca Taton, Florida 33432

★ TELEPHONE: (305) 395-3000
★ CABLES: no
★ TELEX: 803926 Boca Club
★ IN OPERATION: since 1926
★ RESERVATIONS: Hotel Representatives Inc, London and New York/K & K, Frankfurt
★ ROOMS: 912 doubles, singles – rates available
★ SUITES: 39
★ RESTAURANTS: 8 – Top of the Tower, Patio Royale, Cathedral, The Club, Espresso House, Court of the Four Lions, Cabana Club, Boca West, The Court House (at tennis courts) and Halfaway House (at golf course)
★ BARS: 10
★ DISCOTHEQUE: no – but live music and dancing
★ SHOPS: 11 – boutique, men's wear, children's shop, cosmetics, flowers, newsstand
★ CONFERENCE ROOMS: 29 (10 to 1,500)
★ BANQUETING ROOMS: 20 (10 to 1,100)

★ STANDARD BEDROOM SIZE: 35 m²
★ PRIVATE BALCONIES: yes – some
★ SWIMMING POOL: yes – 4, fresh and salt water
★ RECREATIONAL ACTIVITIES: 5 18-hole golf courses, 47 tennis courts, jogging trail, bicycle riding, marina, fishing, sailing, athletic club and health spa
★ GARDENS: yes
★ NO. OF STAFF: 1,450
★ ROOM SERVICE: 07.00–02.00
★ ORIENTATION: all directions
★ CREDIT CARDS: American Express, Master Charge and Visa
★ OWNING COMPANY: The Arvida Corporation
★ GENERAL MANAGER: George Roy
★ PRESIDENT: L. Bert Stephens
★ DISTANCE TO BEACH: directly
★ DISTANCE TO SHOPS: 1 km
★ DISTANCE FROM AIRPORT: Miami 60 km, Palm Beach 40 km, Fort Lauderdale 40 km

This hotel was built back in the mad twenties as a kind of American Moorish castle on the Florida shore – a kind of Citizen Kane place with only slightly less exuberance – great salons with caisson ceilings, a magnificent jumbo-sized lobby and a restaurant designed like a European cathedral. Then it grew and grew, millionaires still came but so did many other affluent Americans because Boca Raton, forever changing, never changed its standards – the highest in the land, rated today by America's most pretigious judges as one of the ten best. Four splendid golf courses and over forty tennis courts; eight restaurants and so many bars that one never need go thirsty; and if you like a resort not to bore you, try this one – it is guaranteed to give you something different to do every hour of the day if you so wish. It also gives you an enormous choice of accommodation – so many that I can't list them here. I rather fancy the grand suites and lovely, spacious rooms of the central Cloister Inn – but there is a pad somewhere for every taste. What is most surprising it works like a dream, with regiments of staff, superb management and chefs that certainly know a Bearnaise. Also worth mentioning is the new Boca Raton Beach Club – latest and mostest.

Boston, Massachusetts

THE COPLEY PLAZA, 138 St. James Avenue, Boston, Massachusetts 02116

- ★ TELEPHONE: 267 5300
- ★ CABLES: no
- ★ TELEX: no
- ★ IN OPERATION: since 1912
- ★ RESERVATIONS: R. M. Brooker, Ltd, Great Britain/American Reservation Systems, U.S.A./C.P. Hotels, Canada
- ★ ROOMS: 460
- ★ SUITES: 35
- ★ RESTAURANTS: 3
- ★ BARS: 3
- ★ DISCOTHEQUE: no – but live music in The Plaza Bar
- ★ SHOPS: 2
- ★ CONFERENCE ROOMS: 22 (50 to 1,100)
- ★ BANQUETING ROOMS: 22 (50 to 1,000)
- ★ STANDARD BEDROOM SIZE: 40 m²

- ★ PRIVATE BALCONIES: no
- ★ SWIMMING POOL: no
- ★ RECREATIONAL ACTIVITIES: no – but special privileges at Boston's most select Country Clubs (by reservation only)
- ★ GARDENS: no
- ★ NO. OF STAFF: 606
- ★ ROOM SERVICE: around the clock
- ★ ORIENTATION: rooms face on to famous Square
- ★ CREDIT CARDS: all major cards
- ★ OWNING COMPANY: Hotels of Distinction Inc
- ★ GENERAL MANAGER: Alan Tremain
- ★ DISTANCE TO SHOPS: walking distance
- ★ DISTANCE FROM AIRPORT: 4 km

The Copley Plaza has been where it is since 1912 but it is a newcomer to our pages. Considering it has been known as 'The Bastion of the Boston Brahmins' for three generations, it is perhaps a little late to be paying our compliments to this highly elegant and very civilised hotel. One English person of quality who got there just before me said it was the only hotel in the United States where they knew how to make tea. It is of course a monument and yet I found some delightful intimate corners. The corridors for instance – everyone knows how dreary hotel corridors can be – are quite charmingly wallpapered and we will also remember it as the only grand hotel we know where books are used as part of the decor scheme in many places and you can retire to the library to read or for tea or conversation. Bedrooms are large, very well furnished, often richly so and the service is quite impeccable – the kind of hotel where the staff instinctively know what sort of person you are. Depending on who you are this may or may not be a good thing. I got the impression that the Copley Plaza *is* 'Borston', with many local gentry to be seen as passing visitors – always a good sign.

THE RITZ-CARLTON HOTEL, 15 Arlington Street, Boston, Massachusetts 02117

- ★ TELEPHONE: (617) 536-5700
- ★ CABLES: Ritzboston
- ★ TELEX: 94-0591

- ★ IN OPERATION: 55 years
- ★ RESERVATIONS: Robert F. Warner, New York

★ ROOMS: 290
★ SUITES: 48
★ RESTAURANTS: 4
★ BARS: 1
★ DISCOTHEQUE: no – but live music in cafe and dining room
★ SHOPS: 7 – dress shop, flowers, barber shop, jeweller, drugstore
★ CONFERENCE ROOMS: 11 (10 to 300)
★ BANQUETING ROOMS: 11 (5 to 250)
★ STANDARD BEDROOM SIZE: 32 m²
★ PRIVATE BALCONIES: no
★ SWIMMING POOL: no
★ GARDENS: no
★ NO. OF STAFF: 465
★ ROOM SERVICE: 06.30–01.00
★ ORIENTATION: rooms face east, north and south
★ CREDIT CARDS: Master Charge, Visa, American Express and Ritz-Carlton
★ OWNING COMPANY: The Ritz-Carlton Hotel Company
★ GENERAL MANAGER: James V. Bennett
★ DISTANCE TO BEACH: 5 km
★ DISTANCE TO SHOPS: walking distance
★ DISTANCE FROM AIRPORT: 4 km

Hotel-fanciers the world over all have their favourites in the great cities and many of them name the Ritz-Carlton as one of the great hotels of our era. From short acquaintance I cannot disagree. This is a noble, elegant, well-bred house which is sensationally comfortable – vast rooms, superb bathrooms and a kind of ageless grace which is quite remarkable combined with a gay, light look. Most bedrooms have a real fireplace with a real logfire in it of an evening if you so wish. The food is real too, a circumstance so rare in the U.S.A. that some visitors never get farther than the Ritz-Carlton. Urbane without being pompous, once they know you and remember you life has the pain quickly removed. One French lady we sent there recently came back rapturous '*Un vrai grand hotel*,' she said.

Chicago, Illinois

THE DRAKE HOTEL, 140 East Walton Place, Chicago, Ill.60611

★ TELEPHONE: (312) 787 2200
★ CABLES: Drakeho
★ TELEX: 910-221-5224
★ IN OPERATION: 59 years
★ RESERVATIONS: Hilton Reservations, worldwide
★ ROOMS: 350 doubles 175 singles
★ SUITES: 101
★ RESTAURANTS: 4 – Avenue One, the Radleigh Rooms, the Cape Cod Room, the Coq d'Or and the Americana Room Coffee Shop
★ BARS: 3
★ DISCOTHEQUE: yes
★ CONFERENCE ROOMS: 20 (15 to 1,100)
★ BANQUETING ROOMS: 20 (10 to 750)
★ SHOPS: 7 – drugstore, beauty salon, florist, jewellery and gift shop,
confectionery shop, liquor store and barber shop
★ STANDARD BEDROOM SIZE: 26 m²
★ PRIVATE BALCONIES: no
★ SWIMMING POOL: no
★ GARDENS: no
★ NO. OF STAFF: 950
★ ROOM SERVICE: 07.00–23.00
★ ORIENTATION: north and south
★ CREDIT CARDS: Visa, Bankamericard, American Express, Diners Club and Drake Credit card
★ OWNING COMPANY: D. H. Venture
★ GENERAL MANAGER: Louis B. Finamore
★ DISTANCE FROM BEACH: walking distance
★ DISTANCE FROM SHOPS: walking distance
★ DISTANCE FROM AIRPORT: 30 km

An English friend who regularly visits Chicago tells me that for him it is the finest hotel in the United States. 'Do you know,' he says, 'that the floor service people inspect your laundry when it comes back, check that everything's there and if there is a button missing, they sew it back on?' Despite its size, it has a feeling of home, has been there for a long time and, oddly enough for a big city hotel, it has what you might call its own beach. One goes from the lobby through what is known to everyone as the North West passage and one is right on Chicago's lakeside sands. Within minutes of the Drake are concert halls, art galleries and the very best shops. Rooms are spacious, all different in style and all of them have pictures, nice knick-knacks and pleasing colour schemes. Everywhere in the hotel are small public rooms where one can sit at ease. In the superbly shining Avenue Restaurant they serve the best food known to me in Chicago and in this cosmopolitan city this is quite a status mark as well as a pleasure. Now the Drake is managed by Hilton and one can only wish it a new lease of life.

Colorado Springs, Colorado

THE BROADMOOR, Box 1439, Lake Avenue & Lake Circle, Colorado Springs Co.80901

- ★ TELEPHONE: (303) 634-7711
- ★ CABLES: no
- ★ TELEX: no
- ★ IN OPERATION: since 1918
- ★ RESERVATIONS: BB & H Hotels Inc, New York/Mr. Robert L. Pfeiffer, Silver Spring/Great Resorts Inc, Chicago
- ★ ROOMS: 510
- ★ SUITES: 50
- ★ RESTAURANTS: 9
- ★ BARS: 9
- ★ DISCOTHEQUE: live music
- ★ SHOPS: 15 – clothing, gifts, antiques, leather goods, drugs etc
- ★ CONFERENCE ROOMS: 37 (up to 2,400)
- ★ BANQUETING ROOMS: 4 (300 to 1,600)
- ★ STANDARD BEDROOM SIZE: 32 m²
- ★ PRIVATE BALCONIES: yes

- ★ SWIMMING POOL: yes – 3, fresh water, 30 m long, 22 m long and kidney-shaped Golf Club Pool
- ★ RECREATIONAL ACTIVITIES: tennis, golf, saunas, skiing, ice skating, boating, skeet and trap
- ★ GARDENS: no
- ★ NO. OF STAFF: 1,150
- ★ ROOM SERVICE: 07.00–22.00
- ★ ORIENTATION: rooms face mountains, lake and city
- ★ CREDIT CARDS: no
- ★ OWNING COMPANY: El Pomar Investment Co
- ★ GENERAL MANAGER: G. Russell Freymuth
- ★ DISTANCE TO SHOPS: 10 minutes
- ★ DISTANCE FROM AIRPORT: 8 km

A hotel with everything? Well, I really cannot think of what else the Broadmoor could have except a name with a happier allusion. This is one of the first of all American self-contained resort hotels and for years visiting foreigners have marvelled at how much could be packed into one place. It is the only hotel I know where indoor tennis courts are actually beautiful as are the three swimming pools. There are three golf courses too, all beautifully combed and manicured. There are nine restaurants, each with its speciality and its own atmosphere. Rooms are vast and the suites are large enough for family and friends too – there is plenty of everything. Broadmoor offers so many activities that one is never bored. It is so vast that it is a full-time job just finding your way around. Service is exceedingly good and very friendly. One tends to stay in after one's arrival which is a mistake because the Colorado Rockies are all around and not to be missed.

Dallas, Texas

FAIRMONT HOTEL, Akard at Ross, Dallas, Texas, 75201

- ★ TELEPHONE: (214) 748-5454
- ★ CABLES: Fairmont
- ★ TELEX: 861 9051
- ★ IN OPERATION: since 1970
- ★ RESERVATIONS: Hotel Representative Inc
- ★ ROOMS: 600
- ★ SUITES: 50
- ★ RESTAURANTS: 3
- ★ BARS: 2
- ★ DISCOTHEQUE: no
- ★ SHOPS: 9
- ★ CONFERENCE ROOMS: 24 (20 to 2,500)
- ★ BANQUETING ROOMS: 24 (20 to 1,900)
- ★ STANDARD BEDROOM SIZE: 35 m²
- ★ PRIVATE BALCONIES: no

- ★ SWIMMING POOL: yes – fresh water, heated
- ★ GARDENS: yes
- ★ NO. OF STAFF: 1,000
- ★ ROOM SERVICE: around the clock
- ★ ORIENTATION: all directions
- ★ CREDIT CARDS: American Express, Master Charge, Diners Club and Carte Blanche
- ★ OWNING COMPANY: Fairmont Hotel Corporation
- ★ GENERAL MANAGER: Julian Abio
- ★ DISTANCE TO SHOPS: walking distance
- ★ DISTANCE FROM AIRPORT: 30 km

Thanks, or perhaps no thanks, to television, everybody the world over knows what Dallas is like. Well, the Fairmont isn't like that and this is a compliment. In this often brash, raucous city with, admittedly, a stunning profile, the Fairmont is elegant, superbly run, very sophisticated and not at all vulgar. It has style. Every one of the king-sized beds has two pillows – one hard and one soft. Towels are best Irish linen and sheets so new one would swear they buy them for each guest. The rooms are among the largest in any American hotel and the whole of Dallas rises around you like some modern fugue. This hotel has probably the highest staff-to-guests ratio in America and it shows, from the minute you step into the lobby to be greeted with the traditional champagne. From then on it's champagne all the way. Decor is ultra modern but carried out with great taste and the food in the three restaurants ranges from American-traditional to the finest Paris can offer.

THE MANSION ON TURTLE CREEK, Turtle Creek Boulevard, Dallas, Texas 75219

★ TELEPHONE: 214-559-2100 (Toll free within Texas 800-442-3408) (Toll free outside of Texas in U.S.A. 800-527-5432)
★ TELEX: 794 946 MANSION DAL
★ IN OPERATION: 1 year
★ RESERVATIONS: direct to hotel
★ ROOMS: 145
★ SUITES: 7 executive suites 3 master suites 2 terrace suites
★ RESTAURANTS: 1
★ BARS: 1 and 1 lounge
★ DISCOTHEQUE: no
★ SHOPS: none
★ CONFERENCE ROOMS: 4 (10 to 200)
★ BANQUETING ROOMS: 4 (10 to 200)
★ STANDARD BEDROOM SIZE: 35 m²
★ SWIMMING POOL: outdoor heated
★ RECREATIONAL ACTIVITIES: pool, jogging,

President's health club and spa within one mile of hotel
★ GARDENS: 1.4 acres of landscaped gardens with courtyard, fountain, oak trees
★ NO. OF STAFF: 300
★ ROOM SERVICE: around the clock
★ ORIENTATION: faces north
★ CREDIT CARDS: American Express, Diners Club, Mastercard, Visa and Carte Blanche
★ OWNING COMPANY: Rosewood Hotels Inc, Dallas, Texas
★ GENERAL MANAGER: Mr. Alexander de Toth
★ DISTANCE TO SHOPS: ¾ km
★ DISTANCE FROM AIRPORT: Dallas/ Ft Worth 30 minutes, Love Field approximately 5 miles

Surprising anyone in the hotel field in the United States is getting rather difficult since this great country now has some of the very finest hostelries in the world. But the arrival on the scene of The Mansion on Turtle Creek did cause a stir – even in Dallas. I recall being on hand shortly after its opening when I saw one well-known American personality (trying to slip past incognito) leaving the hotel shaking his head with a mixture of sadness and envy. And well he might. The Mansion is the latest and the mostest – a superb, smallish hotel centred around what remains of one of those 1920s private palaces of which there are so many in America and the fact that it is run by the '21' people from New York helps. But what matters is the sheer, extravagant beauty of the place – magnificent and often understated decor, superb marble floors and caisson ceilings, furniture made with love, and colours planned by a genius. I especially liked the marvellous Terrace Dining Room but everywhere one's eye is caught by some tiny detail of sheer perfection. Rooms and suites are palatial and quiet and the food, when I was there, was extremely good. Inevitably, only time will tell since hotels, like wine, take a little of that to mature properly. But the first impression is one of delight at seeing what is undoubtedly one of the most beautiful hotels in America.

Hawaii

KAPALUA BAY HOTEL, One Bay Drive, Maui, Hawaii

★ TELEPHONE: 669-5656
★ CABLES: Kapotel
★ TELEX: 6696516
★ IN OPERATION: since October, 1978
★ RESERVATIONS: Regent International Hotels
★ ROOMS: 196
★ SUITES: 3
★ RESTAURANTS: 4 – main dining room, Plantation Veranda, Bay Club and Grill & Bar
★ BARS: 5
★ DISCOTHEQUE: no – but piano and dance music
★ SHOPS: 16 – clothing, sundries, art gallery, sports clothing, men and women speciality shops, 3 jewellery shops, shell shop, artifact shop, realty office, deli and children's shop
★ CONFERENCE ROOMS: 4
★ BANQUETING ROOMS: 2

★ STANDARD BEDROOM SIZE: 39 m^2
★ PRIVATE BALCONIES: yes
★ SWIMMING POOL: yes – fresh water, 23 × 12 m
★ RECREATIONAL ACTIVITIES: 10 tennis courts, 2 golf courses, snorkelling, Hula lessons, lei-making, quilt making and exercise classes
★ GARDENS: yes
★ NO. OF STAFF: 400
★ ROOM SERVICE: 06.45–22.00
★ ORIENTATION: all directions
★ CREDIT CARDS: American Express, Diners Club, Visa and Master Charge
★ OWNING COMPANY: Maui Land and Pineapple Co
★ GENERAL MANAGER: Hans Turnovszky
★ DISTANCE TO BEACH: walking distance
★ DISTANCE TO SHOPS: 9½ km
★ DISTANCE FROM AIRPORT: 6½ km

Undoubtedly one of the finest resort complexes in the whole Pacific, it is not surprising that it should be the brainchild of Laurence Rockefeller (though in this case not owned by him) which is recommendation enough. One is constantly amazed by the American genius for creating resorts that are so well planned, so spacious and so carefully tended that they have no equal in this department. Here, on this superb plantation island of Maui, away from the meretricious glitter of Honolulu, is a haven of rest and good living. There is so much room, both inside and out, that one feels in a special world – green, blue and gold horizons wherever you look and not a hint of speculative building. Apartments are spacious in the extreme, beautifully furnished in a cool and fresh manner and every room has its own ceiling fan – just in case you prefer it to air conditioning. I most certainly do. Public rooms are vast, peopled with graceful and artistic little touches and the service is charmingly polite and attentive. Everything you want is here – golf, tennis, water sports, interesting excursions and, of course, a beach to end all beaches. Everything is quiet and well ordered and that includes the food and drink, specially planned to make you feel good and not greedy.

KONA VILLAGE RESORT, P.O. Box 1299, Kailua-Kona, Hawaii 96740

★ TELEPHONE: (808) 325-5555/ (800) 367-5290
★ CABLES: Coconut
★ TELEX: none
★ IN OPERATION: since 1966

★ RESERVATIONS: New York, Connecticut, New Jersey: (212) 577-3640. Delaware, Mass, N. Hampshire, Penn.: (Areas) 215 & 717) Rhode Isl: (800) 223-6148. All other states: (800) 223-6625. Australia:

20 Willis Av, St Ives 2075, Sydney, Tel. 449-8717. Austria c/o Hotel Bristol, CCA Hotels, Kartnerring, Vienna. London: 49 Brick St, Mayfair, London W1. Tel. (01) 493 6201). Canada: call collect (212) 557-3640. France: c/o Royal Monceau Hotel, 35 Avenue Hoche, 75008 Paris. Italy: Int'l Tourist Reps, Via Giovanni da Procida, Milan 20100. Japan: TVL Centre, Suite 1404-6 Chateau Bunkyo-ku, 113 Tokyo

★ ROOMS: 67
★ SUITES: 14
★ RESTAURANTS: 1 – Hale Moana
★ BARS: 2 – Shipwreck Bar, Talk Story Bar (on beach – weather permitting)
★ DISCOTHEQUE: no – but nightly live entertainment
★ SHOPS: 2 – gift shop, jeweller/handicrafts
★ CONFERENCE ROOMS: 1 (up to 100)
★ BANQUETING ROOMS: none
★ STANDARD BEDROOM SIZE: 27 m² and 20 m²
★ PRIVATE BALCONIES: most rooms
★ SWIMMING POOL: yes – fresh water
★ RECREATIONAL ACTIVITIES: fishing, sailing, scuba diving, snorkelling, outrigger canoes, shuffleboard, volleyball, tennis, ping pong, guided walks, hammocks. Weekly feast with Hawaiin and Polynesian entertainment
★ GARDENS: yes
★ NO. OF STAFF: 110
★ ROOM SERVICE: none
★ ORIENTATION: rooms overlook garden, ocean, lagoon or fishponds
★ CREDIT CARDS: American Express, Diners Club, Carte Blanche, Bankamericard and Master Charge
★ OWNING COMPANY: Cambridge Pacific Inc
★ GENERAL MANAGER: Fred Duerr
★ DISTANCE FROM BEACH: hotel built around beach
★ DISTANCE TO SHOPS: 27 km (Kona)
★ DISTANCE FROM AIRPORT: 10 km

Like they used to say about Los Angeles, it's so nice to know that people who like Honolulu live there or go there! For the rest of us, the much-maligned Hawaiian islands have other treasures – like Kona Village for instance. It is what every Pacific island resort should be like and so often is not: beautiful, simple but practical, gentle and reflective and absolutely natural. The management insists that the speciality of the house is leaving you alone in your own thatched cottage. A few are even built on the water. Others line the magnificent beach and there is no way you can overhear your neighbours. You are on your own. Of course, Kona Village is on what Americans call the Big Island of Hawaii – not Oahu – and just about as far from Waikiki as you could be without swimming home. In addition to this, being American-owned and run, Kona Village has one great plus which is so often lacking in Pacific islands – the bathrooms work, the tableware is clean and if you have to drink water, you can. The food is Technicolour, prepared by people who really know how varied and eye-popping Pacific food can be. As for the place itself, it is built on or close to the site of some ancient Hawaiian sacred grounds. I am full of praise for Kona Village – there are too few places like it.

MAUNA KEA BEACH HOTEL, P.O. Box 218, Kamuela, Hawaii 96743

★ TELEPHONE: (808) 882-7222
★ CABLES: Maunakea Hawaii
★ TELEX: (743) 882-7090
★ IN OPERATION: 16 years
★ RESERVATIONS: Westin Hotels, worldwide
★ ROOMS: 310
★ SUITES: 7
★ RESTAURANTS: 6
★ BARS: 5
★ DISCOTHEQUE: no – live music
★ SHOPS: 7
★ CONFERENCE ROOMS: 2 (20 to 300)
★ BANQUETING ROOMS: 9 (50 to 400)
★ STANDARD BEDROOM SIZE: 21 m²
★ PRIVATE BALCONIES: yes
★ SWIMMING POOL: yes – fresh water
★ RECREATIONAL ACTIVITIES: golf, putting, tennis, snorkelling, surfing, sailing and scuba diving are just some of the activities. There is also horse riding nearby at the hotel's stables
★ GARDENS: yes
★ NO. OF STAFF: 700
★ ROOM SERVICE: 07.00–22.00
★ ORIENTATION: rooms face beach, sea and mountains
★ CREDIT CARDS: none
★ OPERATING COMPANY: Westin Hotels
★ GENERAL MANAGER: Adi W. Kohler

★ DISTANCE TO BEACH: walking distance
★ DISTANCE TO SHOPS: 1 km

★ DISTANCE FROM AIRPORT: 250 km
  (Honolulu)

The legendary Laurence Rockefeller dreamt this one up about twenty years ago and I have the greatest respect for his intelligent vision. The fact that Mauna Kea is now run by another – though very expert company – has not put off the customers and it remains the prototype of the American leisure way of life out there on one of Hawaii's nicer islands. When it comes to beach resorts, Americans should be copied by others – they have the right ideas. In this case, it's 10,000 acres of parkland, planted with half a million tropical plants, beautifully landscaped and next to a superfine white sand beach. There is a golf course (Robert Trent Jones, of course) and so many things to do that you can't possibly get bored. In such a monolith, rooms tend to be rather similar but are very handsomely furnished and with good terraces. The food in the six restaurants has variety enough to please anybody (only the coffee is rather awful). What pleases me most about Mauna Kea above all is the intelligent use it makes of Pacific art forms – there are over 1,000 beautiful artifacts from all over – well chosen, well displayed and of great curiosity value.

Hot Springs, Virginia

THE HOMESTEAD, Hot Springs, Virginia 24445

★ TELEPHONE: (703) 839-5500
★ CABLES: no
★ TELEX: no
★ IN OPERATION: since 1894
★ RESERVATIONS: direct
★ ROOMS: 672
★ SUITES: 82
★ RESTAURANTS: 4
★ BARS: 1
★ DISCOTHEQUE: yes
★ SHOPS: 7
★ CONFERENCE ROOMS: 26 (25 to 1,500)
★ BANQUETING ROOMS: 20 (25 to 1,100)
★ STANDARD BEDROOM SIZE: varying
★ PRIVATE BALCONIES: yes

★ SWIMMING POOL: yes – 3 fresh water
★ RECREATIONAL ACTIVITIES: 3 18-hole golf
  courses, 19 tennis courts, bowling,
  riding and fishing
★ GARDENS: yes
★ NO. OF STAFF: 1,200
★ ROOM SERVICE: around the clock
★ ORIENTATION: south-east, north and
  south
★ CREDIT CARDS: none
★ OWNING COMPANY: Virginia Hot Springs
  Inc
★ GENERAL MANAGER: W. Dan Reichartz
★ DISTANCE FROM AIRPORT: 45 km

Parts of this vast hotel go back to George Washington's time and other bits and pieces have been added by whichever generation of owners felt rich enough to entertain that certain 'folie de grandeur'. The result is without a doubt one of the finest and grandest country resorts in the United States – a place of immense beauty and great charm, with great vistas of colonnades, patios and terraces – all this in 17,000 acres of absolutely gorgeous Virginia countryside. Apart from one new wing whose architecture does not appeal much, The Homestead is one of those places you fall in love with at first sight. What is more (and often rare in North America) the service carried out by a staff who outnumber guests two to one is matchlessly efficient and the food served in any of the four restaurants is good. Breakfasts are a legend. You can play golf (three courses) or just get lost in that splendid landscape of Virginia. The Homestead ought to be a national monument.

Houston, Texas

THE WARWICK HOTEL, Main Street at the Park, Houston, Texas 77005

★ TELEPHONE: (713) 526-1991
★ CABLES: Housintels
★ TELEX: 76-2590
★ IN OPERATION: 18 years

★ RESERVATIONS: Preferred Hotels,
  worldwide
★ ROOMS: 260
★ SUITES: 50

★ RESTAURANTS: 3 – Cafe Vienna, Hunt Room and Warwick Club
★ BARS: 4
★ DISCOTHEQUE: no – but live music
★ SHOPS: 4 – florist, oriental rugs and antiques, jewellery, newspapers and sundries and picture gallery
★ CONFERENCE ROOMS: 7 (35 to 525)
★ BANQUETING ROOMS: 7 (32 to 570)
★ STANDARD BEDROOM SIZE: 35 m²
★ PRIVATE BALCONIES: yes
★ SWIMMING POOL: yes – fresh water, 10 × 13 m
★ RECREATIONAL ACTIVITIES: ladies' and gentlemen's sauna
★ GARDENS: yes
★ NO. OF STAFF: 300
★ ROOM SERVICE: 06.30–02.00
★ ORIENTATION: rooms face all directions
★ CREDIT CARDS: Diners Club, Carte Blanche, Visa, Master Charge and American Express
★ OWNING COMPANY: John W. Mecom Co
★ MANAGING DIRECTOR: Gerald de Schrenck Sill
★ DISTANCE TO SHOPS: 3 km
★ DISTANCE FROM AIRPORT: 34 km

In one edition of this book, I wrote 'If I had to go to the moon via Houston, I wouldn't mind spending my last night in the Warwick's President Suite . . .' One high-born German lady wrote to me and said: 'I have just booked for the moon . . . it can't be more vulgar than this hotel.' I am sorry but I disagree entirely. Like beauty, vulgarity is in the eye of the beholder and as long as one remembers that this is Texas and not gemütlich Vienna, the Warwick is superb. It has borrowed the finest from around the world – Aubusson tapestries, Portuguese marble, panelling from Princess Murat's palaces, Sèvres porcelain and priceless carpets and if, in the Imperial Suite, the dinner service is gold, why, this is Texas and money buys what people want. The rest of the hotel, down to every single detail, is quite ravishingly fresh and beautiful – light, clean colours, lovely textiles, cascades of fresh flowers everywhere and one has the feeling that every morning the master's eye surveys the place. The continental food in the Hunt Room was even better and more soigné than on my last visit and what is more, they had my special brand of Armagnac. The suites may indeed have his-and-hers bathtubs but this, I repeat, is Texas. I have not yet booked my passage to the moon because for the time being I'd rather stay at the Warwick.

Montecito, California

SAN YSIDRO RANCH, 900 San Ysidro Lane, Montecito, California 93108

★ TELEPHONE: (805) 969-5046
★ CABLES: none
★ TELEX: none
★ IN OPERATION: since 1893
★ RESERVATIONS: direct or Mark Allen Travel, London
★ ROOMS: 14
★ SUITES: 24
★ RESTAURANTS: 1 – The Plow & Angel
★ BARS: 1 – The Plow & Angel. Guests can make their own drinks in the Honor Bar until 6.00 p.m. Bar open at pool during busy season
★ DISCOTHEQUE: no – but live entertainment in bar
★ SHOPS: no – but some items available at front desk
★ CONFERENCE ROOMS: 2 – 54 m² (up to 30), 72 m² (up to 50)
★ BANQUETING ROOMS: 1 (up to 30)
★ STANDARD BEDROOM SIZE: 36 m²
★ PRIVATE BALCONIES: most rooms have patios. Deluxe rooms have private jacuzzis
★ SWIMMING POOL: yes – fresh water, heated, 15 m long
★ RECREATIONAL ACTIVITIES: 3 tennis courts, 540 acres of hiking trails, riding and badminton. Croquet available. Golf nearby. Barbecue at poolside on Saturdays
★ GARDENS: flower garden and orange groves
★ NO. OF STAFF: 115
★ ROOM SERVICE: 08.00–10.00, 11.30–14.00 and 18.00–21.00
★ ORIENTATION: rooms overlook gardens, creek or ocean
★ CREDIT CARDS: Visa, Mastercard and American Express.
★ OWNING COMPANY: SYR Corporation. Owners: Susie and Jim Layenson

★ GENERAL MANAGER: Bob DeCock
★ DISTANCE TO BEACH: 3 km (Santa Barbara), 6 km (boat harbour)
★ DISTANCE TO SHOPS: 8 km
★ DISTANCE FROM AIRPORT: 144 km (international), 32 km (local)

This book does not name-drop. It drops hotels. But we had known for a long time that San Ysidro had a guest list second to none, since 1893, too: Galsworthy, Laurence Olivier and Vivien Leigh, Winston Churchill, the Kennedys, etc. And when I got around to visiting it (the world's a big place . . .) I began to understand why. San Ysidro is one of the most private of all private places. The cottages are so remote and hidden away that, as the management says: 'We have to give our room service waiters a compass and a map . . .' It's no joke either – since you get the feeling here that if a guest does not leave his cottage it is because he does not want to meet anyone. How nice. The so-called cottages are nice too – I would have had another word for them maybe since they are all superbly comfortable, all different and very individual, spread across 500 acres of glorious Southern California countryside and well away from noise and bustle. Lots of famous writers have written here and you know what writers are – they do like some choice eating between paragraphs and I suppose even I could write a great novel at San Ysidro where the food, and the wine, are quite superb. They even give you brandy-soaked French toast at breakfast. If you want it that is. Yes, I definitely liked the place – it offers the kind of living you deserve if only the world would let you.

New Orleans, Louisiana

THE PONTCHARTRAIN HOTEL, 2031 St. Charles Avenue, New Orleans, La. 70140

★ TELEPHONE: (504) 524-0581
★ CABLES: no
★ TELEX: 266068 PONT
★ IN OPERATION: 55 years
★ RESERVATIONS: Preferred Hotels Association and Robert F Warner, Inc
★ ROOMS: 53 doubles   10 singles
★ SUITES: 20
★ RESTAURANTS: 2 – Cafe Pontchartrain and Caribbean Room
★ BARS: 1 – The Bayou Bar
★ DISCOTHEQUE: no – but two pianists in The Bayou Bar
★ SHOPS: none
★ CONFERENCE ROOMS: 3 (12 to 65)
★ BANQUETING ROOMS: 3 (12 to 65)
★ STANDARD BEDROOM SIZE: 30 m²
★ PRIVATE BALCONIES: no
★ SWIMMING POOL: no
★ RECREATIONAL FACILITIES: tennis and golf nearby
★ GARDENS: no
★ NO. OF STAFF: 225
★ ROOM SERVICE: 07.00–21.00
★ FURTHER DEVELOPMENTS: Additional conference room space within the next two years to handle top-level board meetings
★ ORIENTATION: on fashionable St. Charles Avenue, two blocks from the Garden District
★ CREDIT CARDS: American Express, Diners Club, Master Charge, Carte Blanche and Bankamericard
★ OWNING COMPANY: Albert Aschaffenburg (privately owned)
★ GENERAL MANAGER: Albert Aschaffenburg (President)
★ DISTANCE TO SHOPS: within walking distance
★ DISTANCE FROM AIRPORT: 15 km

As a one-time Frenchman in voluntary exile on this side of the English Channel for over forty years, I must frankly admit that I have never cared overmuch for New Orleans – a little too much like 'l'ancienne France'. But, as I wrote in the last edition, I am quite willing to return just to stay at the Pontchartrain.

This is a very great hotel indeed because it is itself – individual, the result of having belonged to the same gifted family for near on sixty years. It all shows in the rooms and suites, almost all different, and in the quiet good taste of the smallest item. Nothing jars, nothing shocks and one haughty German count I met there accidentally had to admit that they could not do better back home. Service is faultlessly quiet and attentive – people seem to know what you want or are looking for before you have had time to ask. The lobby is old world in the grand manner but the plumbing, thank goodness, is American. Food in the Caribbean Room turned out to be a very pleasurable experience. In my opinion, this smallish hotel is one of the crown jewels of the American hotel industry. Long may it flourish.

Newport, Rhode Island

INN AT CASTLE HILL, Ocean Drive, Newport, Rhode Island 02840

- ★ TELEPHONE: (401) 849-3800
- ★ CABLES: no
- ★ TELEX: no
- ★ IN OPERATION: 10 years
- ★ RESERVATIONS: direct
- ★ ROOMS: 17 (summer), 10 (winter)
- ★ SUITES: 1
- ★ RESTAURANTS: 1
- ★ BARS: none
- ★ DISCOTHEQUE: piano in lounge, summer Sunday afternoons on lawn
- ★ SHOPS: none
- ★ CONFERENCE ROOMS: 1 (up to 20)
- ★ BANQUETING ROOMS: 2 (20 to 55)
- ★ STANDARD BEDROOM SIZE: 112 m²
- ★ PRIVATE BALCONIES: summer rooms have front porch

- ★ SWIMMING POOL: no
- ★ RECREATIONAL ACTIVITIES: 32 acres of private shoreline for walking, skin diving, beaches
- ★ GARDENS: no
- ★ NO. OF STAFF: 90
- ★ ROOM SERVICE: none
- ★ ORIENTATION: overlooking bay or ocean
- ★ CREDIT CARDS: Visa and Master Charge
- ★ OWNING COMPANY: Inn at Castle Hill Inc
- ★ GENERAL MANAGER: Paul McEnroe (owner)
- ★ DISTANCE TO BEACH: 50 m
- ★ DISTANCE TO SHOPS: 8 km
- ★ DISTANCE FROM AIRPORT: 35 km

I am told that Newport people (very 'iffy-sniffy' as everyone knows . . .) call this sort of place a 'cottage'. Well, well, if it is, I would not mind paying rent for it to the lord of the manor. As it is, all one can do is to spend a night or two there and, as a European, realise once again that there is a good deal more to the American way of life than hamburger stands.

The Inn is absolutely delicious – very grand but not overpowering, filled with quite lovely period pieces often of rare wood and very old vintage and panelled in gleaming chestnut. Floors positively glow when they turn on the Tiffany lamps at night and, quite quickly, you get the feeling that you are going to like this place. That's before you have tasted the food. For myself, it is only in later years that I have come to the conclusion that New England seafood is absolutely tops – sharing Neptunish honours with France's Atlantic coast, and here that seafood is refined into a kind of art form. You just have to taste it to believe it. Outside, the bracing (if that's what they call it . . .) Atlantic roars away and inside the Inn, beautifully managed and serviced, you don't care: let the forces of nature do their worst since you are coccooned in comfortable security.

New York City, New York

THE CARLYLE HOTEL, 35 East 76th Street, New York, N.Y. 10021

- ★ TELEPHONE: 212-744-1600
- ★ CABLES: The Carlyle New York
- ★ TELEX: 620692
- ★ IN OPERATION: 50 years
- ★ RESERVATIONS: direct
- ★ ROOMS: 93
- ★ SUITES: 63
- ★ RESTAURANTS: 2
- ★ BARS: 1
- ★ DISCOTHEQUE: no – but jazz pianist in the bar

- ★ SHOPS: 3 – florist, beauty salon and barber shop
- ★ CONFERENCE ROOMS: 2 (50 to 150)
- ★ BANQUETING ROOMS: 2 (30 to 120)
- ★ STANDARD BEDROOM SIZE: 30 m²
- ★ PRIVATE BALCONIES: yes – some rooms
- ★ SWIMMING POOL: no
- ★ GARDENS: no
- ★ NO. OF STAFF: 300
- ★ ROOM SERVICE: 07.00–01.00

★ ORIENTATION: facing both east side and Central Park from upper floors
★ CREDIT CARDS: American Express, Diners Club, Carte Blanche, Visa and Master Charge
★ OWNING COMPANY: Hotel Carlyle Management Corp
★ GENERAL MANAGER: George Markham
★ DISTANCE TO SHOPS: walking distance
★ DISTANCE FROM AIRPORT: 20 km

The Carlyle was ever a hotel of great distinction, long tradition and a gay and charming decor which is bound to please the most fastidious. Of New York's hotels, it is probably the most intimate and simpatico – people are there to help whatever time of day or night and they are pleased to see you which, even though the guests are among the world's most civilised, is not easy. Service is truly impeccable and nowhere more so than in the two restaurants where the lightness of the decor gives the pleasing appearance of a stage set. Rooms and suites are vast, extremely well and tastefully furnished and so well equipped that one tends to go around to see what could possibly be missing. Food is distinguished and intelligently French and international and the wines are well chosen. The famed Café Carlyle, has been a notable New York rendezvous for a long time. This is a hotel of style, elegance and great quality.

THE MAYFAIR REGENT, 610 Park Avenue, New York, N.Y. 10021

★ TELEPHONE: (212) 288-0800
★ CABLES: Mayrege
★ TELEX: 236257
★ IN OPERATION: 53 years
★ RESERVATIONS: Hotel Representative Inc, worldwide/Regent International Hotels, New Mexico, Tel: 1-800-545-4000
★ ROOMS: 199
★ SUITES: 143
★ RESTAURANTS: 1 – 'Le Cirque'
★ BARS: 1 – 'The Mayfair Lobby Lounge'
★ DISCOTHEQUE: no
★ SHOPS: none
★ CONFERENCE ROOMS: 1 (100)
★ BANQUETING ROOMS: 1 (80)
★ STANDARD BEDROOM SIZE: 86 m^2
★ PRIVATE BALCONIES: no
★ SWIMMING POOL: no
★ GARDENS: no
★ NO. OF STAFF: 186
★ ROOM SERVICE: around the clock
★ ORIENTATION: Park Avenue at 65th Street
★ CREDIT CARDS: American Express, Master Charge, Visa and Diners Club
★ OWNING COMPANY: Regent International Hotels
★ GENERAL MANAGER: Dario Mariotti
★ DISTANCE TO SHOPS: walking distance
★ DISTANCE FROM AIRPORT: 20 km

We all have our weaknesses of course, and our idiosyncrasies – this book is full of the latter. And without denigrating any of the other great New York hostelries, I have a personal confession to make: the Mayfair Regent is the hotel I would choose for myself in this great city. Don't ask me why because the reasons are buried somewhere deep in my subconscious. I just like it, that's all. It's quiet, dignified, comfortable, noiseless and superbly run by a genial management. It also happens to be on Park – for me the only New York avenue worth living on. One does not have a room here – there are only suites, and with closets which in some hotels would pass for bedrooms. Everything is spacious, good-looking, fresh. The new lobby lounge is an absolute delight. As for its restaurant, Le Cirque, one has to make an appointment weeks ahead in order to lunch or dine there on some of the finest French food New York has to offer, served in the grand manner. Nothing is too good or too difficult for this hotel.
One is even given a choice of soap in the bathroom and if it's raining, an umbrella is provided for the foreign visitor who arrived without one – though it must be said that Britishers carry their own to New York (as they do to Khartoum . . .).

THE PIERRE HOTEL, Fifth Avenue and 61st Street, New York, N.Y. 10021

★ TELEPHONE: (212) 838 8000
★ CABLES: Pierreotel
★ TELEX: 12 7426
★ IN OPERATION: 52 years
★ RESERVATIONS: Four Seasons Hotels
★ ROOMS: 315
★ SUITES: 60
★ RESTAURANTS: 2 – Café Pierre and Yellowbird Room
★ BARS: 1

★ DISCOTHEQUE: live music and dancing in the bar

★ SHOPS: 5 – barber shop, beauty salon, florist, news stand and jewellery

★ CONFERENCE ROOMS: 4 (20 to 750)

★ BANQUETING ROOMS: 4 (20 to 850)

★ STANDARD BEDROOM SIZE: 28 m²

★ PRIVATE BALCONIES: no

★ SWIMMING POOL: no

★ GARDENS: none

★ NO. OF STAFF: 550

★ ROOM SERVICE: around the clock

★ ORIENTATION: main facade faces Central Park

★ CREDIT CARDS: American Express, Carte Blanche, Diners Club, Master Charge, Visa

★ OWNING COMPANY: 795 Corporation

★ GENERAL MANAGER: René Sauthier

★ DISTANCE TO SHOPS: walking distance

★ DISTANCE FROM AIRPORT: 20 km

When the Pierre changed management some while back, some people were relieved, others somewhat apprehensive. After all, the Pierre is the Pierre – one of those grand hotels which literally mean New York. I am among those who feel that the Pierre is going to be better than ever under the new regime. Things have only changed marginally so far, which is as it should be since traditions must never be shattered. Decor is faultless, especially since most rooms and suites keep on being remodelled by talented interior artists. The feeling is one of peace and tranquillity and muted pastel shades. It is not often, in a big-city hotel, that someone will telephone you to ask if there is any special service you might require. Now, they even seem to remember the date of your last visit and how you like your breakfast served. This hotel knows that it is the little things that matter. As for the celebrated Café Pierre – may it long endure – it is better than ever.

THE REGENCY HOTEL, 540 Park Avenue (at 61st Street), New York, NY 10021

★ TELEPHONE: (212) 759-4100

★ CABLES: Regency NYK

★ TELEX: 147180

★ IN OPERATION: 20 years

★ RESERVATIONS: Loews Representation International, New York, California, London, Rio de Janeiro, Frankfurt, Tokyo and Toronto

★ ROOMS: 496

★ SUITES: 95

★ RESTAURANTS: 1 – Le Restaurant

★ BARS: 1 cocktail bar

★ DISCOTHEQUE: no

★ SHOPS: 1 news stand

★ CONFERENCE ROOMS: none

★ BANQUETING ROOMS: 3 (10 to 180)

★ STANDARD BEDROOM SIZE: 25 m²

★ PRIVATE BALCONIES: some rooms

★ SWIMMING POOL: no

★ RECREATIONAL ACTIVITIES: none

★ GARDENS: none

★ NO. OF STAFF: 325

★ ROOM SERVICE: around the clock

★ ORIENTATION: mostly south and east

★ CREDIT CARDS: American Express, Carte Blanche, Diners Club, Visa and Master Charge

★ OWNING COMPANY: Loews Corporation

★ MANAGING DIRECTOR: George DeKornfeld

★ DISTANCE TO SHOPS: located in middle of city

★ DISTANCE FROM AIRPORT: 16 km

If only all big-city hotels were like this one. New York is indeed fortunate in having a few of them and the Regency shines among the brightest – a hotel that charms you the minute you walk into its distinguished lobby. This is not one of these built-yesterday-and-awful-tomorrow kind of places but a hotel of great distinction and I am told on good authority that most New York tycoons living on that side of town make it their meeting place. Having partaken of only one dinner (alas) in its restaurant, I can understand why – the food is elegant, very fresh and beautifully served. The same praise goes to the rooms which are among the nicest in New York – rooms without gimmicks but filled with good, solid, well-chosen furniture, extremely good beds and decorated in a civilised, timeless manner which is a pleasure to see. Everything is pin-clean and fresh looking and the service is immediate and silently friendly, especially at breakfast time when one needs all the ego-building one can get. I have known the Regency for a fair long time but it is only now that numerical changes have allowed me to do it justice. It belongs here.

Palm Beach, Florida

THE BREAKERS, South Country Road, Palm Beach, Florida 33480

★ TELEPHONE: 305-655-6611
★ CABLES: no
★ TELEX: 80-3414
★ IN OPERATION: 56 years
★ RESERVATIONS: Robert F. Warner, New York/Morris Associates, London/Hans Regh Associates, Frankfurt
★ ROOMS: 528
★ SUITES: 40
★ RESTAURANTS: 4
★ BARS: 3
★ DISCOTHEQUE: no – but entertainment and dancing nightly
★ SHOPS: 13 – barber shop, beachware, beauty shop, drug store, flower shop, furs, gifts, jewellery and gown shop, menswear, photography, sports, etc
★ CONFERENCE ROOMS: 17 (75 to 1,200)
★ BANQUETING ROOMS: 17 (20 to 900)
★ STANDARD BEDROOM SIZE: 33 to 44 m²
★ PRIVATE BALCONIES: yes – some rooms
★ GARDENS: yes
★ SWIMMING POOL: yes – outdoor salt

water 18½ × 14½ m, and indoor fresh water 8 × 14 m
★ RECREATIONAL ACTIVITIES: tennis, golf, health club and sauna, putting green, driving range, cycling, lawn bowling, shuffleboard, croquet, horse-shoes, children's playground, also fishing, sailing, water skiing and snorkelling all arranged nearby
★ NO. OF STAFF: 1,200
★ ROOM SERVICE: 07.00–23.30
★ ORIENTATION: directly on the ocean to the east with the main façade facing west
★ CREDIT CARDS: Master Charge, Bankamericard, Visa and American Express
★ OWNING COMPANY: Flagler System Inc
★ PRESIDENT: Stayton Addison
★ DISTANCE TO BEACH: on the beach
★ DISTANCE TO SHOPS: 1½ km
★ DISTANCE FROM AIRPORT: 6 km

In olden days American tycoons used to arrive at The Breakers in their own railroad cars. Now all you need is the wish to arrive, a Cadillac or Lincoln, and there you are, in one of America's oldest and most elegant resort hotels because that is what The Breakers is. It's been around so long – by American standards – that it no longer has to advertise. Everybody wants to come here but only a few need apply because Palm Beach is Palm Beach and not for the common herd. If you are feeling at all common give it a miss. There are Florentine ceilings, Venetian arches, Roman courtyards, Flemish tapestries and excellent American bedrooms that are attractively periodless. There are magnificent vistas of well-upholstered corridors and terraces with moulded ceilings and antique American furniture which does not seem at all out of place. It is a beachside hotel with all the sophistication of a grand hotel. There is so much to do – swimming pools, golf, tennis and beachsports that you end up doing just what you like. One dresses for dinner in some truly splendiferous restaurants where the food sometimes matches the decor and, all in all, this is a hotel for civilised people. It is a mere credit card's throw away from Worth Avenue where Cartier, Tiffany and the rest are waiting for you.

San Antonio, Texas

FOUR SEASONS HOTEL, 555 South Alamo, San Antonio, Texas 78205

★ TELEPHONE: (512) 229-1000
★ CABLES: no
★ TELEX: 767-381
★ IN OPERATION: since 1979
★ RESERVATIONS: Central Reservations for Four Seasons Hotels Ltd, New York, Toronto, London, etc
★ ROOMS: 250
★ SUITES: 8

★ RESTAURANTS: 2 – The Anaqua Restaurant and Restoration Bar and Grill located in courtyard area
★ BARS: 2 – Lobby Bar and Palm Terrace Cocktail Lounge
★ DISCOTHEQUE no – but live music
★ SHOPS: 1 – gift shop
★ CONFERENCE ROOMS: 11 (from 54 m² to 126 m² (30 to 400))

★ BANQUETING ROOMS: 1 which divides into 3 of 180 m² (30 to 400)
★ STANDARD BEDROOM SIZE: 24 m²
★ PRIVATE BALCONIES: most rooms
★ SWIMMING POOL: yes – heated, fresh water
★ RECREATIONAL ACTIVITIES: 2 tennis courts, well-equipped exercise rooms with saunas. Golf packages available by special arrangement with local country club. Complimentary bicycles

★ GARDENS: yes
★ NO. OF STAFF: 240
★ ROOM SERVICE: around the clock
★ CREDIT CARDS: American Express, Diners Club, Carte Blanche, Visa, Mastercard and Four Seasons
★ OWNING COMPANY: Four Seasons Hotels Ltd, of Toronto, Canada
★ GENERAL MANAGER: John Indrieri
★ DISTANCE TO SHOPS: walking distance
★ DISTANCE FROM AIRPORT: 13 km

With due respect to all those who live there, J.R. can keep Dallas – I'll have San Antonio, the nicest, most friendly and most civilised city in Texas. And if I get back there, my address will be the Four Seasons. Having had my share of great American hotels, I was amazed to see how different this one could be: a gently palatial place, full of lovely indoor vegetation, a most unusual and graceful lobby and the whole place obviously furnished by someone who decided that this piece would look good here, that piece there, and so on. None of your computer-planned decor here. It is nicely Hispanic (after all, the Alamo is only down the street) but it also seems to have that Tex-Mex mixture which happens to be so successful in San Antonio, a place where people have time to live and time to stroll along their city-bound river. Rooms are ample, fresh and beautifully kept and service is smiling and quick. Since San Antonio is food-conscious, so is this hotel – the menus I had were beyond reproach. They also shine your shoes, give you a newspaper and are ready day and night to help you with any odd wish. That's nice.

San Francisco, California

THE FAIRMONT HOTEL AND TOWER, Atop Nob Hill, San Francisco, California 94106

★ TELEPHONE: (415) 772-5000
★ CABLES: Fairmont
★ TELEX: 372 6002
★ IN OPERATION: 73 years
★ RESERVATIONS: Hotel Representative Inc/R. M. Brooker Ltd
★ ROOMS: 600
★ SUITES: 62
★ RESTAURANTS: 6
★ BARS: 8
★ DISCOTHEQUE: yes – with casual music in the Tonga Room, big band entertainment in the Venetian Room and jazz dancing in the New Orleans Room
★ SHOPS: 11 – fine arts, jewellery, clothing, pharmacy, gifts, cigarettes and liquor
★ CONFERENCE ROOMS: 20 (12 to 2,500)

★ BANQUETING ROOMS: 20 (25 to 1,900)
★ STANDARD BEDROOM SIZE: 30 m²
★ PRIVATE BALCONIES: yes
★ SWIMMING POOL: no
★ GARDENS: there is a main garden area in the interior of the hotel and one in the front
★ NO. OF STAFF: 1,100
★ ROOM SERVICE: around the clock
★ ORIENTATION: rooms face gardens and city
★ CREDIT CARDS: American Express, Visa, Diners Club and Master Charge
★ OWNING COMPANY: Fairmont Hotel Co
★ GENERAL MANAGER: Herman Wiener
★ DISTANCE TO BEACH: 10–12 km
★ DISTANCE TO SHOPS: 500 m
★ DISTANCE FROM AIRPORT: 25 km

Other San Francisco hotels can be excellent too but the Fairmont has two things no one can steal – its address and its rooftop restaurant, the Fairmont Crown which, if you like a thrill, you can reach via the glassbubble of the outside elevator. Up there is a wide-screen view of San Francisco. Those who have weak heads for heights should avoid this conveyance as the sensation produced in the hardiest is that of suddenly walking the high-wire in a circus with no safety-net. But such attractions should not detract from the fact that the Fairmont is a very smart hotel and has been for a long time. It is rich, varied, extremely well run and one of those truly sophisticated places.

They give you your own alarm clock. Everywhere are beautiful carpets, handsome furniture, very good lighting and decor that seems to change as one moves along. Rooms are large and very comfortable, with lovely beds and everything you might wish for. The food is among the best hotel cuisine in a city which is not short of good eating places. You can eat American, French, Polynesian, Japanese – what you will – and it is all served with great distinction.

FOUR SEASONS-CLIFT HOTEL, 495 Geary, San Francisco, Ca. 94102

- ★ TELEPHONE: (415) 775-4700
- ★ CABLES: no
- ★ TELEX: 340647
- ★ IN OPERATION: 66 years
- ★ RESERVATIONS: direct
- ★ ROOMS: 379
- ★ SUITES: 84
- ★ RESTAURANTS: 1 – the French Room
- ★ BARS: 2 – the Redwood Room and Lobby Bar
- ★ DISCOTHEQUE: pianist in the Redwood Room, classical guitarist in Lobby Bar
- ★ SHOPS: none
- ★ CONFERENCE ROOMS: 5 (20 to 225)
- ★ BANQUETING ROOMS: 5 (20 to 150)
- ★ STANDARD BEDROOM SIZE: 81 m²
- ★ PRIVATE BALCONIES: no
- ★ SWIMMING POOL: no
- ★ GARDENS: no
- ★ NO. OF STAFF: 350
- ★ ROOM SERVICE: around the clock
- ★ ORIENTATION: faces west
- ★ CREDIT CARDS: Amexco, Visa, Master Charge, Bankamericard and Diners Club
- ★ OWNING COMPANY: Four Seasons
- ★ GENERAL MANAGER: Paul M. G. Astbury
- ★ DISTANCE TO BEACH: 5 km
- ★ DISTANCE TO SHOPS: walking distance
- ★ DISTANCE FROM AIRPORT: 20 km

I have long had two firm favourites in this lovely city of San Francisco and when one very well travelled hotel man told me that he always stayed elsewhere, I decided on my last visit to try 'elsewhere' – the Four Seasons-Clift – and I must admit that, in a different way, it compares favourably with my other two friends. It is an exceedingly refined and elegant hotel – good taste going right through from the furniture to the silver. Rooms and suites are very large indeed – an ordinary room here would be called an apartment elsewhere – and they are all delightfully furnished with good, solid, unpretentious items – good sofas, nice carpets, immaculate curtains. Everything is in pleasing pastel shades, restful and pleasant, with an occasional flash of brilliant colour, and in general, like most good American hotels, it pays great attention to design-cum-practicality. One is never short of storage space or bathroom space. Service is quiet, efficient and totally unflappable, and I thought that the food in the French Room was of the highest standard and served with an appropriate quiet elegance.

THE STANFORD COURT HOTEL, 905 California Street, San Francisco, California 94108

- ★ TELEPHONE: (415) 989-3500
- ★ CABLES: Stancourt
- ★ TELEX: 34-0899
- ★ IN OPERATION: 8 years
- ★ RESERVATIONS: Preferred Hotels Association, Illinois
- ★ ROOMS: 402
- ★ SUITES: 34
- ★ RESTAURANTS: 2 – Fournou's Ovens and Cafe Potpourri
- ★ BARS: 2
- ★ DISCOTHEQUE: no
- ★ SHOPS: 6
- ★ CONFERENCE ROOMS: 2 (30 to 150)
- ★ BANQUETING ROOMS: 2 (60 to 450)
- ★ STANDARD BEDROOM SIZE: 20 m²
- ★ PRIVATE BALCONIES: no
- ★ SWIMMING POOL: no
- ★ RECREATIONAL ACTIVITIES: golf and tennis close by
- ★ GARDENS: no
- ★ NO. OF STAFF: 375
- ★ ROOM SERVICE: 07.00–24.00
- ★ ORIENTATION: facing California Street and San Francisco Bay
- ★ CREDIT CARDS: American Express, Diners Club, Master Charge, Bankamericard and Visa
- ★ OWNING COMPANY: Royal Stanford Hotel Co

★ GENERAL MANAGER: William F.
  Wilkinson

★ DISTANCE TO SHOPS: 5 minutes' walk

★ DISTANCE FROM AIRPORT: 52 km

Like people, hotels grow, change, mature, develop a very particular personality. Stanford Court is the pride and joy of every discriminating traveller passing through that lovely city of San Francisco and, in its first few years (about the lifetime of this guide), it has attracted more praise, more awards and more bouquets than almost any other hotel in North America and, what is more, it is always changing in small but subtle ways. Corseted in one of those massive Nob Hill mansions of bygone years, Stanford Court is virtually peerless, without reproach. Here you don't even pay for your local telephone calls and while the management don't encourage you to steal their coathangers, they really don't mind all that much. You enter through a discreet courtyard and immediately you know that one man's genius created this place – there are entire walls of Portuguese azulejos, a French provincial restaurant, Fournou's Ovens which even chauvinistic Frenchmen respect, great Baccarat chandeliers and acres of shining marble. Bedrooms are immaculately maintained, very practical and beautifully conceived down to the minutest details. When you eat there you discover that in this department too, intelligence and wit reign as well as good taste – nothing is overdone. Service is the same – they brush your clothes, replace buttons and even get you a new tube of toothpaste when it appears you need it. And when, as the odd Briton, you return around mid-afternoon, the concierge greets you by name, gives you your key and asks whether you would like China or Indian tea.

Santa Fe, New Mexico

RANCHO ENCANTADO, Rt. 4, Box 57C, Santa Fe, New Mexico 87501

★ TELEPHONE: (505) 982-3537

★ CABLES: no

★ TELEX: no

★ IN OPERATION: 15 years

★ RESERVATIONS: direct

★ ROOMS: 36 rooms and suites

★ RESTAURANTS: 1

★ BARS: 1

★ DISCOTHEQUE: no

★ SHOPS: supplies obtainable from Club
  House

★ CONFERENCE ROOMS: 1 (137 m^2)

★ BANQUETING ROOMS: 1 (137 m^2)

★ STANDARD BEDROOM SIZE: 121 m^2

★ PRIVATE BALCONIES: most rooms

★ SWIMMING POOL: yes – fresh water,
  heated, 295 m^2

★ RECREATIONAL ACTIVITIES: tennis,
  billiards, riding and a clubhouse with
  cocktail lounge. Golf available nearby

★ GARDENS: yes

★ NO. OF STAFF: 55

★ ROOM SERVICE: none

★ ORIENTATION: most rooms are
  south/south-west

★ CREDIT CARDS: American Express,
  Master Charge, Visa, Diners Club and
  Carte Blanche

★ OWNING COMPANY: Betty Egan (owner)

★ GENERAL MANAGER: John T. Egan

★ DISTANCE TO SHOPS: 12 km

★ DISTANCE FROM AIRPORT: 112 km

I have not yet met anyone who, having been to Santa Fe, did not fall in love with it at first sight – surely the most charming and most unusual state capital in the United States: American and yet Spanish, traditional and yet venturesome and absolutely beautiful, right there in the middle of Indian America. As for the Rancho Encantado, its long list of return guests shows its pedigree. It is a cheerful, often amusing place run by a very gifted family and you feel that you are a guest in some kind of Western houseparty. It's mostly traditional adobe cottages and buildings, all of them decorated in genuine Indian-Spanish-American style with beautiful tiles and superb Indian rugs, all in very good taste. There are lovely gardens, lots of let's-go land around it and a magnificent swimming pool. The food at Rancho Encantado is well known to most American gourmets as being well above the average and is often innovative and different. All around are some of the greatest Indian pueblos of America and, over it all, the noble profile of the Sangre de Cristo mountains. A marvellous place to be in if you want to get to know that glorious South West.

Saranac Lake, New York

THE POINT, Star Route, Saranac Lake, New York 12983

★ TELEPHONE: (518) 891-5674
★ CABLES: no
★ TELEX: no
★ IN OPERATION: 2 years
★ RESERVATIONS: direct
★ ROOMS: 8
★ SUITES: none
★ RESTAURANTS: 1
★ BARS: there is no bar – this is a private house
★ DISCOTHEQUE: no
★ SHOPS: no
★ CONFERENCE ROOMS: 1 (up to 20)
★ BANQUETING ROOMS: no
★ STANDARD BEDROOM SIZE: 30 m² to 55 m²
★ PRIVATE BALCONIES: some rooms have terraces
★ SWIMMING POOL: no – but private beach on lake

★ RECREATIONAL ACTIVITIES: canoe trips, boating, hiking, tennis, skiing (downhill and cross-country), golf, sailing, skating, badminton, billiards, ping-pong and croquet
★ GARDENS: yes
★ NO. OF STAFF: 9–11
★ ROOM SERVICE: none
★ ORIENTATION: views of mountains in all directions
★ CREDIT CARDS: no
★ OWNING COMPANY: privately owned
★ GENERAL MANAGERS: Edward G. L. Carter and James W. Myhre
★ DISTANCE TO SHOPS: 15 km
★ DISTANCE TO BEACH: on the property
★ DISTANCE TO AIRPORT: domestic 15 km, international 100 km

This is undoubtedly one of the two or three oddest places listed in this book. It is not a hotel (heaven forbid) and not even a guesthouse since the only guests there are people whom the owner, Ted Carter, actually likes. It's really like being invited to a very special houseparty by a man who insists on keeping Armagnac in his boathouse and Vuitton suitcases in the closets. Originally The Point was what they call here in the Adirondacks a 'camp'. A log-cabin if you like, except that in this one, having been built by William Rockefeller in the early thirties, one suspects that the only thing that held the logs together were the French Impressionists. The feeling has not changed much – only the people. It's way up New York State on the shores of Upper Saranac Lake – a jewel if ever there was one – and you arrive in a kind of Cleopatra's barge well stocked with liquids and little titbits and you sail right into the boathouse where sleek speedboats have come to rest. Then come the surprises: The Point is absolutely, but absolutely lovely, a place in which everything you see is total perfection of taste with priceless pieces scattered about in glorious extravagance. The Great Hall is so 'great', with its massive fireplaces and vast couches, that you can't stop looking. Bedrooms are vast, and just the same as the rest of the place – deliciously odd, amusingly grand and yet intimate because this is a lived-in place. One eats with one's host and his co-owner, James Myrhe, a young man who is one of the finest cooks I have ever met, who produces great food like a conjurer, and everything comes on Carter's own family Meissen (eighteenth century and worth 500 dollars a plate . . .). The talk is great, the wine superb and the whole place sparkles with wit and charm. Outside, the great dark green woods of the Adirondacks frame a lake of pure silver and the air is like vintage Pommery. Some of the time you sail, trek, go canoeing or just sit and reflect on your good fortune at just being there.

Scottsdale, Arizona

MARRIOTT'S CAMELBACK INN, P.O. Box 70, 5402 E. Lincoln Dr., Scottsdale, Arizona 85252

★ TELEPHONE: 602 948 1700
★ CABLES: no
★ TELEX: 910 950 1198
★ IN OPERATION: since 1935

★ RESERVATIONS: Marriott Toll Free Reservations, U.S.A./Supranational, London, Paris, Rome and West Germany

★ ROOMS: 400
★ SUITES: 25
★ RESTAURANTS: 3 – Navajo Room, Chaparral and North Pool Buffet
★ BARS: 2 – Oasis and La Cantina
★ DISCOTHEQUE: live music nightly
★ SHOPS: 3
★ CONFERENCE ROOMS: 20 (10 to 1,500)
★ BANQUETING ROOMS: 20 (10 to 1,500)
★ STANDARD BEDROOM SIZE: 46 m²
★ PRIVATE BALCONIES: yes
★ SWIMMING POOL: yes – 2 fresh water
★ RECREATIONAL ACTIVITIES: 10 tennis courts (5 floodlit), 2 18-hole golf courses, 9-hole pitch and putt course, 2 whirlpools, ping pong, shuffleboard, putting green, bicycling, hiking, horse riding and Exer-Trail
★ GARDENS: yes
★ NO. OF STAFF: 600
★ ROOM SERVICE: 07.00–22.00
★ ORIENTATION: all rooms face gardens
★ CREDIT CARDS: American Express, Visa, Carte Blanche, Diners Club and Master Charge
★ OWNING COMPANY: Marriott Hotels Inc
★ GENERAL MANAGER: Dave Rolston
★ DISTANCE TO SHOPS: 5–8 km
★ DISTANCE FROM AIRPORT: 30 km

In my not very humble opinion, anyone who has not seen Arizona has not lived. And anyone who has not tried the grandeur that is Scottsdale·is missing something. You must visit this amazing hostelry which combines the best of the West's free and easy life with civilised luxury – a very rare mixture. Camelback Inn is spread out over unending acres of lush gardens, with the desert in the background, and its Mexican-type casas are very large indeed, often with a living room and a patio and own entrance. They are delightfully cool, very clean and, though furnished 'en serie' the apartments are practical and attractive. Considering the distances, service is remarkably good. What impresses about Camelback Inn is that instead of providing simply wholesome but plain American fare, its food is amazingly varied, served with the touch of the expert on superb table settings. Then there are all the things you can do – swim, sunbathe, play golf, tennis, hiking and riding in the desert and the famous 'Camelback Caravans' which although somewhat showbiz do recapture some of the old adventurous spirit.

Tucson, Arizona

ARIZONA INN, 2200 E. Elm Street, Tucson, Arizona 85719

★ TELEPHONE: (602) 325-1541
★ CABLES: Az Inn-Tuc
★ TELEX: 165523
★ IN OPERATION: 52 years
★ RESERVATIONS: direct
★ ROOMS: 86
★ SUITES: 7
★ RESTAURANTS: 1 main dining room, pool dining room (winter season)
★ BARS: 1 main bar, pool bar (winter season)
★ DISCOTHEQUE: pianist only
★ SHOPS: 1
★ CONFERENCE ROOMS: 5
★ BANQUETING ROOMS: 5 (60 to 205)
★ STANDARD BEDROOM SIZE: all rooms are different but spacious
★ PRIVATE BALCONIES: 40 with patios
★ SWIMMING POOL: yes – outdoor, fresh water and heated
★ RECREATIONAL ACTIVITIES: tennis courts, putting-green, croquet and table tennis. Riding and golf nearby
★ GARDENS: 14 acres of lawns and gardens
★ NO. OF STAFF: 100
★ ROOM SERVICE: 07.00–21.00
★ ORIENTATION: 60 rooms on the ground floor
★ CREDIT CARDS: American Express, Carte Blanche, Master Charge and Visa
★ OWNING COMPANY: family owned
★ GENERAL MANAGER: Robert Minerich
★ DISTANCE TO SHOPS: 3 km
★ DISTANCE FROM AIRPORT: 16 km

By now most of my American friends know that I am nuts about Tucson and I would go anywhere to sing its praises. Cheerful, friendly and civilised in the Spanish-American tradition. And, as they say, the air is so dry it crackles. But it was only on my last visit that I discovered that Tucson also has the Arizona Inn which I swear is the nicest pad in this part of the world. First of all it is a hotel that does not look like one – a sort of cluster of Indian-Spanish-Western adobe buildings ranged around a manicured lawn, lovely gardens and gorgeous swimming pool. The rooms are individually decorated and furnished with great taste and as for the bar, with its Audubons on the walls, it even makes the tequila taste better. But don't let anyone run away with the idea that the Arizona Inn is just another one of those 'simpatico' Western hostelries. It is very high class indeed, very choice, with superb service, cheerful people around and food which is the best within a hundred miles. It is also a very 'private' hotel: you can be yourself and its only rules are those dictated by good taste and decency. And all around is glorious Arizona – mountains and deserts, little pioneer towns, Spanish mission churches and a feeling of personal freedom and wellbeing which is very rare. Don't miss the Arizona Inn – it's the South West as it should be.

TANQUE VERDE RANCH, RT8 Box 66, Tucson, Arizona, 85710

★ TELEPHONE: 602-296-6275
★ CABLES: no
★ TELEX: no
★ IN OPERATION: since 1860
★ RESERVATIONS: direct
★ ROOMS: 60
★ SUITES: 15
★ RESTAURANTS: 3 – main dining room, Mexican Room and Pinata Room
★ BARS: 1
★ DISCOTHEQUE: no
★ SHOPS: 1
★ CONFERENCE ROOMS: 3 (25 to 125)
★ BANQUETING ROOMS: 3 (25 to 125)
★ STANDARD BEDROOM SIZE: 75 m²
★ PRIVATE BALCONIES: yes

★ SWIMMING POOL: yes – fresh water, 1 indoor and 1 outdoor
★ RECREATIONAL ACTIVITIES: tennis, jacuzzi, saunas and exercise room, horse riding, pack trips, nature hikes and bird banding
★ GARDENS: yes
★ NO. OF STAFF: 65
★ ROOM SERVICE: at special request
★ ORIENTATION: desert and mountain views
★ CREDIT CARDS: none
★ OWNING COMPANY: Arizona Sunshine Ranches
★ GENERAL MANAGER: Bob Cote
★ DISTANCE TO SHOPS: 6 km
★ DISTANCE FROM AIRPORT: 40 km

When general manager Bob Cote and I met again last year, we compared notes. Yes, he too had had letters from people suggesting that this travel fellow in lil'ole' England had taken leave of his senses by putting a dude ranch among the best hotels in the world . . . Well, neither of us has changed his mind. Bob still runs one of the fun-most places in the West and I still think Tanque Verde is a winner. As I wrote in the last edition, this is part of our folk memory: 25,000 acres of absolutely virgin Arizona open range, a genuine and original Western ranch with horses everywhere, chuck waggons, saddle rooms, sing-songs and bar-b-cues, fellows in checked shirts and wide hats, the swish of leather boots and bedrooms one could hold a convention in. All this and Tombstone a pistol shot away – what more could one want? It is guaranteed to turn the shyest city gent into Bill Cody in a short while and even the horses know a dude bottom when they feel one. And yes, people still slap me on the back and say 'Howdy, pardner'. I wish they would not. Makes my teeth rattle. Tanque Verde? Just take me back there.

Washington, D.C.

FAIRFAX HOTEL, 2100 Massachusetts Avenue, N.W., Washington D.C. 20008

★ TELEPHONE: 293-2100
★ CABLES: no
★ TELEX: TWX 7108229228
★ IN OPERATION: 52 years
★ RESERVATIONS: Hotel Representative Inc
★ ROOMS: 165
★ SUITES: 16
★ RESTAURANTS: 1

★ BARS: 1
★ DISCOTHEQUE: no – but piano music in bar
★ SHOPS: none
★ CONFERENCE ROOMS: 3 (10 to 60)
★ BANQUETING ROOMS: 3 (10 to 100)
★ STANDARD BEDROOM SIZE: 28 m²
★ PRIVATE BALCONIES: no

★ SWIMMING POOL: no
★ GARDENS: no
★ NO. OF STAFF: 200
★ ROOM SERVICE: around the clock
★ ORIENTATION: north-west
★ FURTHER DEVELOPMENTS: the addition of 105 rooms and 5 banqueting rooms

★ CREDIT CARDS: American Express, Master Charge, Bankamericard, Diners Club and Visa
★ OWNING COMPANY: John B. Coleman Co
★ GENERAL MANAGER: Paul Seligson
★ DISTANCE TO SHOPS: 2 blocks
★ DISTANCE FROM AIRPORT: 16 km

No doubt there are some bad hotels in Washington D.C. Happily, I don't know them. The two I do know are quite splendid and one of them, the redecorated Fairfax, shows a happy blend of tradition, elegance and modernity which does honour to the American capital. It has a colonial – early American – dignity that is a pleasure to see – fine furniture, mostly period, beautifully kept fresh and clean carpets of high quality, an eye for detail which is everywhere. I noticed for instance that messages were relayed twice – once with your key and once in your room – not just shoved under the door but placed in a prominent position. Flowers are always fresh and there are even green plants in your bathroom. Both the restaurant and the bar are traditional American and highly enjoyable.

THE MADISON HOTEL, 15th and M Streets, NW, Washington D.C.20005

★ TELEPHONE: (202) 862-1600
★ CABLES: The Madison
★ TELEX: 64245
★ RESERVATIONS: Hotel Representative Inc
★ ROOMS: 362
★ SUITES: 33
★ RESTAURANTS: 4
★ BARS: 2
★ DISCOTHEQUE: no
★ SHOPS: 2
★ CONFERENCE ROOMS: 10 (50 to 400)
★ BANQUETING ROOMS: 10 (24 to 400)
★ STANDARD BEDROOM SIZE: 28 m^2

★ PRIVATE BALCONIES: no
★ SWIMMING POOL: no
★ GARDENS: no
★ NO. OF STAFF: 370
★ ROOM SERVICE: 07.00–24.00
★ ORIENTATION: north-east
★ CREDIT CARDS: American Express, Master Charge, Bankamericard, Carte Blanche and Diners Club
★ OWNING COMPANY: privately owned
★ PROPRIETOR: Marshall B. Coyne
★ DISTANCE TO SHOPS: 500 m
★ DISTANCE FROM AIRPORT: 34 km

Being in the American capital, the Madison always seems filled with foreign ministers, ambassadors and other peripatetic bigwigs and, as everyone knows, they don't go for the second best. This is a very American and yet international hotel, extremely quiet and refined and run by the people who own it. It shows in every small detail, down to the very personalised service. One never has to mention one's name twice. Breakfast arrives the way one likes it *and* with the newspaper the guest had on his first morning. Rooms are very spacious, beautifully furnished and carpeted and almost totally noiseless. You are never disturbed once you have closed your door. Elegant and tasteful, the food is clearly an un-American activity and the wine-list would not disgrace a grand hotel in France.

White Sulphur Springs, Virginia

THE GREENBRIER, White Sulphur Springs, West Virginia 24986

★ TELEPHONE: (304) 536-1110
★ CABLES: no
★ TELEX: no
★ IN OPERATION: 204 years
★ RESERVATIONS: direct
★ ROOMS: 588 doubles 27 singles
★ SUITES: 85

★ RESTAURANTS: 6
★ BARS: 5
★ DISCOTHEQUE: yes – and live music for dancing
★ SHOPS: 18
★ CONFERENCE ROOMS: 25 (10 to 2,000)
★ BANQUETING ROOMS: 20 (26 to 1,200)

★ STANDARD BEDROOM SIZE: 22 m²
★ PRIVATE BALCONIES: yes – some rooms
★ SWIMMING POOL: yes – fresh water,
  indoor 30 × 12 m and outdoor
  36 × 14 m
★ GARDENS: yes
★ RECREATIONAL FACILITIES: twenty tennis
  courts, three 18-hole golf courses,
  paddle tennis, bowling, horse riding,
  carriage rides, spa, jogging and hiking
  trails, fishing, trap and skeet, putting,
  shuffleboard, billiards, table tennis,
bicycling, ice skating and cross-country
skiing
★ NO. OF STAFF: 1,400
★ ROOM SERVICE: 07.00–24.00
★ ORIENTATION: rooms face all directions
★ CREDIT CARDS: Master Charge, Visa and
  American Express
★ OWNING COMPANY: CSX Inc
★ GENERAL MANAGER: William C. Pitt
  (President and Managing Director)
★ DISTANCE FROM AIRPORT: 15 km

This hotel, one of America's grandest resorts, has won the country's prestigious hotel award no less than 16 times. I have visited it twice and greatly admire it as being the perfect blend of the old world and the new. Here are 6,500 acres of marvellously green Allegheny mountainscape, trails galore, riding, ice skating, bowling, tennis courts and swimming pools both inside and out. It's a vast place and it certainly takes an army to run it. Decor is traditional Southern American furnishings that are quite perfect everywhere both in quality and in upkeep. Originating as a spa, it still runs a health farm side as well as a quite famous school of cookery. Despite its size, Greenbrier has tranquillity and intimacy and is in such a healthy situation that one feels better just being there. Rooms and suites are quite large and very well designed and some have marvellous breakfast balconies overlooking the peaceful green hills. There is so much variety in restaurants and bars that if you stay a week your experiences will all be different. You can also play golf by the way – three 18-hole courses.

YEMEN ARAB REPUBLIC

Sana'a

SANA'A SHERATON HOTEL, P.O. Box 2467, Sana'a,
Yemen Arab Republic

★ TELEPHONE: 221000-237500/8
★ CABLES: no
★ TELEX: 2222 SHSAN YE
★ IN OPERATION: since February, 1981
★ RESERVATIONS: Sheraton Hotels or
  Sheraton Reservation Offices
★ ROOMS: 300
★ SUITES: 6
★ RESTAURANTS: 4 – Coffee Shop, Night
  Club, Poolside Restaurant, Speciality
  Restaurant
★ BARS: 1
★ DISCOTHEQUE: no – but live music
★ SHOPS: 4 – sports, boutique, travel
  agent, pharmacy
★ CONFERENCE ROOMS: 5 – multi-function
  rooms accommodating from 40 to 550
  persons with multi-lingual translation
  facilities and projector booth
★ BANQUETING ROOMS: 5 (40 to 550)

★ STANDARD BEDROOM SIZE: 24 m²
★ PRIVATE BALCONIES: no
★ SWIMMING POOL: yes – fresh water,
  Olympic size
★ RECREATIONAL ACTIVITIES: 2 (floodlit)
  tennis courts, sports and health centre
  with separate gymnasiums, sauna and
  massage
★ GARDENS: yes
★ NO. OF STAFF: 338
★ ROOM SERVICE: around the clock
★ ORIENTATION: all rooms have mountain
  view
★ CREDIT CARDS: all major credit cards
★ OWNING COMPANY: Arab Hotels
  Company, Kuwait
★ GENERAL MANAGER: J. Halbherr
★ DISTANCE TO SHOPS: 5 km
★ DISTANCE FROM AIRPORT: 10 km

The first time I travelled to that little-known and yet amazingly beautiful country, North Yemen, I spent some of my time in a tent and the rest of the time in ancient Arabian caravanserais whose roofs leaked abominably. I did not mind so much – after all the Queen of Sheba wasn't far away. Henceforth, whenever people tell me that hotel chains don't really look after travellers in strange places I shall point with some pride to the Sheraton Corporation's pluck in building a modern hotel on the outskirts of Sana'a, that sand-coloured Chicago of Arabia. A more unlikely place I cannot imagine but this is, for me, the acceptable face of travel capitalism. What's more the hotel works. Bedrooms are international and, thank goodness, so are the bathrooms. Public rooms are handsomely decorated with the odd touch of the country. Service works like a clock. In the main restaurant, you can have escargots, foie gras and shashlik as well as American rib-eye steak. Well, well. How is that for enterprise? And don't say you don't care, because you do. Down the road is the superb Wadi Dhar valley with the former Imam's splendid tower palace. North Yemen? Now you can really go and see for yourself.

YUGOSLAVIA
Belgrade
HOTEL JUGOSLAVIJA, Bul. Edvarda Kardelja 3, 11181 Beograd-YU

★ TELEPHONE: 011/600-222 & 609-444
★ CABLES: Hotel Jugoslavija
★ TELEX: 11777 & 11349 yu hotju
★ IN OPERATION: since 1969
★ RESERVATIONS: Steigenberger Reservation Service, worldwide
★ ROOMS: 186 doubles   308 singles
★ SUITES: 29
★ RESTAURANTS: 3 – 'Panorama', 'Derdap' and 'Zlatan Ovan'
★ BARS: 2
★ DISCOTHEQUE: live music

★ SHOPS: 4 – barber's shop and beauty parlour, souvenirs, newspapers, tobacco, etc
★ CONFERENCE ROOMS: 5 (30 to 1,800)
★ BANQUETING ROOMS: 5 (110 to 1,370)
★ STANDARD BEDROOM SIZE: 23 m²
★ PRIVATE BALCONIES: yes – all rooms
★ SWIMMING POOL: yes – fresh water, 12 × 5 m
★ RECREATIONAL ACTIVITIES: sauna, exercise room and massage
★ GARDENS: yes

★ NO. OF STAFF: 600
★ ROOM SERVICE: around the clock
★ ORIENTATION: rooms overlook the River Danube, park and residential area
★ CREDIT CARDS: Diners Club, American Express, Carte Blanche, Visa, Master Charge, Eurocard, Access and Barclaycard
★ OWNING COMPANY: Hotel Group Metropol
★ GENERAL MANAGER: Mr. Bogoljub Starcevic
★ DISTANCE TO BEACH: by the hotel
★ DISTANCE TO SHOPS: 5 km
★ DISTANCE FROM AIRPORT: 16 km

No one can miss the Jugoslavija – it's that long grey battleship of a place along the banks of the Danube and, although some of the indoor corridors do bear a resemblance to a freeway interchange and the hotel is as modern as tomorrow, I would forgive it all this for the fact that, as big-city hotels go, it is extremely efficient, practical, very clean and surprisingly personal in some little ways. Breakfast arrived with an English-language newspaper and the floor waiter asked me if this was the way I liked the toast – otherwise he'd go away and get another lot. Yugoslavs are very cheerful people, anxious to please, and I never saw a sour face. Rooms tend to be a little mass-produced and homogenous but clean and bright. It is a hotel for visiting politicians and businessmen and as such it works very well – with messages taken and delivered promptly and accurately. As for the food, I soon discovered that the hotel's local dishes were infinitely superior to what passes for international cuisine.

THE TRAVELLER'S NIGHTMARES

For those of us who are in love with the very idea of travel, hotels are wonderful places – hospitable, efficient, glamorous, exciting. Or are they? Sometimes, they are also filled with aggravation, petty annoyances and outright obfuscations – which makes you wonder whether you should have left home in the first place.

Relatively little of this takes place in the hotels listed in this book – that's why they are here. But some does, and over many years of travelling around the world I have collected quite a few of these 'sticking points' and I mention several of them here in the hope (which springs eternal) that at least a few of my hotel manager friends will read this and ask themselves whether their hotels could possibly be guilty.

Ninety per cent of these little contretemps have to do with people – the people who work in hotels – and it makes you wonder occasionally why they chose this particular way of earning a living. They might do better as policemen, customs officers or travelling salesmen. However, they are in the hotel and so are you and there is the rub. One of the curious things about these traveller's nightmares is that some of them are so seemingly unimportant, so transparently wrong and so easy to put right that one cannot understand why someone has not done something about them before.

So here are a few of my traveller's nightmares. How are yours?

★ You have just arrived after fourteen hours in the air. You are tired, dehydrated and anxious to rest your weary head. But the reception clerk does not look at you – he is talking to his girlfriend on the telephone, rifling through old letters or he insists on vanishing behind the partition.

★ He looks up your name and says, sorry, we don't have a reservation for you. You show him your confirmation slip and he turns it over doubtfully as if it were some communication from the Kremlin and then takes fifteen minutes to discover that you were, after all, expected.

★ Reluctantly, he gives you a registration form which, patiently, you fill in – except for your car number (you haven't got a car) but he insists on having your car number.

★ He wants to know how you will pay. Credit card? Cash? Traveller's cheques? Having only just arrived and not yet consumed anything, you tell him that you'll decide when the time comes.

★ In a good hotel, the front office manager or the duty clerk (they are the ones who are not in uniform) takes you along to the elevator and rises with you – to the wrong floor. He looks at your key again and says: 'So sorry – wrong floor . . .'

★ Believing that you normally live in an igloo or an African hut, he shows you your room and how everything works. He explains the television system and always, but *always* turns on the bedside radio full blast (they don't have radio where you come from, of course . . .)

★ He wishes you a pleasant day and leaves you alone – at last. Exhausted and perspiring, you sit on the edge of your bed and wait for your luggage to arrive. And you wait. And wait. You call down. Yes, sir, it's coming right up. You wait some more. The luggage man arrives, carrying your cases with one hand and putting them down the wrong way up. His other hand is by his side – palm upwards. You don't have any of the local small change. That's all right, dollars will do. No coins, mind.

★ Alone at last and even your breath has deserted you because the air conditioning is wrong. It usually is. Africa is suddenly turned into Greenland and Scandinavia becomes what Zaire must be like. You'll soon fix that. But will you? Never – because people who install air conditioning systems always make them foolproof – or guestproof. You try the window. It won't open. Hotels don't like guests who go through the window in desperation. The bathroom is even worse: it has no air at all – period. So you sit there doing what comes naturally, fanning yourself with the room service menu card (that's about the only thing it's good for as you will soon find out . . .)

★ The hotel brochure says that all rooms have refrigerators/bars. Yours has one and you are dying for a drink. Alas, none of the keys you were given fits this one. You wish you had not forgotten your flame-thrower or that Japanese gizmo you got for Christmas. Instead, you suck one of those disgusting 'bonbons' which the airline gave you on the way over. You could of course call for service and ask for someone to come and open it. The thought of waiting some more for someone who may or may not come puts you off. You are tired.

★ Listlessly, you sit down on the bed near the telephone and promptly reach floor level. That's a speciality of hotels: the bed nearest the telephone which is used most goes down like the Great Rift Valley on one side and up like the Himalayas on the other. Cannily, you choose the other bed – at least you'll get some exercise during your stay by running for the phone from one side of the room to the other.

★ You switch on the bedside light. It does not work. You try all the other lights in the room and they work fine – all except the one you need most.

★ The radio is blaring out next door. You call reception and ask them to do something. 'But there is no one in that room, sir,' says the clerk. Not now maybe, but when the maid was there at ten a.m. she had to have Elvis on full blast to help her make the beds and she forgot to turn him off. She *likes* Elvis.

★ Look at the business of messages, now. Invariably, hotel messages are taken by a Pakistani who learnt his English in Guatemala and deciphering them is like doing *The Times* crossword. The possibilities are endless.

★ A red light flashes on your bedside console to let you know that you have a message. You ring and get it. The red light stays on, blinking far into the night. You ring again and ask if you have a message. 'Yes, sir,' says the bright telephone girl, 'Here it is' . . . It's the same message you got three hours ago. You try to go to sleep but the red light still flashes on. There is only one remedy: a bit of Band Aid to mask it. Never travel without Band Aid (and that's not an advertisement).

★ Britain's Prince Philip once made a long and fruitless investigation into why it was that bathwater always goes down the plughole clockwise. I have a problem too. I have discovered that all hotel laundries in the Southern Hemisphere actually live on a diet of shirt buttons. Perhaps one of you dear readers has the answer?

★ Hotel laundries again. They are a lottery. You might get back a pair of Japanese golf socks. Or sixteen handkerchiefs beautifully embroidered with a motto in Hindi. Or nothing at all. Once, I had all my underwear stolen in Nepal – one should not really have to go that far to have one's underwear stolen. Odder still since it would take two normal-sized Nepalis to fill one pair of my undershorts.

★ The colour brochure in your room has been written by a man who only knows adjectives. Did you know that there are four restaurants in this hotel, etc? Mouth-watering. You try the first three and the food goes from bad to worse to impossible. You make a comment and the headwaiter says: 'Ah, but you should try the Rendez-Vous Grill, sir, that's where the real gastronomes go . . .' You eventually make it. Only this is Thursday and yes, you have guessed it, the Rendez-Vous Grill is closed on Thursdays.

★ As a gesture of goodwill, the management kindly left a basket of fruit in your room, beautifully wrapped and topped with a bow. Trouble is that they also left it for the previous guest and the one before him so that by now the apple on top looks like Nefertiti's mummy. You wish they had not bothered.

★ In common with thousands of other hotel loos, yours has one peculiarity: the water keeps on dripping like the well-known Chinese torture and never fills the cistern. This is where your experience as an international plumber comes in. You lift the lid of the cistern, plunge your hand in and adjust the rubber cap that closes the gap. Excellent. But when you have done this every two hours for three days your patience is wearing thin. You call the housekeeper and eventually the plumber comes in, puts the loo right and smashes your bottle of expensive after-shave as he turns around.

★ Loos are tricky things of course. By now, everyone knows that in anglophone countries, one pushes and that in francophone countries, one pulls. What happens if you are in a country outside the linguistic frontiers? Well, there of course is where your experience of the Rubik Cube comes in. Once, in Romania, I had a loo which only flushed when you closed the bathroom door and another time in Mexico I had an even better one – all you had to do was turn off the lights.

★ As one's lady-wife keeps on reminding one, the same applies to that devilish Gallic invention – the bidet. Some are perfect if she wants a shampoo. And if you ever enter the bathroom to find your better half spreadeagled on the ceiling, you'll know where you are: Iceland – they have geysers there.

★ If you want to know what not to buy in any given country, do look at the hotel shops. They have nothing you want and everything you don't want but they do have one thing in common all over the world: they charge three times as much as anyone else.

★ In your room the curtains won't close. There is no pulley at the side and they won't budge when you try to close them by hand. This being an advanced country you discover that one of the twenty-seven buttons on your console actually closes the curtains. Great. But there is a short in this one and when the curtains are drawn all the lights come on. Outside your window, there is a flashing green sign advertising Pepsi Cola in Arabic. I swear I'll never drink the stuff again.

★ Beware of chambermaids. No, I don't mean that way. Unless trained in a certain way, they are experts at barging in on you. You return to your room in the late afternoon, dying for a hot bath and a nice rest. Carefully, you place the 'Do not Disturb' sign on the door handle. You know, 'No molestar' and all that. You are just getting out of your bath, *au naturel, bien sur*, the passkey turns in the lock and the maid catches you just as you are halfway between the bath and your dressing gown.

★ Bathrooms are a special feature of your hotel. Esplendido. Except for one thing: the water won't run away in your washbasin and when you are in a hurry you stand there for ten minutes before you can run more water. That is not an exception, it's the rule in, I would suggest, six out of ten hotels around the world.

★ Once upon a time, your bathtub had two taps – one hot (usually coloured red) and one cold (usually coloured blue). Sometimes you had to guess. Nowadays of course all that is different, much more advanced. You only have one tap, colour-coded and with lots of arrows – the invention of some smart Milan designer with a degree from North Korea and a bathroom fittings plant in Brazil. Naturally you follow the instructions and first the shower comes on when you want a bath. You turn the other way and water pours out scalding hot or cold depending on whether you are North or South of the Equator or if it's Wednesday. The designer incidentally became a millionaire but I regret to report that he ended up in a padded cell in Panama.

★ I'll get in a quick shower, you say to yourself. Good – that will make a new man out of you. Trouble is that the shower system has not been tried or adjusted since the hotel's last annual check and the creature who's just vacated your room was an orang-utang – he loved tropic rain, hot and heavy, and ten seconds after you turn the tap on your entire bathroom is flooded.

★ Breakfast cards are a great invention – at least you don't have to try your best Urdu first thing in the morning. But beware. Your eight thirty breakfast comes in cheerily at five thirty and it is not what you ordered.

★ Your wardrobe (closet to some) is all wrong. If you are in an American or European palace hotel, it's so big that you have to stand on tiptoe to hang your coat. If you are East of Suez, it's been built for a dwarf and your lady's evening dress trails on the floor. Sliding doors are fine in principle. Except that they don't slide and you are reduced to getting your clothes out through an opening two inches wide.

★ Then there are the coathangers – one of the most hazardous and mystifying items in a hotel room. Years ago, some slide rule accountant decided that he would once and for all get rid of those thieving guests who got away with his coathangers. So he and his friends designed a coathanger so vicious as to be unbearable. The top fitting slides along the rail but does not come off. The rest of the hanger does and you spend half your time fitting the bits together. With all the profits the hotels make, one would think they could spare a coathanger or two.

★ Anywhere East of Suez, don't ever ask to have your shoes cleaned unless you are actually wearing them. Shoes are invaluable to the locals and once gone never seen again. I once watched an expensive-looking American gentleman, fully dressed in evening garb, padding along to the front desk in his bare feet and raising hell. He even asked for the American consul's telephone number . . .

★ Room service menus are great. Except that the difference between what they say they have and what they deliver is great too. Your evening snack is a long time coming, cold when you get it and it tastes like a pulped copy of *The New York Times* – all the news that's unfit to eat.

★ The so-called Coffee Shop isn't much better. It's open for 24 hours a day but it takes about that long to get a sandwich and a cup of coffee.

★ Hotel banks and hotel cashiers regard your money with the greatest suspicion. They hold your traveller's cheques at arm's length, turn them over two or three times, look at you to discover if you look like Al Capone and only change them when they really can't see any reason for not doing it – always of course giving you less in the local currency than the daily paper says even if you include their commission. Do what I do: take along your own calculator and work it all out in front of them. It puts them right off.

★ At last, you are going off. You want to make an early start to catch a plane. You swallow your breakfast and you are down to pay your bill, carrying your own luggage so there won't be any waiting around. Trouble is that 76 other people have had the same idea and are ahead of you facing the one and only cashier. One would think hotels would get used to people departing early. Not so. You look at your bill and it does not look like a bill but the kind of computer data that keeps NASA in business and I defy you to find out – quickly – if they have charged you properly.

★ At the door, the luggage man or bellboy is waiting with his hand out. Feeling grumpy you tell him that you carried your own luggage. 'Yes,' he says, 'but I would have carried it for you if you had asked . . .' (True story – it happened in Kenya.)

And so it goes on – the luxury living in the gilded cage of international hotels in which both your wife and your boss think you are indulging. The curious thing is that you soon forget these little aggravations and when, six months later a man in a bar tells you he is going off to Padang, you say: 'Padang? Oh yes. Tell you what. The place you ought to stay at is the Hotel Such-and-Such. Super'. That's what hotels are counting on of course – the passing of time makes the heart grow fonder.

Travel is indeed the greatest thing ever. If you can stand the pace.

HOW
TO TRAVEL
HAPPILY

All I can do is to try to help you with a few general tips I have found useful in many years of travelling all over the world.

CLIMATE AND TRAVEL SEASONS

It is impossible to generalise accurately. My bedside reading is the British Meteorological Office statistics covering the last thirty years month by month in 982 places around the world from Aarhus to Zumbo. But not even that respected publication could tell that it would rain in Greece in September when the cradle of Western Civilisation looked like a suburb of Manchester or Cincinnati.

The travel agent/tour operator is no respecter of the seasons. Either he does not know, or does not care or is so intent on selling you a trip that he will send you to a tropical paradise like the Seychelles for instance in January when, although the temperature is fine, the rainfall is 15 inches for the month. He may also tell you about high season, low season, etc. The thing to remember here is that what makes the high season is not necessarily the glorious weather in the place you are planning to visit, but the terrible climate in your own country which forces the likes of us to emigrate. It is the demand which creates a high season – not the climate. Even the national tourist offices' statistics are open to debate. Naturally they want you to visit their country and many of them are not above doing some creative editing with the facts and figures. If you want to be as sure as you can be consult your own government's meteorological statistics for the world and if you work out a fair average you can't go too far wrong. The first and obvious thing to remember is that the seasons are reversed whether you go North or South of the Equator – i.e. while Scotland freezes in winter, Australians are having a sunny Christmas. This can be confusing.

Here are a few generalities about the main parts of the world.

EUROPE AND THE MEDITERRANEAN

The right time to travel in this temperate continent is between May and October – and that's the time when Europe is overrun with tourists. The Mediterranean area is jam-packed with 20 million tourists in July and August – so don't expect to be alone. Neither can you expect to be truly warm in the Mediterranean in the winter – from Spain to Cyprus, the daily average may be around ten or eleven degrees centigrade though it can be much higher due to micro-climate conditions which affect certain parts due to orientation, mountain protection, etc. You can swim quite happily off a beach in Rhodes in early November and there are climatically favoured places like Almeria (Spain), the Algarve (Portugal), Taormina (Sicily), Southern Crete and Cyprus where the weather is likely to be better than average in the winter months.

It is sensible to give careful study to the orientation of the resort of your choice. If it faces South and is protected from the North by a range of mountains, it is likely to be temperate in winter. Winds like the *mistral* and the *sirocco* (Western Mediterranean), the *bora* (Adriatic) and the *meltemi* (Aegean Sea) must be taken into account. These have their seasons of greater or lesser force.

AFRICA AND THE INDIAN OCEAN

Again it is difficult to generalise but North of the Tropic of Capricorn, it is likely to be drier in our winter than South of the Equator. Avoid inland areas in high summer. The East African coast is affected by the 'big rains' (April/May) and the 'little rains' (October/November). In islands like the Seychelles, the monsoon strikes in December/January/February and to a lesser extent it is the same in Mauritius, but average temperatures will remain around twenty-six degrees centigrade and the islands are likely to be less humid than the continental coast.

NORTH AMERICA

As every New Yorker knows to his cost, the subtropical climate in summer of his own city makes life well-nigh unbearable. Californians know that there is a vast difference between, say, San Diego and San Francisco. The most equable climate is in Florida and the South Western States (not in summer) and further South where, unfortunately, the climate can be turned upside down by Mexico's vertical geography, i.e. you could be chilly in Mexico City and swelter in Acapulco.

THE CARIBBEAN AND SOUTH AMERICA

Together with some Pacific islands, the Caribbean (though not Bermuda) has the most equable climate in the world — hovering around the twenty-six to thirty degrees centigrade mark year round though the rainfall tends to be heavier in the summer months. In South America, apart from altitude factors which can alter things considerably, the further North you go the warmer and rainier it is and the other way around, bearing in mind the fact that because of hemispheric factors, the Rio winter is our summer. I have suffered from heat stroke in Manaos after nearly freezing solid in Sao Paulo the day before.

SOUTHERN ASIA AND THE FAR EAST

This is monsoon country and if you wish to go to India you'd better stay at home from May to September — though the monsoon comes later in the South and differs in timing between the East and West coast. In Singapore, it rains most from November to January while in Hong Kong the big rains come from May to September — though in winter temperatures in the two cities can vary by as much as eight or ten degrees centigrade, Hong Kong being the cooler. Japan has a temperate climate fairly similar to Europe.

CLOTHING

When travelling in hot or tropical countries, there are only two words in your vocabulary — cotton and wool. Reject all synthetic materials, particularly nylon. Wearing them can create serious health hazards, starting with heat rash. The only synthetic material I carry is a plastic shower-coat bought in Japan. It folds down as small as a pack of cards and has repaid the investment a thousand-fold.

Wear loose clothing if you can — nothing restricting — and never start on your travels with new shoes — you'll regret it. Men should take plenty of shirts (hotel laundries are expensive, unpredictable and addicted to eating shirt buttons . . .) and women should take as many light dresses as possible, especially those that fold flat. Remember also that if you are travelling to a tropical country you will find, nine times out of ten, that the locals have long ago designed the most comfortable wear — imitate them and buy some (this applies especially to Africa, India and the East).

I mention wool because a little wool will go a long way when you need it and you never know whether you will or not. My long-time favourite is an alpaca cardigan — light but warm and easy to pack. Alas, it is expensive and fairly delicate. My wife swears by cashmere.

LUGGAGE

There are two schools of thought here — some take as little as possible and others take as much as possible. I confess to belonging to the latter group for two reasons. The first is that I am an eternal optimist and usually hope that there will be porters around (there aren't). The second reason is more important and concerns the number of times I have had to meet Presidents or Prime Ministers or other VIPs in shirtsleeves and I now like to be ready for anything — from climbing the Himalayas to meeting African chiefs or going out on the town. All this is a matter of personal choice.

When it comes to the choice of luggage, watch out: the best is not always the most practical. I love the 'weekend in Monte Carlo' type of leather cases and indeed Gucci or St. Laurent bags but I have become convinced over the years that all airlines share a luggage-mangling mafia that delights in tearing off handles, bashing in corners and breaking the locks – the more beautiful the luggage the greater the temptation. On the whole, I find that moulded cases are still the best and most durable.

HOTEL ROOMS

All the hotels listed in this book are – I think – good ones but that should certainly not prevent you from being inquisitive and asking questions. Here are a few tips:

★ Don't feel shy at asking to see your room before you sign in – hotel people may raise an eyebrow but they will respect you; one does not buy a refrigerator sight unseen.

★ Have a good look around, count the coathangers, inspect the bath and washbasin overflow outlets – if they are clean that's a good sign. Trail a finger inside drawers for dust. Make sure you have the pillows or bolsters you like. Try the shower. Make sure the curtains work. Many hotels are *very* bad at room lighting – so inspect your bedside lighting and if it is not sufficient for you to read by, ask for another lamp. Test the beds for comfort. If you are alone in a double room, *never* choose the bed nearest the telephone: a long succession of guests have been sitting on the edge of this bed to telephone and made it as sway-backed as a camel.

★ Watch out for room service and especially for room service breakfast in any country like the United States where labour is expensive. Charges can be exorbitant. Many good hotels nowadays have adopted the American method of giving you a breakfast order to fill up and hang on your doorknob. I approve of this since it saves time and limits linguistic difficulties at a time of the morning when you can do without them.

★ Tipping. As far as possible, if you can find out, adopt the custom of the country. I have always used a method once explained to me by the late Aga Khan – no mean traveller himself. It's quite simple if a trifle unfair: you tip heavily when you arrive and fairly lightly when you leave. The hotel bush telegraph soon gets going and everybody knows what you are up to and you'll get good service.

★ Most grand hotel *concierges* or head porters are vastly knowledgeable, multi-lingual, helpful and thoroughly familiar with the minor details of travel and tourism. Consult them but try to judge your man. Many are the well-paid end of a mafia which extends to taxi-drivers, car hire companies, restaurants, guides, etc. I always arrive forewarned, that is with the right guidebooks and the right information since this is always handsomely repaid in practice. One of the best I know because of its frankness and lucidity is the Fodor series.

★ Languages. Nobody can expect you to become fluent in Swahili or Serbo-Croat overnight. English is universal and a little French helps quite a bit. Besides this do try to make an effort to master simple words like 'Good Morning', 'Good Night', 'Thank you', 'Where', 'How Much', 'Please', in the local language. People of all nations without exception will be pleased that you have tried. If you are in a country where you cannot even read the alphabet (Arab lands, Japan, etc), ask your hotel porter to write down addresses, etc for your taxi-driver.

★ Be fair, frank and open. If you have any prejudices, leave them at home. Whether a man is red, white, black, yellow or blue, give him a smile and a firm handshake and take him for what he is – not what you would like him to be. Treat people as equals – you'd be surprised how much more fun you will get out of travelling.

HEALTH

I must be lucky for all I ever suffered in two-and-a-half decades of travelling – even in remote countries – was a dose of 'Montezuma's Revenge' in Mexico and another of 'Delhi Belly' in India.

Inquite about the 'jabs' you need if any. Vaccination against smallpox (almost eradicated), yellow fever and cholera are more often than not compulsory. I also believe very strongly in TAB – anti-typhoid vaccination – and rarely travel without insect-repellents, stomach-upsets remedies advocated by my doctor (they vary from country to country), water sterilisation tablets for those countries where genuine mineral water may be hard to get.

Can we drink the water? That's a question most readers always ask and, alas, there is no hard-and-fast rule but over the years one has developed a sixth sense in this – I never drink the water in tropical or backward countries and even in some European countries I have my own particular habits. In Italy, for instance, I will drink the water North of Rome but not South of it. I will drink it in Portugal but not in Spain, in Greece but not in Turkey. It is irrational but all I can say is that it has worked for me – so far.

Apart from accidents, one is convinced that no hotel listed in this book will serve you food that will make you ill. But it is when eating out that you should observe the simplest basic rules: no peeled fruit, no shellfish in polluted areas, no food that you cannot recognise or inquire about.

As for circadian dysrythmia, or jet lag to most of us, habitual travellers are used to it these days. North to South and South to North journeys don't affect anyone, but East to West and vice versa do, and the best physicians recommend a more or less long period of physical rhythm re-adjustment in each case, i.e. don't rush off to a nightclub when your body cycle is still on breakfast time. Be sensible and if you are not sure, ask your airline.

While in the air, make yourself at home – take off your shoes, relax, wear something loose and warm, go to the loo as often as possible and drink lots of liquids but never fizzy drinks – everything from champagne to cokes; try to give them up and stick to fruit juices, wine or whisky.

Finally I can't give you any advice about the final hurdle – the customs man. His genre varies in every country and I have met quite a few. All I can say is this: don't take him for an idiot. Most customs men are very good psychologists and can distinguish at a glance between the holidaymaker who has splashed out a bit on baubles and the professional smuggler. Let discretion be your guide.

AIR TRAVEL

You may well ask: 'That's all very well but after all that how do I avoid all the aggravations connected with air travel?' I sympathise. Having flown well over two million miles I believe that air travel as it is today is one of the most dehumanised and degrading forms of transport imaginable. But one can't have it both ways. One cannot have the benefit of being able to reach Outer Mongolia quickly and then blame the airlines for getting you there. Most airlines, alas, persistently refuse to take the human element into account. All, but really all habitual travellers know that air travel could be simplified, made more comfortable and interesting. No one listens – except another traveller. One can only suggest a few ways – some of them obvious – which will minimise your trauma.

★ If Concorde is going where you are going – take it. Despite its bad press (mostly among those who have never experienced it) it still gets you there twice as fast (and with half the aggravation), your luggage is security-banded and you don't wait around so much.

★ Travel first class if you can. As in everything else, the best costs more and for some of us it is worth it – more legroom, more moving-about room, better food and drink, less herding and an opportunity to complain bitterly if something goes wrong. More loos too – and that makes a great difference on a long flight. First class is supposed to be anti-social but how long is it since you last carried a pack on your back?

★ Take fares, now. Or leave them because the chances are you will never understand them. Even airline people don't and on one occasion recently I was quoted *seven* different fares by the same airline for the same journey. It is a measure of the airlines' giddy death-wish that they will offer you a seat at any price and in the end you'll find that this only works on Wednesdays or on January 2. Take my advice: go shopping for the most awkward, most tiresome, most argumentative travel agent you can find (someone you would *hate* to do business with . . .) and give him your custom. The chances are high that he will get you the best deal.

★ However complicated your journey is – stopovers, side trips, etc – any world airline should be able to issue you with a valid ticket. In principle. But it does not work, despite all the computers and the gizmos. So check it and then check it again because only you know where you want to go and when. Not long ago, one world-famous airline issued me with a ticket for several short, inter-island flights in the Caribbean. When I got to my first take-off point, I discovered that the ticket was based on a two-year-old timetable. Whatever you do examine your ticket carefully, turn it upside down if you like but never take anyone's word that it's all OK.

★ Despite the booking girl's pretty smile, don't believe anything she says when she assures you that you are on the 'waiting-list' unless you can see your name on that list at different times during the waiting period. The girl does not mean to lie but she does, or she is over-ruled by her bosses. Maybe the President's aunt wants to go your way at the last minute and, believe me, she will and you won't. So only accept a firm, OK booking and if you are travelling with, shall we say, an esoteric airline, insist on seeing your name on the passenger list. You won't be popular but you'll take off.

★ Don't be taken in by the airlines' special classes, the businessmen's specials, the club-this and VIP-that. At the time of writing I have counted up to 47 promotional gimmicks of this kind and most of those I have experienced are not worth it. I once reluctantly paid an extra $187 for a system that had been boosted to the skies. I discovered that the only thing I received which economy passengers did not receive was a free drink. A very expensive free drink.

★ If you must travel economy, find out which type of aircraft you will be flying on and ask the airline or the travel agent *in advance* to show you the seating plan adopted by this particular airline. There *are* differences. Make a note of the seat numbers nearest the emergency exits – they always have more legroom.

★ Make up your mind once and for all that there aren't any *good* airports – only bad ones and not-so-bad ones. Reconcile yourself to the fact that when you get to one airport or another, something nasty will happen: air conditioning breakdown, a strike, a power failure and so on. You'll never be disappointed. If you can, especially in Southern Europe, avoid the obvious 'holiday' airports (Gerona, Barcelona, Alicante, Malaga, Venice, Pisa, Nice, Athens, etc). Arrival and departure are guaranteed to put you off air travel for ever. The *worst* international airports I know are Los Angeles, Kennedy, Mexico City, Cairo, Khartoum, Kingston, Dar-es-Salaam, Conakry, Dakar, Kinshasa, Damascus, Baghdad, Delhi, Bombay, Calcutta, Heraklion, Rome and Palermo. I will not name the *next* worst since that would cover all the rest.

★ If you are on a short flight – say anything under three hours – leave the airline's food alone. It will be a good miss. If you think that you really will get hungry, do what a friend of mine does – take your own picnic with you.

★ Avoid airport food and drink at all costs. You are more likely to get food poisoning in an airport than anywhere else in the world.

★ Make up your mind – once and for all – never to buy *anything* in an airport unless you happen to know that the duty free shop is really what it says. Airports are the world's biggest emporiums of rubbish and in all my travels I have been able to count on the fingers of one hand the items that were worth buying.

Apart from that, flying is fun. Getting there is even better.

THE TRAVELLER'S REWARDS

Anyone reading the hotel entries in this book will easily gather that though I very much relish hotels when they are good, they are merely the stopping places in a lifetime of journeys. Travel is my first love and has been for more years than I care to remember. Not just travel for the sake of moving from here to there but travel for what it is: a personal experience so far above any other that it bears no comparison.

In today's society, travel is the best investment anyone can make. And those who say that it is not good value because it is not a 'consumer durable', i.e. once you have got there and come home, that's it – I say nonsense. The travel you like is with you forever and the memories you have stored, sometimes subconsciously, will last you far longer than a motorcar, a television receiver or a personal computer. Travel remains with you in terms of sheer memories, personal discoveries, the widening of your own knowledge, your beliefs and your enjoyment.

Of course, travel's greatest plus is that its effect is never quite the same on two different people. Travel's variety is as great as your own imagination and the things that will delight you may not impress anyone else. You, alone, are facing the world and what you make of it depends on you. For my own part, my years of travelling have yielded sideshows – I once nearly became a lunch snack for crocodiles, I exchanged small talk with a cannibal chief, I got washed away by a Pacific typhoon, I ate fried bat for dinner and I am glad to say that of the 102 countries I have visited so far, only one took the trouble to deport me – because I refused to read the once-compulsory Little Red Book of Chairman Mao. Yet those, and so many others, are the adventurous little sideshows.

People often ask me which are the things I remember most. That's the trick question – like what was the last time you beat your wife. They are speaking of more than two decades and thousands of experiences. Here are one hundred of them, dredged haphazardly from the dark recesses of memory. May you be so lucky!

★ My first and last sight of the Taj Mahal.
★ Standing on Lycabettus in the early morning and watching the sun lighting up the Acropolis.
★ Going to Marib in North Yemen and finding the remains of the Queen of Sheba's palace.
★ Sailing down Mark Twain's Mississipi.
★ A visit to Olympia in the spring.
★ The last time I sat out an afternoon on Siena's Piazza del Campo.
★ Seeing Kanchenjunga from Darjeeling.
★ Standing on the Mount of Beatitudes in Israel and remembering 'Blessed are the poor . . .
★ Visiting Monument Valley looking for John Wayne.
★ Following the Loire from its source to the Atlantic.
★ Seeing the Hermes of Praxiteles for the first time.
★ Sailing up the Amazon to Iquitos.
★ Seeing Bora Bora for the first time.
★ Being the only person on Pigeon Point beach in Tobago.
★ Seeing 'Son et Lumière' at Chenonceau.
★ Discovering the Gol Gumbaz mausoleum in Bijapur, India.
★ Walking into a room in the Prado in Madrid and suddenly coming face to face with Goya's Dos de Mayo.
★ Forgetting time in the little Helenistic city of Side in Southern Turkey.
★ Walking in Venice – at any time.
★ Watching the sun rising over Serengeti.
★ Spending a summer's day in St. Emilion.
★ Cruising down the Sepik River in Papua New Guinea.
★ My first visit to Santiago de Compostela.
★ Sailing in a caique to visit the monasteries of Mount Athos.
★ Any one of my five visits to Petra.

★ Watching 10,000 pilgrims crowding into the Meenakshi Temple in Madurai, Southern India.
★ Sailing Japan's Inland Sea.
★ Visiting the underground churches of Lalibela in Ethiopia.
★ Looking at the Leningrad Winter Palace at dusk on a winter afternoon.
★ Sailing down the Nile before everybody did it.
★ Travelling in Rajasthan and visiting eleven maharajahs' palaces in seven days.
★ Seeing the original – instead of a print – of Botticelli's 'The Birth of Venus' in the Uffizi in Florence.
★ Suddenly discovering the little rococo palace of Amalienburg in Munich.
★ Watching light snow falling around the skyscrapers of New York at night.
★ Watching a kejak dance in Bali.
★ Following the desert road south of the Atlas in Morocco.
★ Seeing the 'charioteer of Delphi'.
★ Crossing the Sahara by car.
★ Climbing the steps of Mihintale in Sri Lanka.
★ Visiting the Palazzo Ducale in Urbino.
★ Seeing Isfahan's Blue Mosque before the ayatollahs' time.
★ Sailing into Hong Kong Harbour at night.
★ Following the Nile in the Sudan from Khartoum to Wadi Halfa.
★ Wandering around the Byzantine churches of Ravenna.
★ Retracing the steps of the great Impressionists and trying to figure out where they set up their easels.
★ Seeing Monreale for the first time.
★ Touring the Mani in the Peloponnese and slowly driving down into Lakonia.
★ Witnessing the full moon festival at Mahabalipuran near Madras.
★ Seeing Durer's 'Self-Portrait' in the Alte Pinakothek in Munich.
★ Making it to Timbuktu.
★ Speedboating on Lake Powell in the Colorado Valley, U.S.A.
★ 'Collecting' village Romanesque churches all the way from Andalusia to Bavaria and from Normandy to Calabria.
★ Seeing Ephesus for the first time.
★ Driving along the valley of the Lot River in France.
★ In Syria, discovering a village where people still speak Aramaic – the language of Christ.
★ Driving along the southern coast of Crete.
★ Visiting the Palladio Theatre at Vicenza.
★ Visiting Chichen Itza for the first time.
★ Watching the Bosphorus from the Iftarye mirador in Istanbul's Topkapi.
★ Waking up at dawn to see the sun rising over the walls of Old Jerusalem.
★ Seeing the spires of Chartres Cathedral over the summer wheatfields.
★ A gala night at the Staatsoper in Vienna.
★ Visiting Segesta in springtime.
★ Seeing the island palaces of Udaipur for the first time.
★ Touring around the birthplaces of the conquistadores in Extremadura.
★ Waking up on my own houseboat on Kashmir's Dal Lake and watching the rising sun turn the Himalayas into pink candyfloss.
★ Seeing the five sensational El Grecos in the village church of Illescas, South of Madrid.
★ Visiting the holy city of Ghardaia in the Sahara.
★ Discovering the old eighteenth century gold-and-diamond rush cities in Brazil's Minas Gerais.
★ Enjoying the game of searching for magnificent and virginal tropical beaches in a world that is supposed to be tourist-polluted – and finding them everywhere.
★ Climbing to the Doi Suthep temple in Chiangmai, Thailand.
★ Sailing in an Arab dhow around the Ras Musandam peninsula in Oman.
★ Driving alone, zigzag fashion, from San Antonio to San Diego.

★ Going to Palmyra for the first time.
★ Driving in England's Cotswolds.
★ Looking at the Chateau of Chambord during a summer storm.
★ Standing on the Megiddo Hill in Israel and looking down at the Vale of Jezreel.
★ Collecting twenty-six Crusaders' Castles in the Middle East.
★ My first sight of the Basilica of Vezelay.
★ Visiting the Alhambra in the early spring when the trees come into bloom.
★ Seeing the walls of Avila for the first time from the Salamanca road.
★ An evening of Mozart in the candle-lit island castle of Herrenchiemsee in Bavaria.
★ Discovering the Treasury of Ste. Foy in Conques.
★ Accidentally entering a small village church in Calabria and finding that it contained the second oldest bible in the world.
★ Looking at the hills of Umbria from a terrace in Todi.
★ Walking along the 'Cours Mirabeau' in Aix-en-Provence.
★ Eating a picnic lunch on the edge of a live volcano crater in Vanuatu.
★ Visiting Fatehpur Sikhri for the first time.
★ Watching canoe racing in Western Samoa.
★ Seeing the Ummayad Mosque in Damascus.
★ Sailing to the Outer Hebrides in a mini-storm.
★ My first sight of Santorini.
★ Meditating close to St. Francis of Assisi's San Damiano Convent.
★ In Egypt's Eastern desert, visiting the Coptic Monastery of St. Paul – inhabited by monks continuously since the year 311A.D.
★ Skindiving on the Great Barrier Reef, Australia.
★ Bryce Canyon, Utah, in the early spring.
★ Driving around Lawrence of Arabia's Wadi Rumm desert in Jordan.
★ Going up-river in Borneo.
★ Having lunch in a 'great house' in Jamaica.
★ Watching Zulus dancing.
★ Making lifelong friends all over the world – a taxi driver in Rio de Janeiro, a doctor in Singapore, a civil servant in India, a rancher in Arizona, a game ranger in Kenya, a village mayor in Greece plus hundreds of others, and if this does not sound too much like a travel brochure cliché, finding that the world is full of wonderful people.